INTERMEDIATE ANALYSIS

THE APPLETON-CENTURY MATHEMATICS SERIES

Edited by Raymond W. Brink

A First Year of College Mathematics, Second Edition
by Raymond W. Brink

College Algebra, Second Edition
by Raymond W. Brink

Algebra—College Course, Second Edition
by Raymond W. Brink

Intermediate Algebra, Second Edition
by Raymond W. Brink

Calculus
by Lloyd L. Smail

Analytic Geometry and Calculus
by Lloyd L. Smail

Solid Analytic Geometry
by John M. H. Olmsted

Intermediate Analysis
by John M. H. Olmsted

The Mathematics of Finance
by Franklin C. Smith

Plane Trigonometry, Revised Edition
by Raymond W. Brink

Spherical Trigonometry
by Raymond W. Brink

Analytic Geometry, Revised Edition
by Raymond W. Brink

Essentials of Analytic Geometry
by Raymond W. Brink

Intermediate Analysis

AN INTRODUCTION TO THE THEORY OF FUNCTIONS OF ONE REAL VARIABLE

by

John M. H. Olmsted

PROFESSOR OF MATHEMATICS
UNIVERSITY OF MINNESOTA

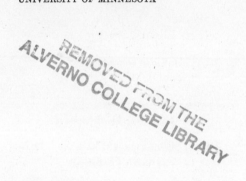

NEW YORK: APPLETON-CENTURY-CROFTS, INC.

PRINTED IN THE UNITED STATES OF AMERICA

PREFACE

~~~~~~

When should the student of mathematics first begin to develop the techniques of a precise analytic proof, complete with "deltas and epsilons"? Such techniques are quite distinct from the manipulative skills normally acquired in the standard elementary and intermediate courses of the mathematics curriculum, and are often not developed until the student is in the graduate school with a course in Advanced Calculus, and possibly several other graduate courses, behind him. It is sometimes difficult for a student to adjust himself to what seems like an entirely new way of thinking, and particularly disturbing to him to realize that what he had considered to be a "proof" is no longer acceptable. Although, under these circumstances, he is not actually faced with *unlearning* things he has acquired, he must at least *relearn* in certain areas.

The author of the present book holds that a student of mathematics should properly begin to make his acquaintance with the tools of analysis as soon as possible after the completion of the first course in calculus. These early overtures may be scattered and limited, but they should be thorough and precise as far as they go. In particular, the student should be encouraged to prove (in full detail) statements which previously he has been persuaded to accept because of their immediate obviousness. Who, for instance, could doubt that if $a_n \to + \infty$, then $2a_n \to + \infty$? On the other hand, how many students fresh from calculus can really *prove* this?

The purpose of this book is to present the basic ideas and techniques of analysis, for functions of a single real variable, in such a way that students who have studied calculus can proceed at whatever pace and degree of intensity are considered suitable. The organization of the book is designed for maximum flexibility. Topics which are of a more difficult or theoretical nature than most of the material normally studied at the level of Intermediate Calculus are starred for possible omission or postponement. For example, the student can learn to differentiate and integrate power series term by term *before* studying uniform convergence. Frequently, if a theorem is easy to understand, whereas its proof is more difficult, only the proof is starred. Occasionally such a proof is presented in a later section or chapter. An instance is the boundedness of a function continuous on a closed interval. Some topics which can be omitted from the starred portions without affecting the continuity of what remains receive double stars. This system of starring and double starring applies to the exercises as well as the text. The resultant arrangement of the contents makes the book unusually adaptable for courses of varying lengths and levels.

The unstarred portions of the book are immediately suitable for any student who has completed a first course in calculus. They contain extremely careful and thorough discussion of elementary ideas and can be reasonably covered in a course with approximately forty-five meetings. Inclusion of most of the singly starred material permits a richer and more substantial course of some sixty meetings. The doubly starred portions of the book, particularly in the exercises, permit the more advanced student to explore well into the graduate curriculum. Instances are the criterion for Riemann integrability in terms of continuity almost everywhere, and the Lebesgue dominated convergence theorem for Riemann and improper integrals; to these the student is led by suitable sequences of exercises.

Special attention should be called to the abundant sets of exercises. These include routine drills for practice, intermediate exercises that extend the material of the text while retaining its character, and advanced exercises that go beyond the standard textual subject matter. Whenever guidance seems desirable, generous hints are included. In this manner the student is led to such items of interest as Weierstrass's theorem on uniform approximation of continuous functions by polynomials, and the construction of a continuous nondifferentiable function. The analytic treatment of the logarithmic, exponential, and trigonometric functions is presented entirely in the exercises, where sufficient hints are given to make these topics available to all. Answers to all problems are given at the end of the book. Illustrative examples abound throughout.

A few words regarding notation should be given. The equal sign $=$ is used for equations, both conditional and identical, and the triple bar sign $\equiv$ is reserved for definitions. For simplicity, if the meaning is clear from the context, neither symbol is restricted to the indicative mood as in "$(a+b)^2 = a^2 + 2ab + b^2$," or "where $f(x) \equiv x^2 + 5$." Examples of subjunctive uses are "let $x = n$," and "let $\epsilon \equiv 1$," which would be read "let x be equal to n," and "let ϵ be defined to be 1," respectively. A similar freedom is granted the inequality symbols. For instance, the symbol $>$ in the following constructions "if $\epsilon > 0$, then $\cdots$," "let $\epsilon > 0$," and "let $\epsilon > 0$ be given," could be translated "is greater than," "be greater than," and "greater than," respectively.

In a few places parentheses are used to indicate alternatives. The principal instances of such uses are heralded by announcements or footnotes in the text. Here again it is hoped that the context will prevent any ambiguity.   Such a sentence as "The function $f(x)$ is integrable from a to b $(a < b)$" would mean that "$f(x)$ is integrable from a to b, where it is assumed that $a < b$," whereas a sentence like "A function having a positive (negative) derivative over an interval is strictly increasing (decreasing) there" is a compression of two statements into one, the parentheses indicating an alternative formulation.

The author wishes to express his deep appreciation of the aid and suggestions given by Professor R. W. Brink of the University of Minnesota in the preparation of the manuscript.   He is also indebted to others, including in particular Professor W. D. Munro of the University of Minnesota, for their friendly and helpful counsel.

Minneapolis

J. M. H. O.

CONTENTS

★Chapter 3

SOME THEORETICAL CONSIDERATIONS

Chapter 4

DIFFERENTIATION

Chapter 5

INTEGRATION

CONTENTS

Chapter 6

SOME ELEMENTARY FUNCTIONS

Chapter 7

INFINITE SERIES OF CONSTANTS

Chapter 8

POWER SERIES

★Chapter 9

UNIFORM CONVERGENCE

INTERMEDIATE ANALYSIS

I

The Real Number System

~~~~~~

101. INTRODUCTION

The reader is already familiar with many of the properties of real numbers. He knows, for example, that $2 + 2 = 4$, that the product of two negative numbers is a positive number, and that if x, y, and z are any real numbers, then $x(y + z) = xy + xz$. The average reader at the level of Calculus usually knows these things because he has been told that they are true—probably by people who know such things simply because they have been told. He knows pretty well why some of these familiar facts (like $2 \cdot 3 = 3 \cdot 2$) are true, but is entitled to be unsure of the reasons for others (like $\sqrt{2} \cdot \sqrt{3} = \sqrt{3} \cdot \sqrt{2}$).

It is important to know that the properties of real numbers which we use almost daily are true, not by *fiat* or *decree*, but by rigorous mathematical *proof*. The situation is not unlike that of Euclidean Plane Geometry. In either case (numbers or geometry), all properties within one particular mathematical system follow by logical inference from a few basic *assumptions*, or *hypotheses*, or *axioms*, which are properties that are "true" only in the relative sense that they are assumed as a working basis for that particular mathematical system. What is true in one system may be false or meaningless in another, but within one logical system "true" means "implied by the axioms."

For the system of real numbers the axioms, as usually given,† are five in number, and are concerned only with the **natural numbers**, $1, 2, 3, \cdots$. These five axioms were given in 1889 by the Italian mathematician G. Peano (1858-1932), and are called the *Peano axioms for the natural numbers*. In the book by Landau, referred to in the footnote, the reader is led by a sequence of steps (consisting of 73 definitions and 301 theorems, most of which are very easy) through the entire construction of the real and complex number systems. The natural numbers are used to build the

---

† For a detailed discussion of the real number system see E. Landau, *Foundations of Analysis* (New York, Chelsea Publishing Company, 1951) or E. W. Hobson, *Theory of Functions* (Washington, Harren Press, 1950).

1

larger system of positive rational numbers (fractions); these in turn form the basis for constructing the positive real numbers; the positive real numbers then lead to the system of all real numbers; finally, the complex numbers are constructed from the real numbers.   In each successive class the basic operations of addition and multiplication and (through the class of real numbers) the relation of order are defined, and shown to be consistent with those of the preceding class considered as a subclass.   The result is the number system as we know it.

In this book we shall begin our discussion of the number system at a point far along the route just outlined.   We shall, in fact, assume that we already have the entire real number system, and *describe* this system by means of a few fundamental properties which we shall accept without further question.   These fundamental properties are so chosen that they give a *complete* description of the real number system, so that all properties of the real numbers are deducible from them.†   For this reason, and to distinguish them from other properties, we call these fundamental properties *axioms*, and refer to them as such in the text.   These axioms are arranged according to three categories: *basic operations*, *order*, and *completeness*.

The present chapter is devoted exclusively to the real number system. The first part of the chapter is elementary in nature, and includes the axioms for the basic operations and order, a review of mathematical induction, a brief treatment of the integers and rational numbers, and a discussion of geometrical representation and absolute value.   The last part, of a more advanced character, is starred for possible omission or postponement, and includes the axiom of completeness and a further treatment of topics introduced earlier.

Except for passing mention, complex numbers are not used in this book. Unless otherwise specified, the word *number* should be interpreted to mean *real number*.

The reader should be advised that many of the properties of real numbers that are given in the Exercises of this chapter are used throughout the book without specific reference.   In many cases (like the laws of cancellation and the unique factorization theorem) such properties, when desired, can be located by means of the index.

102. AXIOMS OF THE BASIC OPERATIONS

The basic operations of the number system are *addition* and *multiplication*.   As shown below, *subtraction* and *division* can be defined in terms of these two.   The axioms of the basic operations are further subdivided into three subcategories: *addition*, *multiplication*, and *addition and multiplication*.

† For a proof of this fact and a discussion of the axioms of the real number system, see G. Birkhoff and S. MacLane, *A Survey of Modern Algebra* (New York, The Macmillan Company, 1944).   Also cf. Ex. 13, § 116.

I. Addition

(i) *Any two numbers, x and y, have a unique sum, $x + y$.*

(ii) *The **associative law** holds.   That is, if x, y, and z are any numbers,*
$$x + (y + z) = (x + y) + z.$$

(iii) *There exists a number 0 such that for any number x, $x + 0 = x$.*

(iv) *Corresponding to any number x there exists a number $-x$ such that*
$$x + (-x) = 0.$$

(v) *The **commutative law** holds.   That is, if x and y are any numbers,*
$$x + y = y + x.$$

The number 0 of axiom (*iii*) is called **zero.**

The number $-x$ of axiom (*iv*) is called the **negative** of the number x. The difference between x and y is defined:
$$x - y \equiv x + (-y).$$

The resulting operation is called **subtraction.**

Some of the properties that can be derived from Axioms I alone are given in Exercises 1-7, § 103.

II. Multiplication

(i) *Any two numbers, x and y, have a unique product, xy.*

(ii) *The **associative law** holds.   That is, if x, y, and z are any numbers,*
$$x(yz) = (xy)z.$$

(iii) *There exists a number $1 \neq 0$ such that for any number x, $x \cdot 1 = x$.*

(iv) *Corresponding to any number $x \neq 0$ there exists a number x^{-1} such that $x \cdot x^{-1} = 1$.*

(v) *The **commutative law** holds.   That is, if x and y are any numbers,*
$$xy = yx.$$

The number 1 of axiom (*iii*) is called **one** or **unity.**

The number x^{-1} of axiom (*iv*) is called the **reciprocal** of the number x. The **quotient** of x and y ($y \neq 0$) is defined:
$$\frac{x}{y} \equiv x \cdot y^{-1}.$$

The resulting operation is called **division.**

Some of the properties that can be derived from Axioms II alone are given in Exercises 8-11, § 103.

III. Addition and Multiplication

(i) *The **distributive law** holds.   That is, if x, y, and z are any numbers,*
$$x(y + z) = xy + xz.$$

The distributive law, together with Axioms I and II, yields further familiar relations, some of which are given in Exercises 12-33, § 103.

103. EXERCISES

In Exercises 1-33, prove the given statement or establish the given equation.

1. There is only one number having the property of the number 0 of Axiom I
(*iii*).   *Hint:* Assume that the numbers 0 and 0′ both have the property.   Then
simultaneously $0' + 0 = 0'$ and $0 + 0' = 0$.

2. The **law of cancellation for addition** holds: $x + y = x + z$ implies
$y = z$.   *Hint:* Let $(-x)$ be a number satisfying Axiom I (*iv*).   Then
$$(-x) + (x + y) = (-x) + (x + z).$$
Use the associative law.

3. The negative of a number is unique.   *Hint:* If y has the property of
$-x$ in Axiom I (*iv*), § 102, $x + y = x + (-x) = 0$.   Use the law of cancellation, given in Exercise 2.

4. $-0 = 0$.

5. $-(-x) = x$.

6. $0 - x = -x$.

7. $-(x + y) = -x - y; -(x - y) = y - x$.   *Hint:* By the uniqueness of
the negative it is sufficient for the first part to prove that
$$(x + y) + [(-x) + (-y)] = 0.$$
Use the commutative and associative laws.

8. There is only one number having the property of the number 1 of Axiom
II (*iii*).

9. The **law of cancellation for multiplication** holds: $xy = xz$ implies $y = z$
if $x \neq 0$.

10. The reciprocal of a number ($\neq 0$) is unique.

11. $1^{-1} = 1$.

12. $x \cdot 0 = 0$.   *Hint:* $x \cdot 0 + 0 = x \cdot 0 = x(0 + 0) = x \cdot 0 + x \cdot 0$.   Use the law
of cancellation on the extreme members.

13. Zero has no reciprocal.

14. If $x \neq 0$ and $y \neq 0$, then $xy \neq 0$.   Equivalently, if $xy = 0$, then either
$x = 0$ or $y = 0$.   *Hint:* Assume $x \neq 0$, $y \neq 0$, and $xy = 0$.   Then
$$x^{-1}(xy) = x^{-1} \cdot 0 = 0.$$
Use the associative law to infer $y = 0$.

15. If $x \neq 0$, then $x^{-1} \neq 0$ and $(x^{-1})^{-1} = x$.

16. $\dfrac{x}{y} = 0$ ($y \neq 0$) if and only if $x = 0$.

17. $\dfrac{1}{x} = x^{-1}$ ($x \neq 0$).

18. If $x \neq 0$ and $y \neq 0$, then $(xy)^{-1} = x^{-1}y^{-1}$, or $\dfrac{1}{xy} = \dfrac{1}{x} \cdot \dfrac{1}{y}$.

19. If $b \neq 0$ and $d \neq 0$, then $\dfrac{a}{b} = \dfrac{ad}{bd}$.
Hint: $(ad)(bd)^{-1} = (ad)(d^{-1}b^{-1}) = a[(dd^{-1})b^{-1}] = ab^{-1}$.

20. If $b \neq 0$ and $d \neq 0$, then $\dfrac{a}{b} \cdot \dfrac{c}{d} = \dfrac{ac}{bd}$.

21. If $b \neq 0$ and $d \neq 0$, then $\dfrac{a}{b} + \dfrac{c}{d} = \dfrac{ad + bc}{bd}$.

Hint: $(bd)^{-1}(ad + bc) = (b^{-1}d^{-1})(ad) + (b^{-1}d^{-1})(bc)$.

22. $(-1)(-1) = 1$. *Hint:* $(-1)(1 + (-1)) = 0$. The distributive law gives $(-1) + (-1)(-1) = 0$. Add 1 to each member.

23. $(-1)x = -x$.

Hint: Multiply each member of the equation $1 + (-1) = 0$ by x.

24. $(-x)(-y) = xy$.

Hint: Write $-x = (-1)x$ and $-y = (-1)y$.

25. $-(xy) = (-x)y = x(-y)$.

26. $-\dfrac{x}{y} = \dfrac{-x}{y} = \dfrac{x}{-y}$ $(y \neq 0)$.

27. $x(y - z) = xy - xz$.

★28. $(x - y) + (y - z) = x - z$.

★29. $(a - b) - (c - d) = (a + d) - (b + c)$.

★30. $(a + b)(c + d) = (ac + bd) + (ad + bc)$.

★31. $(a - b)(c - d) = (ac + bd) - (ad + bc)$.

★32. $a - b = c - d$ if and only if $a + d = b + c$.

33. The general linear equation $ax + b = 0$, $a \neq 0$, has a unique solution $x = -b/a$.

104. AXIOMS OF ORDER

In addition to the basic *operations*, the real numbers have an *order relation* subject to certain axioms. One form of these axioms expresses order in terms of the primitive concept of *positiveness:*

(*i*) *Some numbers have the property of being positive.*

(*ii*) *For any number x exactly one of the following three statements is true:*
$x = 0$; *x is positive;* $-x$ *is positive.*

(*iii*) *The sum of two positive numbers is positive.*

(*iv*) *The product of two positive numbers is positive.*

Definition I. *The symbols $<$ and $>$ (read "less than" and "greater than," respectively) are defined by the statements*

$$x < y \text{ if and only if } y - x \text{ is positive;}$$
$$x > y \text{ if and only if } x - y \text{ is positive.}$$

Definition II. *The number x is **negative** if and only if $-x$ is positive.*

Definition III. *The symbols $\leqq$ and $\geqq$ (read "less than or equal to" and "greater than or equal to," respectively) are defined by the statements*

$$x \leqq y \text{ if and only if either } x < y \text{ or } x = y;$$
$$x \geqq y \text{ if and only if either } x > y \text{ or } x = y.$$

NOTE 1. The two statements $x < y$ and $y > x$ are equivalent. The two statements $x \leq y$ and $y \geq x$ are equivalent.

NOTE 2. The *sense* of an inequality of the form $x < y$ or $x \leq y$ is said to be the **reverse** of that of an inequality of the form $x > y$ or $x \geq y$.

NOTE 3. The simultaneous inequalities $x < y$, $y < z$ are usually written $x < y < z$, and the simultaneous inequalities $x > y$, $y > z$ are usually written $x > y > z$. Similar interpretations are given the compound inequalities $x \leq y \leq z$ and $x \geq y \geq z$.

105. EXERCISES

In Exercises 1-24, prove the given statement or establish the given equation.

1. $x > 0$ if and only if x is positive.

2. The **transitive law** holds for $<$ and for $>$: $x < y$, $y < z$ *imply* $x < z$; $x > y$, $y > z$ *imply* $x > z$. (Cf. Ex. 19.)

3. The **law of trichotomy** holds: *for any x and y, exactly one of the following holds:* $x < y$, $x = y$, $x > y$.

4. Addition of any number to both members of an inequality preserves the order relation: $x < y$ implies $x + z < y + z$. A similar fact holds for subtraction. *Hint:* $(y + z) - (x + z) = y - x$.

5. $x < 0$ if and only if x is negative.

6. The sum of two negative numbers is negative.

7. The product of two negative numbers is positive. *Hint:* $xy = (-x)(-y)$. (Cf. Ex. 24, § 103.)

8. The square of any nonzero real number is positive.

9. $1 > 0$.

10. The equation $x^2 + 1 = 0$ has no real root.

11. The product of a positive number and a negative number is negative.

12. The reciprocal of a positive number is positive. The reciprocal of a negative number is negative.

13. $0 < x < y$ imply $0 < \dfrac{1}{y} < \dfrac{1}{x}$.

14. Multiplication or division of both members of an inequality by a positive number preserves the order relation: $x < y$, $z > 0$ imply $xz < yz$ and $x/z < y/z$.

15. Multiplication or division of both members of an inequality by a negative number reverses the order relation: $x < y$, $z < 0$ imply $xz > yz$ and $x/z > y/z$.

16. $a < b$, $c < d$ imply $a + c < b + d$.

17. $0 < a < b$, $0 < c < d$ imply $ac < bd$ and $a/d < b/c$.

18. If x and y are nonnegative numbers, then $x < y$ if and only if $x^2 < y^2$ (cf. Ex. 10, § 107).

19. The transitive law holds for $\leq$ (also for $\geq$): $x \leq y$, $y \leq z$ imply $x \leq z$. (Cf. Ex. 2.)

20. $x \leq y$, $y \leq x$ imply $x = y$.

21. $x + x = 0$ implies $x = 0$, $x + x + x = 0$ implies $x = 0$.

22. $x^2 + y^2 \geq 0$; $x^2 + y^2 > 0$ unless $x = y = 0$.

23. If x is a fixed number satisfying the inequality $x < \epsilon$ for every positive number ϵ, then $x \leq 0$. *Hint:* If x were positive one could choose $\epsilon = x$.

24. There is no largest number, and therefore the real number system is infinite. (Cf. Ex. 11, § 109.) *Hint:* $x + 1 > x$.

25. If $x < a < y$ or if $x > a > y$, then a is said to be **between** x and y. Prove that if x and y are distinct numbers, their arithmetic mean $\frac{1}{2}(x + y)$ is between them.

26. If $x^2 = y$, then x is called a **square root** of y. By Exercise 8, if such a number x exists, y must be nonnegative, and if $y = 0$, $x = 0$ is the only square root of y. Show that if a positive number y has square roots, it has exactly two square roots, one positive and one negative. The unique positive square root is called **the square root** and is written $\sqrt{y}$. It is shown in § 214 that such square roots do exist. *Hint:* Let $x^2 = z^2 = y$. Then

$$x^2 - z^2 = (x - z)(x + z) = 0.$$

Therefore $x = z$ or $x = -z$.

106. POSITIVE INTEGERS AND MATHEMATICAL INDUCTION

In the development of the real number system, as discussed briefly in the Introduction, the natural numbers become absorbed in successively larger number systems, losing their identity but not their properties, and finally emerge in the real number system as **positive integers**, $1, 2, 3, \cdots$.

The *positive integers* have certain elementary properties that follow directly from the role of the natural numbers in the construction of the number system (cf. § 115 for further remarks):

   (*i*) *The "positive integers" are positive.* (Cf. Ex. 9, § 105.)

   (*ii*) *If n is a positive integer, $n \geq 1$.*

  (*iii*) $2 = 1 + 1, 3 = 2 + 1, 4 = 3 + 1, 5 = 4 + 1, \cdots$.

  (*iv*) $0 < 1 < 2 < 3 < 4 < \cdots$.

   (*v*) *The sum and product of two positive integers are positive integers.*

  (*vi*) *If m and n are positive integers, and $m < n$, then $n - m$ is a positive integer.*

 (*vii*) *If n is a positive integer, there is no positive integer m such that $n < m < n + 1$.*

An important property of the positive integers, one which validates mathematical induction, is a rewording of the fifth Peano axiom for the natural numbers:

Axiom of Induction. *If S is a set of positive integers with the two properties* (*i*) *S contains the number 1, and* (*ii*) *whenever S contains the positive integer n it also contains the positive integer $n + 1$, then S contains all positive integers.*

An immediate consequence is the theorem:

Fundamental Theorem of Mathematical Induction. *For every positive integer n let $P(n)$ be a proposition which is either true or false. If (i) $P(1)$ is true and (ii) whenever this proposition is true for the positive integer n it is also true for the positive integer $n + 1$, then $P(n)$ is true for all positive integers n.*

Proof: Let S be the set of positive integers for which $P(n)$ is true, and use the Axiom of Induction.

Another consequence (less immediate) of the Axiom of Induction is the principle:

Well-ordering Principle. *Every nonempty set of positive integers (that is, every set of positive integers which contains at least one member) contains a smallest member.*

Proof. Let T be an arbitrary set of positive integers which contains at least one member, and assume that T has no smallest member. We shall obtain a contradiction by letting S be the set of all positive integers n having the property that every member of T is greater than n. Clearly 1 is a member of S, since every member of T is at *least* equal to 1, and if a member of T were *equal* to 1 it would be the smallest member of T (property (ii) above). Now suppose n is a member of S. Then every member of T is greater than n and therefore (property (vii) above) is at least $n + 1$. But by the same argument as that used above, any member of T equal to $n + 1$ would be the smallest member of T. Therefore every member of T is greater than $n + 1$ and $n + 1$ belongs to S. Consequently every positive integer is a member of S, and T must be empty.

We state two general laws which are familiar to all, whose detailed proofs by mathematical induction are given in § 115.

General Associative Laws. *Any two sums (products) of the n numbers $x_1, x_2, \cdots, x_n$ in the same order are equal regardless of the manner in which the terms (factors) are grouped by parentheses.*

Illustration. Let $a = x_1(x_2(x_3(x_4x_5)))$ and $b = ((x_1x_2)(x_3x_4))x_5$. We shall show that $b = a$ by using the associative law of § 102 to transform b step by step into a. A similar sequence of steps would transform any product of the five numbers into the "standard" product a, and hence justify the theorem for $n = 5$. We start by thinking of the products (x_1x_2) and (x_3x_4) as single numbers and use the associative law to write $b = (x_1x_2)((x_3x_4)x_5)$. Repeating this method we have: $b = (x_1x_2)(x_3(x_4x_5)) = x_1(x_2(x_3(x_4x_5))) = a$.

NOTE. As a consequence of the general associative laws any sum or product can be written without parentheses, since the omission of such parentheses leads to no ambiguity, thus: $x_1 + x_2 + \cdots + x_n$ and $x_1x_2 \cdots x_n$.

General Commutative Laws. *Any two sums (products) of the n numbers* $x_1, x_2, \cdots, x_n$ *are equal regardless of the order of the terms (factors).*

Illustration. Let $a = x_1 x_2 x_3 x_4 x_5$ and $b = x_4 x_1 x_5 x_2 x_3$. We shall show that $b = a$ by using the commutative law of § 102 to transform b step by step into a. We first bring x_1 to the left-hand end: $b = (x_4 x_1)(x_5 x_2 x_3) = (x_1 x_4)(x_5 x_2 x_3) = x_1 x_4 x_5 x_2 x_3$. Next we take care of x_2: $b = x_1 x_4 (x_5 x_2) x_3 = x_1 (x_4 x_2) x_5 x_3 = x_1 x_2 x_4 x_5 x_3$. Finally, after x_3 is moved two steps to the left, the form a is reached.

The following examples illustrate the principles and uses of mathematical induction:

Example 1. Establish the formula

(1) $$1^2 + 3^2 + 5^2 + \cdots + (2n - 1)^2 = \frac{n(4n^2 - 1)}{3}$$

for every positive integer n.

Solution. Let $P(n)$ be the proposition (1). Direct substitution shows that $P(1)$ is true. We wish to show that whenever $P(n)$ is true for a *particular* positive integer n it is also true for the positive integer $n + 1$. Accordingly, we assume (1) and wish to establish

(2) $$1^2 + 3^2 + 5^2 + \cdots + (2n - 1)^2 + (2n + 1)^2 = \frac{(n + 1)[4(n + 1)^2 - 1]}{3}.$$

On the assumption that (1) is correct (for a particular value of n), we can rewrite the left-hand member of (2) by grouping:

$$[1^2 + 3^2 + \cdots + (2n - 1)^2] + (2n + 1)^2 = \frac{n(4n^2 - 1)}{3} + (2n + 1)^2.$$

Thus verification of (2) reduces to verification of

(3) $$\frac{n(4n^2 - 1)}{3} + (2n + 1)^2 = \frac{(n + 1)(4n^2 + 8n + 3)}{3},$$

which, in turn, is true (divide by 3) by virtue of

(4) $4n^3 - n + 3(4n^2 + 4n + 1) = (4n^3 + 8n^2 + 3n) + (4n^2 + 8n + 3).$

By the Fundamental Theorem of Mathematical Induction, (1) is true for all positive integers n.

Example 2. Prove the *general distributive law:*

(5) $$x(y_1 + y_2 + \cdots + y_n) = xy_1 + xy_2 + \cdots + xy_n.$$

Solution. Let $P(n)$ be the proposition (5). $P(1)$ is a triviality, and $P(2)$ is true by the distributive law III(i), § 102. We wish to show now that the truth of (5) for a particular positive integer n implies the truth of $P(n + 1)$:

(6) $x(y_1 + y_2 + \cdots + y_n + y_{n+1}) = xy_1 + xy_2 + \cdots + xy_n + xy_{n+1}.$

By using the distributive law of § 102 and the assumption (5), we can rewrite the left-hand member of (6) as follows:

$$x[(y_1 + \cdots + y_n) + y_{n+1}] = x(y_1 + \cdots + y_n) + xy_{n+1}$$
$$= (xy_1 + \cdots + xy_n) + xy_{n+1}.$$

Since this last expression is equal to the right-hand member of (6), the truth of $P(n)$, or (5), is established for all positive integers n by the Fundamental Theorem of Mathematical Induction.

107. EXERCISES

1. Prove that $2 + 2 = 4$. *Hint:* Use the associative law with $4 = 3 + 1 = (2 + 1) + 1$.

2. Prove that $2 \cdot 3 = 6$.

3. Prove that $6 + 8 = 14$ and that $3 \cdot 4 = 12$.

4. Prove that the sum and product of n positive integers are positive integers.

5. Prove that any product of nonzero numbers is nonzero.

6. Prove that if $x_1 \neq 0$, $x_2 \neq 0$, $\cdots$, $x_n \neq 0$, then $(x_1 x_2 \cdots x_n)^{-1} = x_1^{-1} x_2^{-1} \cdots x_n^{-1}$.

7. Prove that if $x_1 < x_2, x_2 < x_3, \cdots, x_{n-1} < x_n$ (usually written $x_1 < x_2 < \cdots < x_n$), then $x_1 < x_n$.

8. Prove that any sum or product of positive numbers is positive.

9. Use mathematical induction to prove that if n is any positive integer, then $x^n - y^n = (x - y)(x^{n-1} + x^{n-2}y + \cdots + xy^{n-2} + y^{n-1})$. *Hint:* $x^{n+1} - y^{n+1} = x^n(x - y) + y(x^n - y^n)$.

10. Prove that if x and y are nonnegative numbers and n is a positive integer, then $x > y$ if and only if $x^n > y^n$. *Hint:* Use Ex. 9. (Cf. Ex. 18, § 105.)

11. Establish the inequality $2^n > n$, where n is a positive integer.

12. Establish the formula $1 + 2 + \cdots + n = \frac{1}{2}n(n + 1)$. (Cf. Ex. 38.)

13. Establish the formula (cf. Ex. 39)
$$1^2 + 2^2 + \cdots + n^2 = \tfrac{1}{6}n(n + 1)(2n + 1).$$

14. Establish the formula (cf. Ex. 40)
$$1^3 + 2^3 + \cdots + n^3 = \tfrac{1}{4}n^2(n + 1)^2 = (1 + 2 + \cdots + n)^2.$$

15. Establish the formula (cf. Ex. 41)
$$1^4 + 2^4 + \cdots + n^4 = \tfrac{1}{30}n(n + 1)(2n + 1)(3n^2 + 3n - 1).$$

★16. Let A be a nonempty set of real numbers with the property that whenever x is a member of A and y is a member of A then $x - y$ is a member of A. Prove that whenever $x_1, x_2, \cdots, x_n$ are members of A then $x_1 + x_2 + \cdots + x_n$ is a member of A.

17. Establish the law of exponents: $a^m a^n = a^{m+n}$, where a is any number and m and n are positive integers. *Hint:* Hold m fixed and use induction on n.

18. Establish the law of exponents:

$$\frac{a^m}{a^n} = \begin{cases} a^{m-n} \text{ if } m < n, \\ \dfrac{1}{a^{n-m}} \text{ if } n < m, \end{cases}$$

where a is any nonzero number and m and n are positive integers.

19. Establish the law of exponents: $(a^m)^n = a^{mn}$, where a is any number and m and n are positive integers.

20. Establish the law of exponents: $(ab)^n = a^n b^n$, where a and b are any numbers and n is a positive integer. Generalize to m factors.

21. Establish the law of exponents $\left(\dfrac{a}{b}\right)^n = \dfrac{a^n}{b^n}$, where a and b are any numbers ($b \neq 0$) and n is a positive integer.

22. A positive integer m is a **factor** of a positive integer p if and only if there exists a positive integer n such that $p = mn$. A positive integer p is called **composite** if and only if there exist integers $m > 1$ and $n > 1$ such that $p = mn$. A positive integer p is **prime** if and only if $p > 1$ and p is not composite. Prove that if m_i, $i = 1, 2, \cdots, n$, are integers > 1, then $m_1 m_2 \cdots m_n > n$. Hence prove that any integer > 1 is either a prime or a product of primes. (Cf. Ex. 29.)

23. Two positive integers are **relatively prime** if and only if they have no common integral factor greater than 1. A fraction p/q, where p and q are positive integers, is **in lowest terms** if and only if p and q are relatively prime. Prove that any quotient of positive integers is equal to such a fraction in lowest terms. (Cf. Ex. 33.)

★24. Prove that the positive integers are **Archimedean** (cf. § 114): If a and b are positive integers, then there exists a positive integer n such that $na > b$. *Hint:* $ba \geqq b$.

★25. Prove the **Fundamental Theorem of Euclid**: *If a and b are positive integers, there exist unique numbers n and r, each of which is either 0 or a positive integer and where $r < a$, such that*
$$b = na + r.$$
Hint: For existence, let $n + 1$ be the smallest positive integer such that $(n + 1)a > b$ (cf. Ex. 24).

★26. Prove that a prime number p cannot be a factor of the product of two positive integers, a and b, each of which is less than p. *Hint:* Assuming that p is a factor of ab, let c be the smallest positive integer such that p is a factor of ac, and let n be a positive integer such that $nc < p < (n + 1)c$ (cf. Ex. 24). Then $p - nc$ is a positive integer less than c having the property assumed for c !

★27. Prove that if a prime number p is a factor of the product of two positive integers, a and b, then p is a factor of either a or b (or both). *Hint:* Use Exs. 25 and 26.

★28. Prove that if a prime number p is a factor of the product of n positive integers a_1, a_2, $\cdots$, a_n, then p is a factor of at least one of these numbers. (Cf. Ex. 27.)

★29. Prove the **Unique Factorization Theorem**: *Every positive integer greater than 1 can be represented in one and only one way as a product of primes. Hint:* Assume $p_1 p_2 \cdots p_m$ and $q_1 q_2 \cdots q_n$ are two nonidentical factorizations of a positive integer. Cancel all identical prime factors from both members of the equation $p_1 p_2 \cdots p_m = q_1 q_2 \cdots q_n$. A prime number remains which is a factor of both members but which violates Ex. 28. (Cf. Ex. 22.)

★30. Prove that if a, b, and c are positive integers such that a and c are relatively prime and b and c are relatively prime, then ab and c are relatively prime. (Cf. Ex. 23.)

★31. Prove that if a, b, and c are positive integers such that a and c are relatively prime and c is a factor of ab, then c is a factor of b. (Cf. Ex. 23.)

★32. Prove that two positive integers each of which is a factor of the other are equal.

★33. Prove that if a fraction p/q, where p and q are positive integers, is in lowest terms, then p and q are uniquely determined. (Cf. Ex. 23.)

34. If n is a positive integer, **n factorial**, written $n\,!$, is defined: $n\,! \equiv 1\cdot2\cdot3\cdot$ $\cdots\cdot n$. **Zero factorial** is defined: $0\,! \equiv 1$. If r is a positive integer or zero and if $0 \leqq r \leqq n$, the binomial coefficient $\binom{n}{r}$ (also written $_nC_r$) is defined:

$$\binom{n}{r} \equiv \frac{n\,!}{(n-r)\,!\,r\,!}.$$

Prove that $\binom{n}{r}$ is a positive integer. *Hint:* Establish the law of *Pascal's Triangle* (cf. any College Algebra text): $\binom{n+1}{r} = \binom{n}{r-1} + \binom{n}{r}$.

35. Prove the **Binomial Theorem** for positive integral exponents (cf. V, § 807): *If x and y are any numbers and n is a positive integer,*

$$(x+y)^n = \binom{n}{0}x^n + \binom{n}{1}x^{n-1}y + \cdots + \binom{n}{r}x^{n-r}y^r + \cdots + \binom{n}{n}y^n.$$

(Cf. Ex. 34.)

36. The **sigma summation notation** is defined:

$$\sum_{k=m}^{n} f(k) \equiv f(m) + f(m+1) + \cdots + f(n), \text{ where } n \geqq m. \quad \text{Prove:}$$

(*i*) k is a **dummy variable:** $\sum_{k=m}^{n} f(k) = \sum_{i=m}^{n} f(i)$.

(*ii*) $\sum$ is **additive:** $\sum_{k=m}^{n} [f(k) + g(k)] = \sum_{k=m}^{n} f(k) + \sum_{k=m}^{n} g(k)$.

(*iii*) $\sum$ is **homogeneous:** $\sum_{k=m}^{n} cf(k) = c \sum_{k=m}^{n} f(k)$.

(*iv*) $\sum_{k=m}^{n} 1 = n - m + 1$.

★**37.** A useful summation formula is

(1) $\sum_{k=1}^{n} [f(k) - f(k-1)] = f(n) - f(0)$. Establish this by mathematical induction.

★**38.** By means of Exercises 36 and 37 *derive* the formula of Exercise 12. *Hint:* Let $f(n) \equiv n^2$. Then (1) becomes

$$\sum_{k=1}^{n} [k^2 - (k-1)^2] = \sum_{k=1}^{n} (2k-1) = n^2, \quad \text{or}$$

$$2\sum_{k=1}^{n} k = n^2 + n.$$

★**39.** By means of Exercises 36-38, *derive* the formula of Exercise 13. *Hint:* Let $f(n) \equiv n^3$ in (1).

★**40.** By means of Exercises 36-39, *derive* the formula of Exercise 14.

★**41.** By means of Exercises 36-40, *derive* the formula of Exercise 15.

★**42.** Use mathematical induction to prove that $\sum_{k=1}^{n} k^m$ is a polynomial in n of degree $m+1$ whose leading coefficient (coefficient of the term of highest degree) is $1/(m+1)$. (Cf. Exs. 36-41.)

★**43.** If $a_1, a_2, \cdots, a_n$ and $b_1, b_2, \cdots, b_n$ are real numbers, show that

$$\left(\sum_{i=1}^{n} a_i^2\right)\left(\sum_{i=1}^{n} b_i^2\right) - \left(\sum_{i=1}^{n} a_i b_i\right)^2 = \sum_{1 \le i < j \le n} (a_i b_j - a_j b_i)^2.$$

Hence establish the **Schwarz (or Cauchy) inequality**:

$$\left(\sum_{i=1}^{n} a_i b_i\right)^2 \le \sum_{i=1}^{n} a_i^2 \sum_{i=1}^{n} b_i^2.$$

(Cf. Ex. 29, § 503; Ex. 26, § 711; Ex. 14, § 717.)

★**44.** By use of Exercise 43, establish the **Minkowski inequality**:

$$\sqrt{\sum_{i=1}^{n} (a_i + b_i)^2} \le \sqrt{\sum_{i=1}^{n} a_i^2} + \sqrt{\sum_{i=1}^{n} b_i^2}.$$

Hint: Square both members of the Minkowski inequality, expand each term on the left, cancel identical terms that result, divide by 2, and reverse steps. (Cf. Ex. 30, § 503; Ex. 14, § 717.)

108. INTEGERS AND RATIONAL NUMBERS

In order to rely as little as possible on the constructive process behind real numbers, we shall formulate definitions of integers and rational numbers in terms of the more primitive concept of *positive integer*. Having done this in order to achieve an economy in basic concepts, we must suffer the consequence of being forced to prove "obvious" statements. For instance, we all know that the sum of two integers is an integer, yet the student is asked to prove this elementary fact in Exercise 1 of the following section! Inspection of the following two definitions and of the hint accompanying that exercise should dispel any confusion.

Definition I.   *A number x is a **negative integer** if and only if $-x$ is a positive integer. A number x is an **integer** if and only if it is 0 or a positive integer or a negative integer.*

Definition II.   *A number x is a **rational number** if and only if there exist integers p and q, where $q \ne 0$, such that $x = p/q$. The real numbers that are not rational are called **irrational**.*

109. EXERCISES

1. Prove that the sum of two integers is an integer. *Hint:* Consider all possible cases of signs. For the case $m > -n > 0$, use property (vi), § 106.

2. Prove that the product of two integers is an integer.

3. Prove that the difference between two integers is an integer.

4. Prove that the quotient of two integers need not be an integer.

5. Prove that the integers are rational numbers.

6. Prove that the sum, difference, and product of two rational numbers are rational numbers, and that the quotient of two rational numbers the second of which is nonzero is a rational number.

7. Define integral powers a^n, where $a \neq 0$ and n is any integer, and establish the laws of exponents of Exercises 17-21, § 107, for integral exponents.

8. The square root of a positive number was defined in Exercise 26, § 105. Existence is proved in § 214. Prove that $\sqrt{2}$ is irrational. That is, prove that there is no positive rational number whose square is 2. *Hint:* Assume $\sqrt{2} = p/q$, where p and q are relatively prime positive integers (cf. Ex. 23, § 107). Then $p^2 = 2q^2$, and p is even and of the form $2k$. Repeat the argument to show that q is also even!

★9. Assume that $f(x) \equiv a_0 x^n + a_1 x^{n-1} + \cdots + a_{n-1} x + a_n$ is a polynomial with integral coefficients $a_0, \cdots, a_n$, of which the leading coefficient a_0 and the constant term a_n are nonzero. Prove that if p/q is a rational root of the equation $f(x) = 0$, where p and q are relatively prime integers (that is, they are nonzero and they have no common integral factor greater than 1; cf. Ex. 23, § 107), then p is a factor of a_n and q is a factor of a_0. *Hint:* By assumption $a_0 p^n + a_1 p^{n-1} q + \cdots + a_n q^n = 0$. Use Ex. 31, § 107, and the fact that each of p and q is a factor of n of these terms, and therefore also of the remaining term.

★10. Prove that a positive integer m cannot have a rational nth root (n is a positive integer), unless m is a perfect nth power (of a positive integer), and hence generalize Exercise 8. *Hint:* Use Ex. 9.

★11. Prove that a positive rational number p/q, where p and q are relatively prime positive integers, cannot have a rational nth root (n is a positive integer) unless both p and q are perfect nth powers. (Cf. Ex. 23, § 107; Ex. 10 above.)

★12. Let a and b be any two nonzero integers, and consider the set

$$G(a, b) \equiv \{ma + nb\}$$

consisting of all numbers of the form $ma + nb$, where m and n are arbitrary integers. Prove that $G(a, b)$ consists precisely of all integral multiples of a positive integer k. *Hint:* Show first that whenever c and d belong to $G(a, b)$, so do $c + d$ and $c - d$, and that whenever c belongs to $G(a, b)$ and h is an arbitrary integer, then ch belongs to $G(a, b)$. Then let k be the smallest positive integer in $G(a, b)$. If there were a member of $G(a, b)$ not a multiple of k, use the Fundamental Theorem of Euclid (Ex. 25, § 107) to obtain a contradiction.

★13. Prove that the number k of Exercise 12 is unique. Prove that k is a factor of both a and b, and that any common factor of a and b is a factor of k. (In other words, k is the *highest common factor* of a and b.)

★14. Prove that if a and b are relatively prime integers, there exist integers m and n such that

$$ma + nb = 1.$$

(Cf. Exs. 12-13.)

NOTE. In the following problems, **nonzero polynomial** means any polynomial different from the **zero polynomial** all of whose coefficients are zero.

★15. Prove the *Fundamental Theorem of Euclid for polynomials: If $f(x)$ and $g(x)$ are nonzero polynomials, there exist unique polynomials $Q(x)$ and $R(x)$, where $R(x)$ either is 0 or has degree less than that of $g(x)$, such that*

$$f(x) = Q(x)g(x) + R(x).$$

The polynomials $Q(x)$ and $R(x)$ are called the **quotient** and **remainder**, respectively, when $f(x)$ is divided by $g(x)$. (Cf. Ex. 25, § 107.)

★**16.** Let $f(x)$ and $g(x)$ be any two nonzero polynomials, and consider the set

$$G(f, g) \equiv \{\phi(x)f(x) + \psi(x)g(x)\}$$

consisting of all polynomials of the form $\phi f + \psi g$, where ϕ and ψ are arbitrary polynomials. Prove that $G(f, g)$ consists precisely of all polynomial multiples of a nonzero polynomial $P(x)$. *Hint:* See Ex. 12, observing that $P(x)$ is not uniquely determined, but is any nonzero polynomial in $G(f, g)$ of lowest degree.

★**17.** State and prove the analogue of Exercise 13 for Exercise 16. *Hint:* $P(x)$ is unique except for a nonzero constant factor.

★**18.** Prove that if $f(x)$ and $g(x)$ are relatively prime polynomials (that is, they are nonzero and have only constants as common polynomial factors), there exist polynomials $\phi(x)$ and $\psi(x)$ such that

$$\phi(x)f(x) + \psi(x)g(x) = 1.$$

(Cf. Exs. 16-17.)

★**19.** Prove that any fraction of the form $N(x)/f(x)g(x)$, where $N(x)$ is a polynomial and $f(x)$ and $g(x)$ are relatively prime polynomials, can be written in the form

$$\frac{N(x)}{f(x)g(x)} = \frac{A(x)}{f(x)} + \frac{B(x)}{g(x)},$$

where $A(x)$ and $B(x)$ are polynomials. *Hint:* Take the equation of Ex. 18, divide by $f(x)g(x)$, and multiply by $N(x)$.

★**20.** Prove that if $f(x)$ and $g(x)$ are nonconstant polynomials and if the degree of $N(x)$ is less than that of $f(x)g(x)$, then the polynomials $A(x)$ and $B(x)$ of Exercise 19 can be chosen so that their degrees are less than those of $f(x)$ and $g(x)$, respectively. *Hint:* Write

$$\frac{N(x)}{f(x)g(x)} = \frac{\Phi(x)}{f(x)} + \frac{\Psi(x)}{g(x)},$$

where $\Phi(x)$ and $\Psi(x)$ are polynomials, and write $\Phi(x) = Q(x) f(x) + A(x)$, where the degree of $A(x)$ is less than that of $f(x)$, and define $B(x) \equiv \Psi(x) + Q(x) g(x)$. Under the assumption that the degree of $B(x)$ is at least that of $g(x)$, obtain a contradiction from the equation $N(x) = A(x)g(x) + B(x)f(x)$.

★**21.** Prove that any fraction of the form $A(x)/[p(x)]^n$, where $A(x)$ and $p(x)$ are nonconstant polynomials and n is a positive integer, and where the degree of the numerator $A(x)$ is less than that of the denominator $[p(x)]^n$, can be written in the form

$$\frac{A(x)}{[p(x)]^n} = \frac{B(x)}{[p(x)]^{n-1}} + \frac{C(x)}{[p(x)]^n},$$

where $B(x)$ and $C(x)$ are polynomials such that $B(x)$ either is 0 or has degree less than that of $[p(x)]^{n-1}$, and $C(x)$ either is 0 or has degree less than that of $p(x)$. *Hint:* Use Ex. 15 to write $A(x) = B(x)p(x) + C(x)$.

★**22.** Recall the fact from College Algebra that any real polynomial (any polynomial with real coefficients) of positive degree can be factored into real linear and quadratic factors; more precisely, as a constant times a product of factors of the form $(x + a)$ and $(x^2 + bx + c)$, where the discriminant $b^2 - 4c$ is negative. Use this fact and those contained in Exercises 19-21 to prove the

Fundamental Theorem on Partial Fractions (used in Integral Calculus): *Any quotient of real polynomials, where the degree of the numerator is less than that of the denominator, can be expressed as a sum of fractions of the form*

$$\frac{A}{(x + a)^m} \quad \text{and} \quad \frac{Bx + C}{(x^2 + bx + c)^n},$$

where A, B, and C are constants and m and n are positive integers.

110. GEOMETRICAL REPRESENTATION AND ABSOLUTE VALUE

The reader has doubtless made use of the standard representation of real numbers by means of points on a straight line. It is conventional, when considering this line to lie horizontally as in Figure 101, to adopt a

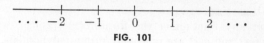

FIG. 101

uniform scale, with numbers increasing to the right and decreasing to the left. With an appropriate axiomatic system for Euclidean geometry† there is a one-to-one correspondence between real numbers and points on a line. That is, to any real number there corresponds precisely one point of the line, and to any point of the line, there corresponds precisely one real number. For this reason it is often immaterial whether one speaks of *numbers* or *points*. In this book we shall frequently use these two words interchangeably, and feel free, for example, to speak of the *point* 3. In this sense, in Figure 101, positive numbers lie to the right of the point 0, and $x < y$ if and only if the point x is to the left of the point y. Again, if $x < z$, then the number y satisfies the simultaneous inequalities $x < y < z$ if and only if the point y is between the points x and z (cf. Ex. 25, § 105). Properties of the real numbers, axiomatized and obtained in this chapter, lend strength to our intuitive conviction that a straight line with a number scale furnishes a reliable picture of the real number system.

Definition I. *If a and b are any two real numbers such that $a < b$, the* **open interval** *from a to b, written (a,b), is the set of all numbers x between a and b, $a < x < b$. The* **closed interval** *from a to b, written $[a,b]$, includes the points a and b and is the set of all x such that $a \leq x \leq b$. The* **half-open intervals** *$(a,b]$ and $[a,b)$ are defined by the inequalities $a < x \leq b$ and $a \leq x < b$, respectively. In any of these cases the interval is called a* **finite interval** *and the points a and b are called* **end-points**. *Infinite intervals are denoted and defined as follows, the point a, where it appears, being the*

† Cf. D. Hilbert, *The Foundations of Geometry* (La Salle, Ill., The Open Court Publishing Company, 1938).

end-point *of the interval:* $(a, +\infty), x > a; [a, +\infty), x \geqq a; (-\infty, a), x < a;$ $(-\infty, a], x \leqq a; (-\infty, +\infty),$ *all* x.† *Any point of an interval that is not an end-point is called an* **interior point** *of the interval.*

Definition II. *The* **absolute value** *of a number* x, *written* $|x|$, *is defined:*

$$|x| \equiv \begin{cases} x \text{ if } x \geqq 0, \\ -x \text{ if } x < 0. \end{cases}$$

The absolute value of a number can be thought of as its *distance* from the **origin** 0 in Figure 101. Similarly, the absolute value of the difference between two numbers, $|x - y|$, is the distance between the two points x and y. Some of the more useful properties of the absolute value are given below. For hints for some of the proofs, see § 111.

Properties of Absolute Value

   I. $|x| \geqq 0$; $|x| = 0$ *if and only if* $x = 0$.
  II. $|xy| = |x| \cdot |y|$.
 III. $\left|\dfrac{x}{y}\right| = \dfrac{|x|}{|y|}$ $(y \neq 0)$.
  IV. *If* $\epsilon > 0$, *then*
       (*i*) *the inequality* $|x| < \epsilon$ *is equivalent to the simultaneous inequalities* $-\epsilon < x < \epsilon$;
       (*ii*) *the inequality* $|x| \leqq \epsilon$ *is equivalent to the simultaneous inequalities* $-\epsilon \leqq x \leqq \epsilon$.
   V. *The* **triangle inequality**‡ *holds:* $|x + y| \leqq |x| + |y|$.
  VI. $|-x| = |x|$; $|x - y| = |y - x|$.
 VII. $|x|^2 = x^2$; $|x| = \sqrt{x^2}$. (Cf. Ex. 26, § 105.)
VIII. $|x - y| \leqq |x| + |y|$.
  IX. $\big|\, |x| - |y|\, \big| \leqq |x - y|$.

Definition III. *A* **neighborhood** *or* **epsilon-neighborhood** *of a point* a *is an open interval of the form* $(a - \epsilon, a + \epsilon)$, *where* ϵ *is a positive number.*

By Property IV, the neighborhood $(a - \epsilon, a + \epsilon)$ consists of all x satisfying the inequalities $a - \epsilon < x < a + \epsilon$, or $-\epsilon < x - a < \epsilon$, or $|x - a| < \epsilon$. It consists, therefore, of all points whose distance from a is less than ϵ. The point a is the midpoint of each of its neighborhoods.

---

† These infinite intervals are also sometimes designated directly by means of inequalities: $a < x < +\infty$, $a \leqq x < +\infty$, $-\infty < x < a$, $-\infty < x \leqq a$, and $-\infty < x < +\infty$, respectively.

‡ Property V is called the *triangle inequality* because the corresponding inequality for complex numbers states that any side of a triangle is less than or equal to the sum of the other two.

111. EXERCISES

1. Prove Property I, § 110.

2. Prove Property II, § 110.

3. Prove Property III, § 110. *Hint:* Use Property II with $z = x/y$, so that $x = yz$.

4. Prove Property IV, § 110.

5. Prove Property V, § 110. *Hint:* For the case $x > 0$ and $y < 0$,
$$x + y < x + 0 < x - y = |x| + |y|,$$
$$-(x + y) = -x - y < x - y = |x| + |y|.$$
Use Property IV. Consider all possible cases of sign.

6. Prove Property VI, § 110.

7. Prove Property VII, § 110.

8. Prove Property VIII, § 110.

9. Prove Property IX, § 110. *Hint:* The inequality $|x| - |y| \leq |x - y|$ follows by Property V from $|(x - y) + y| \leq |x - y| + |y|$.

10. Prove that $|x_1 \cdot x_2 \cdots x_n| = |x_1| \cdot |x_2| \cdots \cdot |x_n|$.

11. Prove the *general triangle inequality:*
$$|x_1 + x_2 + \cdots + x_n| \leq |x_1| + |x_2| + \cdots + |x_n|.$$

12. Replace by an equivalent single inequality:
$$x > a + b, \quad x > a - b.$$

In Exercises 13-24, find the values of x that satisfy the given inequality or inequalities. Express your answer without absolute values.

13. $|x - 2| < 3$. | **14.** $|x + 3| \geq 2$.

15. $|x - 5| < |x + 1|$. *Hint:* Square both members. (Cf. Ex. 18, § 105.)

★16. $|x - 4| > x - 2$. | **★17.** $|x - 4| \leq 2 - x$.

★18. $|x - 2| > x - 4$. | **★19.** $|x^2 - 2| \leq 1$.

★20. $x^2 - 2x - 15 < 0$. *Hint:* Factor and graph the left-hand member.

★21. $x^2 + 10 < 6x$. | **★22.** $|x + 5| < 2|x|$.

★23. $x < x^2 - 12 < 4x$. | **★24.** $|x - 7| < 5 < |5x - 25|$.

In Exercises 25-28, solve for x, and express your answer in a simple form by using absolute value signs.

★25. $\dfrac{x - a}{x + a} > 0$. | **★26.** $\dfrac{a - x}{a + x} \geq 0$.

★27. $\dfrac{x - 1}{x - 3} > \dfrac{x + 3}{x + 1}$. | **★28.** $\dfrac{x - a}{x - b} > \dfrac{x + a}{x + b}$.

In Exercises 29-38, sketch the graph. (These problems presuppose Analytic Geometry.)

★29. $y = |x|$. | **★30.** $y = \dfrac{x}{|x|}$.

★31. $y = x \cdot |x|$. | **★32.** $y = \sqrt{|x|}$.

★33. $y = |\,|x| - 1|$. | **★34.** $|y| = |x|$.

★35. $|y| < |x|$. | **★36.** $|x| + |y| = 1$.

★**37.** $|x| + |y| < 1.$ ★**38.** $|x| - |y| \leqq 1.$

112. SOME FURTHER PROPERTIES

In this section we give a few relations which exist between *certain* real numbers (integers and rational numbers, to be precise) and real numbers *in general.* In the constructive development of the real number system, discussed in the introduction, these properties follow easily and naturally from the definitions. From the point of view of a set of axioms descriptive of the real numbers, it is of interest that the properties of this section are implied by the properties listed as axioms in other sections of this chapter, in particular the axiom of completeness (cf. § 114 for statements and proofs not given in this section).

(*i*) *If x is any real number there exists a positive integer n such that $n > x$.*

(*ii*) *If x is any real number there exist integers m and n such that*

$$m < x < n.$$

(*iii*) *If x is any real number there exists a unique integer n such that*

$$n \leqq x < n + 1.$$

(*iv*) *If ϵ is any positive number there exists a positive integer n such that*

$$\frac{1}{n} < \epsilon.$$

(*v*) *The rational numbers are **dense** in the system of real numbers. That is, between any two distinct real numbers there is a rational number (in fact, there are infinitely many).*

We defer to § 114 the proof of (*i*) and present here the proofs of the remaining properties on the assumption that (*i*) is true.

Proof of (*ii*). According to (*i*), let n be a positive integer such that $n > x$, let p be a positive integer such that $p > -x$, and let $m \equiv -p$.

Proof of (*iii*). *Existence:* By (*ii*) there exist integers r and s such that $r < x < s$. If x is an integer, let $n = x$. If x is not an integer, x must lie between two consecutive integers of the finite set $r, r + 1, r + 2, \cdots$, s. *Uniqueness:* If m and n are distinct integers such that $m \leqq x < m + 1$ and $n \leqq x < n + 1$, assume $n < m$. Then $n < m \leqq x < n + 1$, in contradiction to property (*vii*), § 106.

Proof of (*iv*). Let $n > 1/\epsilon$, by (*i*).

Proof of (*v*). Let a and b be two real numbers, where $a < b$, or $b - a > 0$. Let q be a positive integer such that $\frac{1}{q} < b - a$, by (*iv*). We now seek an integer p so that $\frac{p}{q}$ shall satisfy the relation

$$a < \frac{p}{q} \leqq a + \frac{1}{q} < b.$$

This will hold if p is chosen so that $aq < p \leqq aq + 1$, or $p - 1 \leqq aq < p$, according to (iii).   With this choice of p and q we have found a rational number $r_1 \equiv p/q$ between a and b.   A second rational number r_2 must exist between r_1 and b, a third between r_2 and b, etc.

113. EXERCISES

1. Prove that if r is a nonzero rational number and x is irrational, then $x \pm r$, $r - x$, xr, x/r, r/x are all irrational.   *Hint for* $x + r$: If $x + r = s$, a rational number, then $x = s - r$.

2. Prove that the irrational numbers are dense in the system of real numbers.   *Hint:* Let x and y be any two distinct real numbers, assume $x < y$, and find a rational number p/q between $\sqrt{2}\, x$ and $\sqrt{2}\, y$.   Then divide by $\sqrt{2}$.   (Cf. Ex. 8, § 109, and Ex. 1, above.)

3. Prove that the sum of two irrational numbers may be rational.   What about their product?

★**4.** Prove that the **binary numbers,** $p/2^n$, where p is an integer and n is a positive integer, are dense in the system of real numbers.   (Cf. Ex. 11, § 107, and Ex. 5, below.)

★**5.** Prove that the **terminating decimals** $\pm d_{-m}d_{-m+1} \cdots d_{-1}d_0.d_1d_2 \cdots d_n$, where d_i is an integral digit ($0 \leqq d_i \leqq 9$), are dense in the system of real numbers.   *Hint:* Each such number is of the form $p/10^q$, where p is an integer and q is a positive integer.   (Cf. Ex. 4.)

NOTE.   Decimal expansions are treated in Exercises 28-30, § 711.

6. Prove that if x and y are two fixed numbers and if $y \leqq x + \epsilon$ for every positive number ϵ, then $y \leqq x$.   Prove a corresponding result as a consequence of an inequality of the form $y < x + \epsilon$; of the form $y \geqq x - \epsilon$; of the form $y > x - \epsilon$.   (Cf. Ex. 23, § 105.)

★**7.** Axioms I (i), (ii), (iii), and (iv), § 102, define a **group.**   That is, any set of objects with one operation (in this case addition) satisfying these axioms is *by definition* a group.   Show that the set of all nonzero numbers with the operation of multiplication (instead of addition) is a group.

★**8.** Axioms I, II, and III, § 102, define a **field.**   That is, any set of objects with two operations satisfying these axioms is *by definition* a field.   Show that the set of five elements 0, 1, 2, 3, 4, with the following addition and multiplication tables, is a field:

	0	1	2	3	4
0	0	1	2	3	4
1	1	2	3	4	0
2	2	3	4	0	1
3	3	4	0	1	2
4	4	0	1	2	3

Addition

	0	1	2	3	4
0	0	0	0	0	0
1	0	1	2	3	4
2	0	2	4	1	3
3	0	3	1	4	2
4	0	4	3	2	1

Multiplication

Hint: The sum (product) of any two elements is the remainder left after division by 5 of the real-number sum (product) of the corresponding two numbers.

★**9.** Prove that the integers form a group but not a field. (Cf. Exs. 7 and 8.)

★**10.** Prove that the rational numbers form a field. (Cf. Ex. 8.)

★**11.** Axioms I, II, and III, § 102, and the axioms of § 104 define an **ordered field**. That is, any set of objects with two operations and an order relation satisfying these axioms is *by definition* an ordered field. Prove that the rational numbers form an ordered field. Prove that any ordered field is infinite. (Cf. Ex. 8, above, and Ex. 24, § 105.)

★**12.** Any set whose members can be put into a one-to-one correspondence with the natural numbers is called **denumerable** or **enumerable**. Thus the set of positive integers is denumerable. Prove that the set of all integers is denumerable. *Hint:* Arrange the integers as follows: $0, 1, -1, 2, -2, 3, -3, \cdots$, and count them off: first, second, third, etc.

★**13.** Prove that the set of positive rational numbers is denumerable. (Cf. Ex. 12.) *Hint:* Represent each positive rational as a quotient of relatively prime positive integers (cf. Ex. 23, § 107), and arrange them as follows, and count them off as indicated:

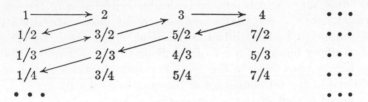

★**14.** Prove that the set of all rational numbers is denumerable. (Cf. Ex. 12.) *Hint:* Let the positive rationals be (cf. Ex. 13) $r_1, r_2, r_3, \cdots$, and arrange the rationals: $0, r_1, -r_1, r_2, -r_2, \cdots$.

NOTE. It is shown in Exercise 30, § 711, that not all infinite sets are denumerable, and that, in fact, the set of real numbers is not.

★★**15.** An expression of the form

$$a_1 + \cfrac{1}{a_2 + \cfrac{1}{a_3 + \cfrac{1}{a_4}}}, \quad \text{written} \quad a_1 + \frac{1}{a_2+}\frac{1}{a_3+}\frac{1}{a_4},$$

and, more generally, an expression of the form

$$(1) \qquad\qquad a_1 + \frac{1}{a_2+}\frac{1}{a_3+} \cdots \frac{1}{a_n},$$

where a_1 is a nonnegative integer and $a_2, \cdots, a_n$ are positive integers with $a_n > 1$, is called a **simple continued fraction.**† Prove that any positive rational number can be expressed in one and only one way as a simple continued fraction.

---

† For a treatment of continued fractions, see George Chrystal, *Algebra* (New York, Chelsea Publishing Company, 1952) or B. M. Stewart, *Number Theory* (New York, The Macmillan Company, 1952).

★★16. Show that the numbers

$$1, 1 + \frac{1}{2} = \frac{3}{2}, 1 + \frac{1}{2+} \frac{1}{2} = \frac{7}{5}, 1 + \frac{1}{2+} \frac{1}{2+} \frac{1}{2} = \frac{17}{12}, 1 + \frac{1}{2+} \frac{1}{2+} \frac{1}{2+} \frac{1}{2} = \frac{41}{29}, \cdots$$

satisfy the *recursion relation:* if p/q is any one, the next is $(p + 2q)/(p + q)$. Also show that they are alternately less than and greater than $\sqrt{2}$. Finally, prove that each is closer to $\sqrt{2}$ than its predecessor and that if ϵ is an arbitrary positive number there exists a number r in this set such that $|r - \sqrt{2}| < \epsilon$. *Hint:* If r is any member of the set, the next member is $(r + 2)/(r + 1)$, and $\left(\frac{r + 2}{r + 1} - \sqrt{2}\right) / (\sqrt{2} - r) = \frac{\sqrt{2} - 1}{r + 1} < \frac{1}{2}$. Make use of Ex. 11, § 107, and Property (iv), § 112.

★★17. If x is an irrational number, under what conditions on the rational numbers a, b, c, and d, is $(ax + b)/(cx + d)$ rational?

★114. AXIOM OF COMPLETENESS

The remaining axiom of the real number system can be given in any of several forms, all of which involve basically the ordering of the numbers. We present here the one that seems to combine most naturally a fundamental simplicity and an intuitive reasonableness. It is based on the idea of an **upper bound** of a set of numbers; that is, a number that is at least as large as anything in the set. For example, the number 10 is an upper bound of the set consisting of the numbers -15, 0, 3, and 7. It is also an upper bound of the set consisting of the numbers -37, 2, 5, 8, and 10. The number 16 is an upper bound of the open intervals $(-3, 6)$ and $(8, 16)$, and also of the closed intervals $[-31, -2]$ and $[15, 16]$. However, 16 is *not* an upper bound of the set of numbers -6, 13, and 23, nor of the open interval $(8, 35)$, nor of the set of all integers. There is *no* number x that is an upper bound of the set of all positive real numbers, for x is not greater than or equal to the real number $x + 1$. (Cf. Ex. 24, § 105.)

If, for a given set A of numbers, there is some number x that is an upper bound of A, the set A is said to be **bounded above.** This means that the corresponding set B of points on a number scale does not extend indefinitely to the right but, rather, that there is some point x at least as far to the right as any point of the given set (Fig. 102).

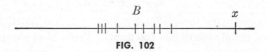

FIG. 102

Whenever a set is bounded above, it has *many* upper bounds. For example, if x is an upper bound, so is $x + 1$ and, indeed, so is any number greater than x. An appropriate question: "Is there any upper bound *less* than x?"   If the answer to this question is "No," then x is the smallest of all possible upper bounds and is called the **least upper bound**† of the set.   Since two numbers cannot be such that each is less than the other, there cannot be *more* than one such *least* upper bound.   When a number x is a least upper bound of a set, it is therefore called *the* least upper bound of the set.   Furthermore, in this case, we say that the set *has x* as its least upper bound, whether x is a member of the set or not.   Thus the open interval (a, b) and the closed interval $[a, b]$, where $a < b$, both have b as their least upper bound, whereas b is a member of only the *closed* interval.

The essential question now is whether a given set has a least upper bound. Of course, if a set is not bounded above it has no upper bound and *a fortiori* no *least* upper bound.   Suppose a set *is* bounded above.   Then does it have a least upper bound?   The final axiom gives the answer.

Axiom of Completeness.   *Any nonempty set of real numbers that is bounded above has a least upper bound.*

This axiom can be thought of geometrically as stating that there are no "gaps" in the number scale.   For instance, if a single point x were removed from the number scale (Fig. 103), the remaining numbers would

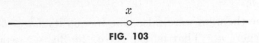

FIG. 103

no longer be complete, since the set consisting of all numbers less than x would be bounded above (e.g., by $x + 1$), but would have no least upper bound (if y is an upper bound, then $x < y$ and $x < \frac{1}{2}(x + y) < y$, so that $\frac{1}{2}(x + y)$ is a smaller upper bound).   (Cf. Ex. 25, § 105.)

It might seem that the axiom of completeness is biased or one-sided. Why should we speak of *upper* bounds and *least* upper bounds, when we might as naturally consider *lower* bounds and *greatest* lower bounds? The answer is that it is immaterial, as far as the axiomatic system is concerned, whether we formulate completeness in terms of upper bounds or lower bounds.   This fact is illustrated by Theorem I, below, whose statement is actually *equivalent* to the axiom of completeness.   **Lower bounds** and **greatest lower bounds** are defined in strict imitation of upper bounds and least upper bounds.   A set is **bounded below** if and only if it has a lower bound.   A set is **bounded** if and only if it is bounded both below and above; in other words, if and only if it is contained in some finite interval.

Theorem I.   *Any nonempty set of real numbers that is bounded below has a greatest lower bound.*‡

† The least upper bound of a set A is also called the **supremum** of A, abbreviated sup(A) (pronounced "supe of A").

‡ The greatest lower bound of a set A is called the **infimum** of A, abbreviated inf(A) (pronounced "inf of A").

Proof. The set obtained by changing every member of the given set to its negative is bounded above by the negative of any lower bound of the original set. (Look at the number scale with a mirror.) By the axiom of completeness the new set then has a least upper bound, whose negative must be the greatest lower bound of the original set. (Look at the number scale directly again, without the mirror.)

We shall now show that the axiom of completeness implies the first property of § 112 (Corollary, below). In essence, this property is an algebraic formulation of a basic principle of Euclidean geometry known as the *Archimedean property*.† This principle states that any length (however large) can be exceeded by repeatedly marking off a given length (however small), each successive application starting where the preceding one stopped. (A midget ruler, if used a sufficient number of times, can measure off an arbitrarily large distance.) For real numbers this principle, again called the **Archimedean property,** has the following formal statement and proof.

Theorem II. *If a and b are positive numbers, there is a positive integer n such that na > b.*

Proof. If the theorem were false, the inequality $na \leq b$ would hold for all positive integers n. That is, the set $a, 2a, 3a, \cdots$ would be bounded above. Let c be the least upper bound of this set. Then $na \leq c$ for all n, and hence $(n + 1)a \leq c$ for all n. Therefore $na + a \leq c$, or $na \leq c - a$, for all n. Thus $c - a$ is an upper bound that is *less* than the *least* upper bound c. This is the desired contradiction.

Corollary ((*i*), § 112). *If x is any real number there exists a positive integer n such that n > x.*

Proof. If $x \leq 0$, let $n = 1$. If $x > 0$, use Theorem II with $a = 1$ and $b = x$.

★115. FURTHER REMARKS ON MATHEMATICAL INDUCTION

If the real number system is considered as defined by the descriptive axioms of this chapter rather than by the constructive development outlined in the Introduction, the simple properties of positive integers given in § 106 are no longer obvious. However, they are still true if we superimpose on the axiomatized real number system the structure of the natural numbers given by the Peano axioms. The positive integers greater than 1 are then defined inductively, $2 \equiv 1 + 1$, $3 \equiv 2 + 1$, $\cdots$, and the remaining properties of § 106 are proved by mathematical induction. We

† Cf. D. Hilbert, *op. cit.*

omit further discussion and refer the reader to the book by Birkhoff and MacLane cited in the footnote on page 2.

We present now the formal detailed proofs by mathematical induction of the general associative and commutative laws stated in § 106. For simplicity of notation we restrict ourselves to the multiplicative form.

Proof of the general associative law. Let $P(n)$ be the proposition: "Any product of the m numbers $x_1, x_2, \cdots, x_m$, in that order, is equal to the special product $x_1(x_2(x_3(\cdots(x_{m-1}x_m)\cdots))))$, whenever $m \leq n$." For $n = 1$ and $n = 2$ the proposition is trivial, and for $n = 3$ it follows from the associative law, $(x_1x_2)x_3 = x_1(x_2x_3)$. Assume now the truth of $P(n)$, for a fixed n, and consider any possible form for the product of the $n + 1$ numbers $x_1, x_2, \cdots, x_{n+1}$, in that order. Such a product must have the form ab, where a and b are products of at most n of the x's. By the induction assumption that $P(n)$ is true, each of these two factors can be rewritten, if necessary, in the form $a = x_1y$ and $b = x_{k+1}z$, where y is either 1 or a product of the factors $x_2, \cdots, x_k$, and z is either 1 or a product of the factors $x_{k+2}, \cdots, x_{n+1}$. By the associative law of § 102, $ab = (x_1y)(x_{k+1}z) = x_1(y(x_{k+1}z))$. Again using the induction hypothesis, we can write the product $y(x_{k+1}z)$ in the special form $x_2(x_3(\cdots(x_nx_{n+1})\cdots))$. This fact, with the aid of the Fundamental Theorem of Mathematical Induction, § 106, establishes the truth of $P(n)$ for every positive integer n. Finally, since any two products of n numbers in a given order are equal to the same special product, they must be equal to each other.

Proof of the general commutative law. Let $P(n)$ be the proposition: "Any two products of n numbers are equal regardless of the order of the factors." For $n = 1$ the proposition is trivial and for $n = 2$ it follows from the commutative law of § 102: $x_2x_1 = x_1x_2$. Assume now the truth of $P(n)$ for a particular n and consider any possible product of the $n + 1$ numbers $x_1, x_2, \cdots, x_{n+1}$. This product must have the form xx_1y, where x is either 1 or the product of some of the x's and y is either 1 or the product of some of the x's. By the commutative and associative laws, $xx_1y = (xx_1)y = (x_1x)y = x_1(xy)$. The product xy contains the n factors $x_2, x_3, \cdots, x_{n+1}$ which, by the induction assumption that $P(n)$ is true, can be rearranged according to the order of the subscripts. Therefore $P(n + 1)$ follows from $P(n)$, and application of the Fundamental Theorem completes the proof.

★116. EXERCISES

★1. Prove that the system of integers satisfies the axiom of completeness. (Cf. Ex. 2, below.)

★2. Prove that the system of rational numbers does not satisfy the axiom of completeness. *Hint:* Consider the set S of all rational numbers less than $\sqrt{2}$. Then S has an upper bound in the system of rational numbers (the rational number 2 is one such).   Assume that S has a least upper bound r. Use the density of the rational numbers to show that if $r < \sqrt{2}$ then r is not even an upper bound of S, and that if $r > \sqrt{2}$ then r is not the *least* upper bound of S.

★3. Let x be a real number and let S be the set of all rational numbers less than x.   Show that x is the least upper bound of S.

★4. Prove that if S is a bounded nonempty set there is a smallest closed interval I containing S.   That is, I has the property that if J is any closed interval containing S, then J contains I.

★5. Prove by counterexample that the statement of Exercise 4 is false if the word *closed* is replaced by the word *open*.

★6. Prove that if S is a set of numbers dense in the system of real numbers, and if any finite number of points are deleted from S, the remaining set is still dense.

★7. Let S be a nonempty set of numbers bounded above, and let x be the least upper bound of S.   Prove that x has the two properties corresponding to an arbitrary positive number ϵ: (i) every element s of S satisfies the inequality $s < x + \epsilon$; (ii) at least one element s of S satisfies the inequality $s > x - \epsilon$.

★8. Prove that the two properties of Exercise 7 characterize the least upper bound.   That is, prove that a number x subject to these two properties is the least upper bound of S.

★★9. Prove the analogue of Exercise 7 for greatest lower bounds.

★★10. Prove the analogue of Exercise 8 for greatest lower bounds.

★★11. Prove **Dedekind's Theorem**: *Let the real numbers be divided into two nonempty sets A and B such that (i) if x is an arbitrary member of A and if y is an arbitrary member of B then x < y and (ii) if x is an arbitrary real number then either x is a member of A or x is a member of B.   Then there exists a number c (which may belong to either A or B) such that any number less than c belongs to A and any number greater than c belongs to B.*

★★12. Prove that the real number system is both minimal and maximal in the sense that it is impossible to have two systems R and S both satisfying the axioms of this chapter, where every member of R belongs to S but not every member of S belongs to R, and where the members of R are combined algebraically and related by order in the same way whether they are thought of as members of R or as members of S.   *Hint:* The multiplicative unit 1 of S must be the multiplicative unit of R, and therefore R must contain all rational members of S.   Since R is dense in S and complete it must be the same as S.

★★13. Discuss the essential uniqueness of the real number system in the following sense: Prove that if R and S are any two "real number systems" subject to the axioms of this chapter, then it is possible to establish a one-to-one correspondence between their members which preserves algebraic operations and order.   *Hint:* Let correspond, first, the additive units 0 and $0'$, then the multiplicative units 1 and $1'$, then the positive integers n and n', then the integers n and n', and then the rational numbers p/q and p'/q', and show that these correspondences preserve operations and order.   Finally, since any real number is the least upper bound of all rational numbers less than it (Ex. 3), the correspondence can be extended to all elements of R and S.

NOTE. By virtue of Exercise 13 it is possible to describe completely the real number system by the definition: *The real numbers are a complete ordered field.* (Cf. Ex. 11, § 113.)

2

Functions, Sequences, Limits, Continuity

~~~~~~

201. FUNCTIONS AND SEQUENCES

Whenever one says that y is a function of x, one has in mind some mechanism that assigns values to y corresponding to given values of x. The most familiar examples are real-valued functions of a real variable given by formulas, like $y = 3x^2 - 12x$ or $y = \pm\sqrt{x^2 - 4}$. These and other examples (where the variables x and y need not be related by formula, or even be real numbers) are given below.

Definition I. *Let D and R be two sets of objects. Then $y = f(x)$ is called a **function** with **domain** (of definition) D and **range** (of values) R if and only if to each member x of D there corresponds at least one member y of R, and for each member y of R there is at least one member x of D to which y corresponds. The general member of D and the general member of R are called the **independent** and the **dependent variable,** respectively. In case no two members of R correspond to the same member of D, $f(x)$ is called **single-valued**. In case R consists of just one object, $f(x)$ is called a **constant** function. In case D consists of real numbers, $f(x)$ is called a function of a **real variable**. In case R consists of real numbers, $f(x)$ is called **real-valued**. The symbol $f(x_0)$ denotes the members of R that correspond to the member x_0 of D.*

Example 1. The function $y = 3x^2 - 12x$ is defined for all real numbers. If we take D to be the set of all real numbers, R consists of all real numbers $\geqq -12$, since the function has an absolute minimum (cf. § 409) when $x = 2$. The function is a single-valued real-valued function of a real variable.

Example 2. The function of Example 1 restricted to the domain $D \equiv (1, 5)$ (the open interval from 1 to 5) has range R equal to the half-open interval $[-12, 15)$. This function is not the same as that of Example 1, since it has a different domain. It is also, however, a single-valued real-valued function of a real variable.

Example 3. The function $y = \sqrt{x^2 - 4}$ with domain D consisting of all real numbers x such that $|x| \geqq 2$ is a single-valued real-valued function of a real variable, with range R consisting of all nonnegative real numbers.　(Cf. § 214.)

Example 4.　The function $y = \pm\sqrt{x^2 - 4}$ with the same domain as the function of Example 3 is real-valued, but is single-valued only for $x = \pm 2$. Otherwise it is double-valued.　Its range is the set of all real numbers.

Example 5.　The **bracket function** or **greatest integer function,** $f(x) \equiv [x]$, is defined to be the largest integer less than or equal to x, with domain all real numbers (Fig. 201).　It is a single-valued real-valued function of a real variable.　Its range is the set of all integers.

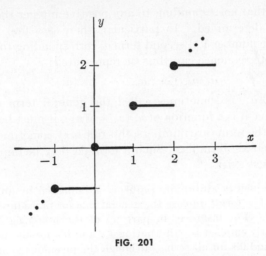

FIG. 201

Example 6.　Let D be the closed interval $[0, 1]$, and define $f(x)$, for x in D, to be 1 if x is rational and 0 if x is irrational.　(See Fig. 202.)　Then R consists of the two numbers 0 and 1.

Example 7.　Let D be the contestants in a radio quiz show and define $f(x)$ as follows: If x is a contestant who has correctly answered all questions, then

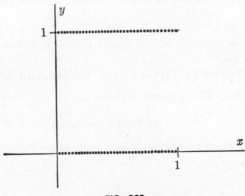

FIG. 202

$f(x) \equiv n$ where n is the number of dollars of prize money; if x is a contestant who has incorrectly answered a question, then $f(x)$ is a box of breakfast food. In this example $f(x)$ is a single-valued function. In some cases its value is a real number, and in some cases its value is a box of breakfast food.

A type of function of particular importance in mathematics is specified in the following definition.

Definition II. *An* **infinite sequence** *is a single-valued function whose domain of definition is the positive integers.*

This means that corresponding to any positive integer there is a unique value or **term** determined. In particular, there is a first term a_1 corresponding to the number 1, a second term a_2 corresponding to the number 2, etc. An infinite sequence can thus be represented:

$$a_1, a_2, \cdots, a_n, \cdots, \text{ or } \{a_n\}.$$

The nth term, a_n, is sometimes called the **general term** of the infinite sequence. Since it is a function of n, $(a_n = f(n))$, it must be prescribed by some rule. If the terms are numbers, this rule may sometimes be expressed as a simple algebraic formula. Such a formula may be impractical, but a definite rule must exist.

NOTE 1. Frequently an infinite sequence is indicated by an explicit listing of only the first few terms, in case the general rule for procedure is clear *beyond reasonable doubt*. For instance, in part (c) of the following Example 8 the rule that is clearly implied by alternating 1's and 0's for the first six terms is alternating 1's and 0's for all terms, although the ingenious artificer could construct any number of infinite sequences that start with alternating 1's and 0's (the terms could continue by being identically 0, or with alternating 6's and 7's, for example). Such interpretations, we hold, are not only unnatural, but deliberately mischievous.

NOTE 2. For convenience, if the meaning is clear, the single word *sequence* will be used henceforth to mean *infinite sequence*.

Example 8. Give a rule for obtaining the general term for each of the following sequences:

(a) $\frac{1}{2}, -\frac{2}{5}, \frac{3}{8}, -\frac{4}{11}, \cdots$;   (b) $1, \frac{1}{1}, \frac{1}{2}, \frac{1}{3}, \cdots$;

(c) $1, 0, 1, 0, 1, 0, \cdots$;   (d) $1, 2, 3, 1, 2, 3, 1, 2, 3, \cdots$;

(e) $\frac{1}{2}, \frac{1}{3}, \frac{1}{4}, \frac{1}{9}, \frac{1}{8}, \frac{1}{27}, \cdots$.

Solution. (a) The factor $(-1)^n$ or $(-1)^{n+1}$ is a standard device to take care of alternating signs. The general term is $(-1)^{n+1} \dfrac{n}{3n - 1}$. (b) If $n = 1$, $a_n = 1$; if $n > 1$, $a_n = \dfrac{1}{n - 1}$. (c) First formulation: if n is odd, $a_n = 1$; if n is even, $a_n = 0$. Second formulation: $a_{2n-1} = 1$; $a_{2n} = 0$. Third formulation: $a_n = \frac{1}{2}[(-1)^{n+1} + 1]$. (d) $a_{3n-2} = 1$; $a_{3n-1} = 2$; $a_{3n} = 3$. (e) $a_{2n-1} = \dfrac{1}{2^n}$; $a_{2n} = \dfrac{1}{3^n}$.

202. LIMIT OF A SEQUENCE

A sequence is said to **tend toward,** or **converge to,** a number if and only if the absolute value of the difference between the general term of the sequence and this number is less than any preassigned positive number (however small) whenever the subscript n of the general term is sufficiently large.

Symbolically, this is written

$$\lim_{n \to +\infty} a_n = a \quad \text{or} \quad \lim_{n \to \infty} a_n = a \quad \text{or} \quad a_n \to a,$$

where a_n is the nth term of the sequence and a is the number to which it converges. If $\{a_n\}$ converges to a, a is called the **limit** of the sequence.

A more concise form of the definition given above is the following:

Definition I. *The sequence $\{a_n\}$ has the* **limit** *a, written* $\lim\limits_{n \to +\infty} a_n = a$, *if and only if corresponding to an arbitrary positive number ϵ there exists a number $N = N(\epsilon)$ such that $|a_n - a| < \epsilon$ whenever $n > N$.*

NOTE 1.   In conformity with the discussion following Definition III, § 110, the statement that $\{a_n\}$ converges to a is equivalent to the statement that every neighborhood of a contains all of the terms of $\{a_n\}$ *from some point on*, and is also equivalent to the statement that every neighborhood of a contains all but a finite number of the terms of $\{a_n\}$ (that is, all of the terms except for a finite number of the subscripts).

If a sequence converges to some number, the sequence is said to be **convergent**; otherwise it is **divergent.**

The concept of an *infinite limit* is important, and will be formulated in precise symbolic form.   As an exercise, the student should reformulate the following definition in his own words, without the use of mathematical symbols.

Definition II. *The sequence $\{a_n\}$ has the limit $+\infty$, written*

$$\lim_{n \to +\infty} a_n = +\infty, \quad or \quad a_n \to +\infty,$$

if and only if corresponding to an arbitrary number B (however large) there exists a number $N = N(B)$ such that $a_n > B$ whenever $n > N$; the sequence $\{a_n\}$ has the limit $-\infty$, written

$$\lim_{n \to +\infty} a_n = -\infty, \; or \; a_n \to -\infty,$$

if and only if corresponding to an arbitrary number B (however large its negative) there exists a number $N = N(B)$ such that $a_n < B$ whenever $n > N$; the sequence has the limit ∞ (unsigned infinity), written

$$\lim_{n \to +\infty} a_n = \infty, \text{ or } a_n \to \infty,$$

if and only if $\lim\limits_{n \to +\infty} |a_n| = +\infty.$

NOTE 2. Although the word *limit* is applied to both the finite and infinite cases, the word *converge* is used only for finite limits. Thus, a sequence tending toward $+\infty$ diverges.

NOTE 3. In any extensive treatment of limits there are numerous statements which can be interpreted to apply to both finite and infinite cases, and which are of such a nature that the proofs for the finite and infinite particularizations are in essence identical. In such instances these proofs can be combined into a single proof by appropriate extensions of the word *neighborhood*. We define "neighborhoods of infinity" as follows: (*i*) a **neighborhood of** $+\infty$ is an open interval of the form $(a, +\infty)$; (*ii*) a **neighborhood of** $-\infty$ is an open interval of the form $(-\infty, b)$; (*iii*) a **neighborhood of** ∞ is the set of all x satisfying an inequality of the form $|x| > a$. With these conventions, for example, all cases of Definitions I and II can be included in the following single formulation for $\lim\limits_{n \to +\infty} a_n = a$ (where a may be a number, or $+\infty$, $-\infty$, or ∞): *Corresponding to every neighborhood N_a of a there exists a neighborhood $N_{+\infty}$ of $+\infty$ such that whenever n belongs to $N_{+\infty}$, a_n belongs to N_a.* In the sequel we formulate theorems and proofs separately for the finite and infinite forms, but suggest that the student interested in exploring the simplifying techniques available with general neighborhoods try his hand at combining the separate formulations into unified ones. A word of warning is in order, however: Do not confuse infinite symbols with numbers, and write such nonsense as $|a_n - \infty| < \epsilon$ when dealing with an infinite limit! It is to avoid such possible confusion of ideas that we have adopted the policy of maintaining (in the main) the separation of the finite and infinite.

Definition III. *A **subsequence** of a sequence is a sequence whose terms are terms of the original sequence arranged in the same order. That is, a subsequence of a sequence $\{a_n\}$ has the form $a_{n_1}, a_{n_2}, a_{n_3}, \cdots$, where*

$$n_1 < n_2 < n_3 < \cdots.$$

It is denoted by $\{a_{n_k}\}$.

Example 1. The sequence $\frac{1}{2}, \frac{1}{4}, \frac{1}{8}, \cdots$ is a subsequence of the sequence $\frac{1}{2}, \frac{1}{3}, \frac{1}{4}, \frac{1}{9}, \frac{1}{8}, \cdots$ of Example 8, § 201. The sequence $0, 1, 0, 1, 0, 1, \cdots$ is a subsequence of the sequence $1, 0, 1, 0, 0, 1, 0, 0, 0, 1, \cdots$.

Example 2. Show that the following sequences converge to 0:

(*a*) $1, \frac{1}{2}, \frac{1}{3}, \cdots, \frac{1}{n}, \cdots$; (*b*) $\frac{1}{2}, \frac{1}{4}, \frac{1}{8}, \cdots, \frac{1}{2^n}, \cdots$; (*c*) $\frac{1}{2}, -\frac{1}{4}, \frac{1}{8}, \cdots, \frac{(-1)^{n+1}}{2^n}, \cdots$.

Solution. (*a*) Since $|a_n - a| = |\frac{1}{n} - 0| = \frac{1}{n}$, and since $\frac{1}{n} < \epsilon$ whenever $n > 1/\epsilon$, we can choose as the function $N(\epsilon)$ of Definition I the expression $1/\epsilon$. (Cf. § 112.) (*b*) By Ex. 11, § 107, $2^n > n$ for all positive integers, so that we can choose $N(\epsilon) = 1/\epsilon$. (Cf. Ex. 14, § 205.) (*c*) This reduces immediately to (*b*).

Example 3. Find the limit of each sequence: (a) $\frac{1}{2}, \frac{3}{4}, \frac{7}{8}, \cdots, 1 - \frac{1}{2^n}, \cdots$.
(b) $3, 3, 3, \cdots, 3, \cdots$; (c) $1, \frac{1}{2}, 1, \frac{3}{4}, 1, \frac{7}{8}, \cdots$.

Solution. (a) The expression $|a_n - 1|$ is equal to $\frac{1}{2^n}$, which is less than any preassigned positive number whenever n is sufficiently large, as shown in Example 2, (b). Therefore the limit is 1. (b) The absolute value of the difference between the general term and 3 is identically zero, which is less than any preassigned positive number for *any* n, and certainly for n sufficiently large. Therefore the limit is 3. (c) By combining the reasoning in parts (a) and (b) we see that the general term differs numerically from 1 by less than any preassigned positive number if n is sufficiently large. The odd-numbered terms form a subsequence identically 1, while the even-numbered terms form a subsequence which is the sequence of part (a). The limit is 1.

Example 4. Show that each of the following sequences diverges:

(a) $1, 2, 1, 2, 1, 2, \cdots$; (b) $1, 2, 4, 8, 16, \cdots$;
(c) $1, 2, 1, 3, 1, 4, \cdots$; (d) $1, -2, 4, -8, 16, \cdots$.

Solution. (a) If $\{a_n\}$ converges to a, *every* neighborhood of a must contain all terms from some point on, and therefore must contain both numbers 1 and 2. On the other hand, no matter what value a may have, a neighborhood of a of length less than 1 cannot contain both of these points! (b) No finite interval about any point can contain all terms of this sequence, from some point on. The limit is $+\infty$. (c) The comment of part (b) applies to this sequence, since there is a subsequence tending toward $+\infty$. This sequence has no limit, finite or infinite. (d) The subsequence of the odd-numbered terms tends toward $+\infty$, and that of the even-numbered terms tends toward $-\infty$. The sequence of absolute values tends toward $+\infty$, so that the sequence itself has the limit ∞.

203. EXERCISES

In Exercises 1-10, draw the graph of the given function, assuming the domain of definition to be as large as possible. Give in each case the domain and the range of values. The bracket function $[x]$ is defined in Example 5, § 201, and square roots are discussed in § 214. (Also cf. Exs. 5-10, § 216.)

1. $y = \sqrt{x^2 - 9}$.   **2.** $y = \pm\sqrt{25 - x^2}$.
3. $y = \sqrt{-x}$.   **4.** $y = \pm\sqrt{|x|}$.
5. $y = \sqrt{4x - x^2}$.   **6.** $y = \sqrt{|x^2 - 16|}$.
7. $y = x - [x]$.   **8.** $y = (x - [x])^2$.
9. $y = \sqrt{x - [x]}$.   **10.** $y = [x] + \sqrt{x - [x]}$.

In Exercises 11-18, give a rule for finding the general term of the sequence.

11. $2, \frac{4}{3}, \frac{6}{5}, \frac{8}{7}, \cdots$.   **12.** $\frac{1}{3}, -\frac{1}{6}, \frac{1}{11}, -\frac{1}{18}, \frac{1}{27}, \cdots$.
13. $1, -1, \frac{1}{2}, -\frac{1}{6}, \frac{1}{24}, -\frac{1}{120}, \cdots$.   **14.** $1, 2, 24, 720, 40320, \cdots$.
15. $1 \cdot 3, 1 \cdot 3 \cdot 5, 1 \cdot 3 \cdot 5 \cdot 7, 1 \cdot 3 \cdot 5 \cdot 7 \cdot 9, \cdots$.
16. $1, 2, 3, 2, 1, 2, 3, 2, 1, \cdots$.

17. $-1, 1, 1, -2, 2, 2, -3, 3, 3, -4, 4, 4, \cdots$.

18. $1, 2 \cdot 4, 1 \cdot 3 \cdot 5, 2 \cdot 4 \cdot 6 \cdot 8, 1 \cdot 3 \cdot 5 \cdot 7 \cdot 9, \cdots$.

In Exercises 19-24, find the limit of the sequence and justify your contention (cf. Exs. 25-30).

19. $2, 2, 2, 2, 2, \cdots$.   **20.** $\frac{3}{2}, \frac{5}{4}, \frac{7}{6}, \cdots, \frac{2n+1}{2n}, \cdots$.

21. $\frac{3}{5}, \frac{3}{7}, \frac{5}{9}, \frac{5}{11}, \frac{7}{13}, \frac{7}{15}, \cdots$.   **22.** $1, 4, 9, 16, \cdots, n^2, \cdots$.

23. $\frac{3}{7}, -\frac{8}{7}, \frac{13}{7}, -\frac{18}{7}, \cdots$.   **24.** $9, 16, 21, 24, \cdots, 10n - n^2, \cdots$.

In Exercises 25-30, give a simple explicit function $N(\epsilon)$ or $N(B)$, in accord with Definition I or II, for the sequence of the indicated Exercise.

★**25.** For Ex. 19.   ★**26.** For Ex. 20.   ★**27.** For Ex. 21.

★**28.** For Ex. 22.   ★**29.** For Ex. 23.   ★**30.** For Ex. 24.

In Exercises 31-34, prove that the given sequence has no limit, finite or infinite.

31. $1, 5, 1, 5, 1, 5, \cdots$.   **32.** $1, 2, 3, 1, 2, 3, 1, 2, 3, \cdots$.

33. $1, 2, 1, 4, 1, 8, 1, 16, \cdots$.   **34.** $2^1, 2^{-2}, 2^3, 2^{-4}, 2^5, 2^{-6}, \cdots$.

204. LIMIT THEOREMS FOR SEQUENCES

Theorem I. *The alteration of a finite number of terms of a sequence has no effect on convergence or divergence or limit. In other words, if $\{a_n\}$ and $\{b_n\}$ are two sequences and if M and N are two positive integers such that $a_{M+n} = b_{N+n}$ for all positive integers n, then the two sequences $\{a_n\}$ and $\{b_n\}$ must either both converge to the same limit or both diverge; in case of divergence either both have the same infinite limit or neither has an infinite limit.*

Proof. If $\{a_n\}$ converges to a, then every neighborhood of a contains all but a finite number of the terms of $\{a_n\}$, and therefore all but a finite number of the terms of $\{b_n\}$. Proof for the case of an infinite limit is similar.

Theorem II. *If a sequence converges, its limit is unique.*

Proof. Assume $a_n \to a$ and $a_n \to a'$, where $a \neq a'$. Take neighborhoods of a and a' so small that they have no points in common. Then each must contain all but a finite number of the terms of $\{a_n\}$. This is clearly impossible.

Theorem III. *If all terms of a sequence, from some point on, are equal to a constant, the sequence converges to this constant.*

Proof. Any neighborhood of the constant contains the constant and therefore all but a finite number of the terms of the sequence.

Theorem IV. *Any subsequence of a convergent sequence converges, and its limit is the limit of the original sequence.* (Cf. Ex. 12, § 205.)

Proof. Assume $a_n \to a$. Since every neighborhood of a contains all but a finite number of terms of $\{a_n\}$ it must contain all but a finite number of terms of any subsequence.

Definition I. *A sequence is **bounded** if and only if all of its terms are contained in some interval. Equivalently, the sequence $\{a_n\}$ is bounded if and only if there exists a positive number P such that $|a_n| \leq P$ for all n.*

Theorem V. *Any convergent sequence is bounded.* (Cf. Ex. 2, § 205.)

Proof. Assume $a_n \to a$, and choose a definite neighborhood of a, say the open interval $(a - 1, a + 1)$. Since this neighborhood contains all but a finite number of terms of $\{a_n\}$, a suitable enlargement will contain these missing terms as well.

Definition II. *If $\{a_n\}$ and $\{b_n\}$ are two sequences, the sequences $\{a_n + b_n\}$, $\{a_n - b_n\}$, and $\{a_n b_n\}$ are called their **sum, difference,** and **product,** respectively. If $\{a_n\}$ and $\{b_n\}$ are two sequences, where b_n is never zero, the sequence $\{a_n/b_n\}$ is called their **quotient.** The definitions of sum and product extend to any finite number of sequences.*

Theorem VI. *The sum of two convergent sequences is a convergent sequence, and the limit of the sum is the sum of the limits:*

$$\lim_{n \to +\infty} (a_n + b_n) = \lim_{n \to +\infty} a_n + \lim_{n \to +\infty} b_n.$$

(Cf. Ex. 4, § 205.) *This rule extends to the sum of any finite number of sequences.*

Proof. Assume $a_n \to a$ and $b_n \to b$, and let $\epsilon > 0$ be given. Choose N so large that the following two inequalities hold *simultaneously* for $n > N$:

$$|a_n - a| < \tfrac{1}{2}\epsilon, \quad |b_n - b| < \tfrac{1}{2}\epsilon.$$

Then, by the triangle inequality, for $n > N$

$$|(a_n + b_n) - (a + b)| = |(a_n - a) + (b_n - b)|$$
$$\leq |a_n - a| + |b_n - b| < \tfrac{1}{2}\epsilon + \tfrac{1}{2}\epsilon = \epsilon.$$

The extension to the sum of an arbitrary number of sequences is provided by mathematical induction. (Cf. Ex. 3, § 205.)

Theorem VII. *The difference of two convergent sequences is a convergent sequence, and the limit of the difference is the difference of the limits:*

$$\lim_{n \to +\infty} (a_n - b_n) = \lim_{n \to +\infty} a_n - \lim_{n \to +\infty} b_n.$$

Proof. The details are almost identical with those of the preceding proof. (Cf. Ex. 6, § 205.)

Theorem VIII. *The product of two convergent sequences is a convergent sequence and the limit of the product is the product of the limits:*

$$\lim_{n \to +\infty} (a_n b_n) = \lim_{n \to +\infty} a_n \cdot \lim_{n \to +\infty} b_n.$$

(Cf. Ex. 5, § 205.)   *This rule extends to the product of any finite number of sequences.*

Proof.   Assume $a_n \to a$ and $b_n \to b$. We wish to show that $a_n b_n \to ab$ or, equivalently, that $a_n b_n - ab \to 0$. By addition and subtraction of the quantity ab_n and by appeal to Theorem VI, we can use the relation

$$a_n b_n - ab = (a_n - a)b_n + a(b_n - b)$$

to reduce the problem to that of showing that both sequences $\{(a_n - a)b_n\}$ and $\{a(b_n - b)\}$ converge to zero.   The fact that they do is a consequence of the following lemma:

Lemma.   *If $\{c_n\}$ converges to 0 and $\{d_n\}$ converges, then $\{c_n d_n\}$ converges to 0.*

Proof of lemma.   By Theorem V the sequence $\{d_n\}$ is bounded, and there exists a positive number P such that $|d_n| \leq P$ for all n. If $\epsilon > 0$ is given, choose N so large that $|c_n| < \epsilon/P$ for $n > N$.   Then for $n > N$,

$$|c_n d_n| = |c_n| \cdot |d_n| < (\epsilon/P) \cdot P = \epsilon.$$

This inequality completes the proof of the lemma, and hence of the theorem.

The extension to the product of an arbitrary number of sequences is provided by mathematical induction.   (Cf. Ex. 3, § 205.)

Theorem IX.   *The quotient of two convergent sequences, where the denominators and their limit are nonzero, is a convergent sequence and the limit of the quotient is the quotient of the limits:*

$$\lim_{n \to +\infty} \frac{a_n}{b_n} = \frac{\lim_{n \to +\infty} a_n}{\lim_{n \to +\infty} b_n}.$$

Proof.   Assume $a_n \to a$, $b_n \to b$, and that b and b_n are nonzero for all n. Inasmuch as $a_n/b_n = (a_n) \cdot (1/b_n)$, Theorem VIII permits the reduction of this proof to that of showing that $1/b_n \to 1/b$ or, equivalently, that

$$\frac{1}{b_n} - \frac{1}{b} = \frac{b - b_n}{b} \cdot \frac{1}{b_n} \to 0.$$

Let $c_n \equiv (b - b_n)/b$ and $d_n \equiv 1/b_n$ and observe that the conclusion of the Lemma of Theorem VIII is valid (with no change in the proof) when the sequence $\{d_n\}$ is assumed to be merely bounded (instead of convergent). Since the sequence $\{c_n\} = \{(b - b_n) \cdot (1/b)\}$ converges to zero (by this same lemma), we have only to show that the sequence $\{d_n\} = \{1/b_n\}$ is bounded. We proceed now to prove this fact.   Since $b \neq 0$, we can choose neighborhoods of 0 and b which have no points in common.   Since $b_n \to b$, the neighborhood of b contains all but a finite number of the terms of $\{b_n\}$, so that only a finite number of these terms can lie in the neighborhood of 0. Since b_n is nonzero for all n, there is a (smaller) neighborhood of 0 that excludes *all* terms of the sequence $\{b_n\}$. If this neighborhood is the open interval $(-\epsilon, \epsilon)$, where $\epsilon > 0$, then for all n, $|b_n| \geq \epsilon$, or $|d_n| = |1/b_n| \leq 1/\epsilon$. The sequence $\{d_n\}$ is therefore bounded, and the proof is complete.

Theorem X. *Multiplication of the terms of a sequence by a nonzero constant k does not affect convergence of divergence. If the original sequence converges, the new sequence converges to k times the limit of the original, for any constant k:*

$$\lim_{n \to +\infty} (k\, a_n) = k \cdot \lim_{n \to +\infty} a_n.$$

Proof. This is a consequence of Theorems III and VIII.

Theorem XI. *If $\{a_n\}$ is a sequence of nonzero numbers, then $a_n \to \infty$ if and only if $1/a_n \to 0$; equivalently, $a_n \to 0$ if and only if $1/a_n \to \infty$.*

Proof. If $|a_n| \to +\infty$ and if $\epsilon > 0$ is given, there exists a number N such that for $n > N$, $|a_n| > 1/\epsilon$, and therefore $|1/a_n| < \epsilon$. Conversely, if $1/a_n \to 0$ and B is any given *positive* number, there exists a number N such that for $n > N$, $|1/a_n| < 1/B$, and therefore $|a_n| > B$.

Theorem XII. *If $a > 1$, $\lim\limits_{n \to +\infty} a^n = +\infty$.*

Proof. Let $p \equiv a - 1 > 0$. Then $a = 1 + p$, and by the Binomial Theorem (cf. Ex. 35, § 107), if n is a positive integer,

$$a^n = (1 + p)^n = 1 + np + \frac{n(n-1)}{2}\, p^2 + \cdots \geq 1 + np.$$

Therefore, if B is a given positive number and if $n > B/p$, then

$$a^n \geq 1 + np > 1 + B > B.$$

Theorem XIII. *If $|r| < 1$, $\lim\limits_{n \to +\infty} r^n = 0$.*

Proof. This is a consequence of the two preceding theorems.

Definition III. *A sequence $\{a_n\}$ is* **monotonically increasing** *(***decreasing***),*† *written $a_n \uparrow$ $(a_n \downarrow)$, if and only if $a_n \leq a_{n+1}$ $(a_n \geq a_{n+1})$ for every n. A sequence is* **monotonic** *if and only if it is monotonically increasing or, monotonically decreasing.*

Theorem XIV. *Any bounded monotonic sequence converges. If $a_n \uparrow$ $(a_n \downarrow)$ and if $a_n \leq P$ $(a_n \geq P)$ for all n, then $\{a_n\}$ converges; moreover, if $a_n \to a$, then $a_n \leq a \leq P$ $(a_n \geq a \geq P)$ for all n.*

† Parentheses are used here to indicate an alternative statement. For a discussion of the use of parentheses for alternatives, see the Preface.

★*Proof.* We give the details only for the case $a_n \uparrow$ (cf. Ex. 7, § 205). Since the set A of points consisting of the terms of the sequence $\{a_n\}$ is bounded above, it has a least upper bound a (§ 114), and since P is an upper bound of A, the following inequalities must hold for all n: $a_n \leq a \leq P$. To prove that $a_n \to a$ we let ϵ be a given positive number and observe that there must exist a positive integer N such that $a_N > a - \epsilon$ (cf. Ex. 7, § 116). Therefore, for $n > N$, the following inequalities hold:

$$a - \epsilon < a_N \leq a_n \leq a < a + \epsilon.$$

Consequently $a - \epsilon < a_n < a + \epsilon$, or $|a_n - a| < \epsilon$, and the proof is complete.

NOTE. As a consequence of Theorem XIV we can say in general that *any monotonic sequence has a limit* (finite, $+\infty$, or $-\infty$), and that the limit is finite if and only if the sequence is bounded. (The student should give the details in Ex. 7, § 204.)

Theorem XV. *If $a_n \leq b_n$ for all n, and if $\lim\limits_{n \to +\infty} a_n$ and $\lim\limits_{n \to +\infty} b_n$ exist (finite, $+\infty$, or $-\infty$), then $\lim\limits_{n \to +\infty} a_n \leq \lim\limits_{n \to +\infty} b_n$.*

Proof. If the two limits are finite we can form the difference

$$c_n \equiv b_n - a_n$$

and, by appealing to Theorem VII, reduce the problem to the special case: *if $c_n \geq 0$ for all n and if $C \equiv \lim\limits_{n \to +\infty} c_n$ exists and is finite then $C \geq 0$.* By the definition of a limit, for any positive ϵ we can find values of n (arbitrarily large) such that $|c_n - C| < \epsilon$. Now if $C < 0$, let us choose $\epsilon \equiv -C > 0$. We can then find arbitrarily large values of n such that $|c_n - C| = |c_n + \epsilon| < \epsilon$, and hence $c_n + \epsilon < \epsilon$. This contradicts the nonnegativeness of c_n. On the other hand, if it is assumed that $a_n \to +\infty$ and $b_n \to B$ (finite), we may take $\epsilon \equiv 1$ and find first an N_1 such that $n > N_1$ implies $a_n > B + 1$, and then an N_2 such that $n > N_2$ implies $b_n < B + 1$. Again the inequality $a_n \leq b_n$ is contradicted (for n greater than both N_1 and N_2). The student should complete the proof for the cases $a_n \to A$ (finite), $b_n \to -\infty$ and $a_n \to +\infty$, $b_n \to -\infty$.

205. EXERCISES

1. Prove that if two subsequences of a given sequence converge to distinct limits, the sequence diverges.

2. Show by a counterexample that the converse of Theorem V, § 204, is false. That is, a bounded sequence need not converge.

3. Prove the extensions of Theorems VI and VIII, § 204, to an arbitrary finite number of sequences.

4. Prove that if $a_n \to +\infty$ and either $\{b_n\}$ converges or $b_n \to +\infty$, then $a_n + b_n \to +\infty$.

5. Prove that if $a_n \to +\infty$ and either $b_n \to b > 0$ or $b_n \to +\infty$, then $a_n b_n \to +\infty$. Prove that if $a_n \to \infty$ and $b_n \to b \neq 0$, then $a_n b_n \to \infty$.

6. Prove Theorem VII, § 204.

7. Prove Theorem XIV, § 204, for the case $a_n \downarrow$, and the statement of the Note that follows. *Hint:* Let $b_n \equiv -a_n$ and use Theorem XIV, § 204, for the case $b_n \uparrow$. Cf. Ex. 23.

8. Show by counterexamples that the sum (difference, product, quotient) of two divergent sequences need not diverge.

9. Prove that if the sum and the difference of two sequences converge, then both of the sequences converge.

10. Prove that $a_n \to 0$ if and only if $|a_n| \to 0$.

11. Prove that $a_n \to a$ implies $|a_n| \to |a|$. Is the converse true? Prove, or give a counterexample. *Hint:* Use Property IX, § 110.

12. Prove that if a sequence has the limit $+\infty$ $(-\infty, \infty)$ then any subsequence has the limit $+\infty$ $(-\infty, \infty)$.

13. Prove that if $a_n \leq b$ $(a_n \geq b)$ and $a_n \to a$, then $a \leq b$ $(a \geq b)$. Show by an example that from the strict inequality $a_n < b$ $(a_n > b)$ we cannot infer the strict inequality $a < b$ $(a > b)$.

14. Prove that if $0 \leq a_n \leq b_n$ and $b_n \to 0$, then $a_n \to 0$. More generally, prove that if $a_n \leq b_n \leq c_n$ and $\{a_n\}$ and $\{c_n\}$ converge to the same limit, then $\{b_n\}$ also converges to this same limit.

15. Prove that if x is an arbitrary real number, there is a sequence $\{r_n\}$ of rational numbers converging to x. *Hint:* By the density of the rationals $((v)$, § 112$)$, there is a rational number r_n in the open interval $\left(x - \dfrac{1}{n}, x + \dfrac{1}{n} \right)$.

★★16. If $\{s_n\}$ is a given sequence, define $\sigma_n \equiv \dfrac{1}{n}(s_1 + s_2 + \cdots + s_n)$. Prove that if $\{s_n\}$ converges to 0 then $\{\sigma_n\}$ also converges to 0. (Cf. Ex. 17.) *Hint:* Let m be a positive integer $< n$, and write

$$\sigma_n = \frac{1}{n}(s_1 + \cdots + s_m) + \frac{1}{n}(s_{m+1} + \cdots + s_n).$$

If $\epsilon > 0$, first choose m so large that whenever $k > m$, $|s_k| < \frac{1}{2}\epsilon$. Holding m fixed, choose $N > m$ and so large that $|s_1 + \cdots + s_m|/N < \frac{1}{2}\epsilon$. Then choose $n > N$, and consider separately the two groups of terms of σ_n, given above.

★★17. With the notation of Exercise 16, prove that if $\{s_n\}$ converges, then $\{\sigma_n\}$ also converges and has the same limit. Show by the example $0, 1, 0, 1, \cdots$ that the convergence of $\{\sigma_n\}$ does not imply that of $\{s_n\}$. Can you find a divergent sequence $\{s_n\}$ such that $\sigma_n \to 0$? *Hint:* Assume $s_n \to l$, let $t_n \equiv s_n - l$, and use the result of Ex. 16.

★★18. With the notation of Exercise 16, prove that if $\lim\limits_{n \to +\infty} s_n = +\infty$, then $\lim\limits_{n \to +\infty} \sigma_n = +\infty$. Show by the example $0, 1, 0, 2, 0, 3, \cdots$ that the reverse implication is not valid. *Hint:* If B is a given positive number, first choose m so large that whenever $k > m$, $s_k > 3B$. Then choose $N > 3m$ and so large that $|s_1 + \cdots + s_m|/N < B$. Then follow the hint of Ex. 16.

★★19. Show by the example $1, -1, 2, -2, 3, -3, \cdots$ that with the notation of Exercise 16, $\lim\limits_{n \to +\infty} s_n = \infty$ does not imply $\lim\limits_{n \to +\infty} \sigma_n = \infty$. Can you find an example where $\lim\limits_{n \to +\infty} s_n = \infty$ and $\lim\limits_{n \to +\infty} \sigma_n = 0$?

★★20. A number x is called a **limit point** of a sequence $\{a_n\}$ if and only if there exists some subsequence of $\{a_n\}$ converging to x. Prove that x is a limit point of $\{a_n\}$ if and only if corresponding to $\epsilon > 0$ the inequality $|a_n - x| < \epsilon$ holds for infinitely many values of the subscript n. Show by an example that this does not mean that $|a_n - x| < \epsilon$ must hold for infinitely many *distinct* values of a_n.

★★21. Prove that a bounded sequence converges if and only if it has exactly one limit point. (Cf. Ex. 20.)

★★22. Explain what you would mean by saying that $+\infty$ $(-\infty)$ is a limit point of a sequence $\{a_n\}$. Prove that a sequence is unbounded above (below) if and only if $+\infty$ $(-\infty)$ is a limit point of the sequence. Show how the word "bounded" can be omitted from Exercise 21. (Cf. Ex. 20.)

★★23. Prove Theorem XIV, § 204, for the case $a_n \downarrow$, directly (without reference to the case $a_n \uparrow$), using the principle of *greatest lower bound*.

★★24. Formulate the results of Exercises 12-14, 16, § 113, in terms of the language of sequences.

206. LIMITS OF FUNCTIONS

In this section we recall and extend some of the basic limit concepts of elementary calculus. Before formalizing the appropriate definitions for such limits as $\lim\limits_{x \to a} f(x)$ and $\lim\limits_{x \to +\infty} f(x)$, let us agree on one thing. It will be implicitly assumed, whenever a limit of a function is concerned, that there is some substance to the relations written down, and that *the quantities symbolized exist for at least some values of the independent variable neighboring the limiting value of that variable*. For example, when we write $\lim\limits_{x \to a} f(x)$ we shall assume that every neighborhood of the point a contains at least one point x different from a for which the function $f(x)$ is defined;† and when we write $\lim\limits_{x \to +\infty} f(x)$ we shall assume that for any number N there exists a number x of the domain of definition of $f(x)$ such that $x > N$.

A function $f(x)$ is said to **tend toward** or **approach** or **have** a limit L as x approaches a number a if and only if the absolute value of the difference between $f(x)$ and L is less than any preassigned positive number (however small) whenever the point x belonging to the domain of definition of $f(x)$ is sufficiently near a but not equal to a. This is expressed symbolically:

$$\lim_{x \to a} f(x) = L.$$

† In the terminology of the next chapter (§ 309), a is a *limit point* of the domain of definition D of $f(x)$. It can be shown that every neighborhood of a contains *infinitely many* points of D.

If in this definition the independent variable x is restricted to values greater than a, we say that x approaches a from the **right** or from **above** and write

$$\lim_{x \to a+} f(x) = L.$$

Again, if x is restricted to values less than a, we say that x approaches a from the **left** or from **below** and write

$$\lim_{x \to a-} f(x) = L.$$

The terms *undirected limit* or *two-sided limit* may be used to distinguish the first of these three limits from the other two in case of ambiguity arising from use of the single word *limit*.

A more concise formulation for these limits is given in the following definition:

Definition I. *The function $f(x)$ has the limit L as x approaches a, written*

$$\lim_{x \to a} f(x) = L, \quad or \quad f(x) \to L \ as \ x \to a,$$

if and only if corresponding to an arbitrary positive number ϵ there exists a positive number $\delta = \delta(\epsilon)$ such that $0 < |x - a| < \delta$ implies $|f(x) - L| < \epsilon$, for values of x for which $f(x)$ is defined;† $f(x)$ has the limit L as x approaches a from the right (left),‡ written

$$\lim_{x \to a+} f(x) = L, \quad or \quad f(x) \to L \ as \ x \to a+$$

$$(\lim_{x \to a-} f(x) = L, \quad or \quad f(x) \to L \ as \ x \to a-),$$

if and only if corresponding to an arbitrary positive number ϵ there exists a positive number $\delta = \delta(\epsilon)$ such that $a < x < a + \delta$ $(a - \delta < x < a)$ implies $|f(x) - L| < \epsilon$, for values of x for which $f(x)$ is defined. These one-sided limits (if they exist) are also denoted:

$$f(a+) \equiv \lim_{x \to a+} f(x), \quad f(a-) \equiv \lim_{x \to a-} f(x).$$

Since the definition of limit employs only values of x different from a, it is completely immaterial what the value of the function is at $x = a$ or, indeed, whether it is defined there at all. Thus a function can fail to have a limit as x approaches a only by its misbehavior for values of x *near* a but not *equal* to a. Since $\lim_{x \to a} f(x)$ exists if and only if $\lim_{x \to a+} f(x)$ and

---

† An open interval with the midpoint removed is called a **deleted neighborhood** of the missing point. The inequalities $0 < |x - a| < \delta$, then, define a deleted neighborhood of the point a.

‡ Parentheses are used here and in the following two definitions to indicate an alternative statement. For a discussion of the use of parentheses for alternatives, see the Preface.

$\lim\limits_{x\to a-} f(x)$ both exist and are equal (cf. Exs. 13-14, § 208), $\lim\limits_{x\to a} f(x)$ may fail to exist either by $\lim\limits_{x\to a+} f(x)$ and $\lim\limits_{x\to a-} f(x)$ being unequal or by either or both of the latter failing to exist in one way or another. These possibilities are illustrated in Example 1 below.

Limits as the independent variable becomes infinite have a similar formulation:

Definition II. *The function $f(x)$ has the limit L as x becomes positively (negatively) infinite, written*

$$f(+\infty) \equiv \lim_{x\to+\infty} f(x) = L, \quad or \quad f(x) \to L \text{ as } x \to +\infty$$

$$(f(-\infty) \equiv \lim_{x\to-\infty} f(x) = L, \quad or \quad f(x) \to L \text{ as } x \to -\infty),$$

if and only if corresponding to an arbitrary positive number ϵ there exists a number $N = N(\epsilon)$ such that $x > N$ $(x < N)$ implies $|f(x) - L| < \epsilon$, for values of x for which $f(x)$ is defined.

In an analogous fashion, infinite limits can be defined. Only a sample definition is given here, others being requested in the Exercises of § 208.

Definition III. *The function $f(x)$ has the limit $+\infty\,(-\infty)$ as x approaches a, written*

$$\lim_{x\to a} f(x) = +\infty \ (-\infty), \quad or \quad f(x) \to +\infty \ (-\infty) \text{ as } x \to a,$$

if and only if corresponding to an arbitrary number B there exists a positive number $\delta = \delta(B)$ such that $0 < |x - a| < \delta$ implies $f(x) > B$ $(f(x) < B)$, for values of x for which $f(x)$ is defined.

As with limits of sequences it is often convenient to use an *unsigned infinity*, ∞. When we say that a variable, dependent or independent, tends toward ∞, we shall mean that its absolute value approaches $+\infty$. Thus $\lim\limits_{x\to\infty} f(x) = L$ is defined as in Definition II, with the inequality $x > N$ replaced by $|x| > N$, and $\lim\limits_{x\to a} f(x) = \infty$ is equivalent to $\lim\limits_{x\to a} |f(x)| = +\infty$.

Example 1. Discuss the limits of each of the following functions as x approaches 0, $0+$, and $0-$, and in each case sketch the graph: (a) $f(x) \equiv \dfrac{x^2 + x}{x}$ if $x \neq 0$, undefined for $x = 0$; (b) $f(x) \equiv |x|$ if $x \neq 0$, $f(0) \equiv 3$; (c) the **signum function,** $f(x) \equiv \text{sgn } x \equiv 1$ if $x > 0$, $f(x) \equiv \text{sgn } x \equiv -1$ if $x < 0$, $f(0) \equiv \text{sgn } 0$ $\equiv 0$; (d)† $f(x) \equiv \sin\dfrac{1}{x}$ if $x \neq 0$, $f(0) \equiv 0$; (e) $f(x) \equiv \dfrac{1}{x}$ if $x \neq 0$, undefined if $x = 0$; (f) $f(x) \equiv \dfrac{1}{x^2}$ if $x \neq 0$, undefined if $x = 0$.

† For illustrative examples and exercises the familiar properties of the trigonometric functions will be assumed. An analytic treatment is given in §§ 603-604.

Solution. The graphs are given in Figure 203. In part (*a*) if $x \neq 0$, $f(x)$ is identically equal to the function $x + 1$, and its graph is therefore the straight line $y = x + 1$ with the single point $(0, 1)$ deleted; $\lim\limits_{x \to 0} f(x) = f(0+) = f(0-) = 1$. In part (*b*) $\lim\limits_{x \to 0} f(x) = f(0+) = f(0-) = 0$. The fact that $f(0) = 3$ has no bearing on the statement of the preceding sentence. For the signum function (*c*), $f(0+) = 1$, $f(0-) = -1$, and $\lim\limits_{x \to 0} f(x)$ does not exist. In part (*d*) all three limits fail to exist. In part (*e*) $f(0+) = +\infty$, $f(0-) = -\infty$, and $\lim\limits_{x \to 0} f(x) = \infty$ (unsigned infinity) (cf. Exs. 31-32, § 208). In part (*f*), $f(0+) = f(0-) = \lim\limits_{x \to 0} f(x) = +\infty$ (cf. Ex. 32, § 208).

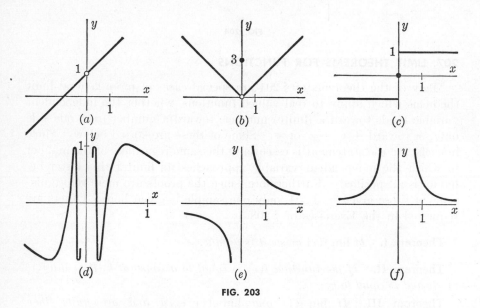

(*a*)   (*b*)   (*c*)

(*d*)   (*e*)   (*f*)

FIG. 203

★**Example 2.** Show that $\lim\limits_{x \to 2} \dfrac{x^2 - x + 18}{3x - 1} = 4$. Find an explicit function $\delta(\epsilon)$ as demanded by Definition I.

Solution. Form the absolute value of the difference:

(1) $$\left| \frac{x^2 - x + 18}{3x - 1} - 4 \right| = \left| \frac{x^2 - 13x + 22}{3x - 1} \right| = |x - 2| \cdot \left| \frac{x - 11}{3x - 1} \right|.$$

We wish to show that this expression is small if x is near 2. The first factor, $|x - 2|$, is certainly small if x is near 2; and the second factor, $\left| \dfrac{x - 11}{3x - 1} \right|$, is not dangerously large if x is near 2 and at the same time not too near $\frac{1}{3}$. Let us make this precise by first requiring that $\delta \leq 1$. If x is within a distance less than δ of 2, then $1 < x < 3$, and hence also $-10 < x - 11 < -8$ and $2 < 3x - 1 < 8$, so that $|x - 11| < 10$ and $|3x - 1| > 2$. Thus the second factor is less than $\frac{10}{2} = 5$. Now let a positive number ϵ be given. Since the expression (1) will be less than ϵ if simultaneously $|x - 2| < \frac{\epsilon}{5}$ and $\left|\frac{x - 11}{3x - 1}\right| < 5$,

we have only to take $\delta = \delta(\epsilon)$ to be the smaller of the two numbers 1 and $\frac{\epsilon}{5}$,

$\delta(\epsilon) \equiv \min\left(1, \frac{\epsilon}{5}\right)$. The graph of this function $\delta(\epsilon)$ is shown in Figure 204.

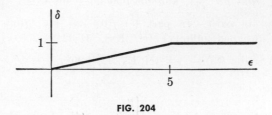

FIG. 204

207. LIMIT THEOREMS FOR FUNCTIONS

Many of the theorems of § 204 are special cases of more general limit theorems which apply to real valued functions, whether the independent variable tends toward a (finite) number, toward a number from one side only, or toward $+\infty$, $-\infty$ or ∞. Some of these are stated below. Since in each case the statement is essentially the same regardless of the manner in which the independent variable approaches its limit,† this latter behavior is unspecified. Furthermore, since the proofs are mere reformulations of those given in § 204, only one sample is given here. Others are requested in the Exercises of § 208.

Theorem I. *If* $\lim f(x)$ *exists it is unique.*

Theorem II. *If the function* $f(x)$ *is equal to a constant* k, *then* $\lim f(x)$ *exists and is equal to* k.

Theorem III. *If* $\lim f(x)$ *and* $\lim g(x)$ *exist and are finite, then* $\lim [f(x) + g(x)]$ *exists and is finite, and*

$$\lim [f(x) + g(x)] = \lim f(x) + \lim g(x).$$

In short, the limit of the sum is the sum of the limits. This rule extends to the sum of any finite number of functions.

Theorem IV. *Under the hypotheses of* Theorem III, *the limit of the difference is the difference of the limits:*

$$\lim [f(x) - g(x)] = \lim f(x) - \lim g(x).$$

† The word *limit* has been given specific meaning in this chapter only for functions, but it is convenient to extend its use to apply to *both* dependent and independent variables. The reader should recognize, however, that such an isolated statement as "the limit of the variable v is l" is meaningless, and takes on meaning only if v is associated with another variable, thus: $\lim\limits_{x \to a} v(x) = l$, or $\lim\limits_{v \to l} f(v) = k$.

Theorem V. *Under the hypotheses of* Theorem III, *the limit of the product is the product of the limits:*

$$\lim\,[f(x)\,g(x)] = \lim f(x)\cdot\lim g(x).$$

This rule extends to the product of any finite number of functions.

Proof for the case $x \to a$. Assume $f(x) \to L$ and $g(x) \to M$ as $x \to a$. We wish to show that $f(x)\,g(x) \to LM$ or, equivalently, that

$$f(x)\,g(x) - LM \to 0,\ \text{as}\ x \to a.$$

By addition and subtraction of the quantity $L\cdot g(x)$ and by appeal to Theorem III, we can use the relation

$$f(x)\,g(x) - LM = [f(x) - L]g(x) + L[g(x) - M]$$

to reduce the problem to that of showing that $[f(x) - L]g(x) \to 0$ and $L[g(x) - M] \to 0$ as $x \to a$. The fact that they do is a consequence of the following lemma:

Lemma. *If* $\phi(x) \to 0$ *and* $\psi(x) \to \mu$ *as* $x \to a$, *then* $\phi(x)\psi(x) \to 0$ *as* $x \to a$.

Proof of lemma. First, by letting $\epsilon = 1$ in the definition of $\lim\limits_{x\to a} \psi(x) = \mu$, we observe that there is a positive number δ_1 such that for x in the deleted neighborhood $0 < |x - a| < \delta_1$ the values of the function $\psi(x)$ lie in the neighborhood $(\mu - 1, \mu + 1)$, and are therefore bounded. Let P be a positive number such that $0 < |x - a| < \delta_1$ implies $|\psi(x)| \leqq P$. Now let ϵ be an arbitrary positive number, and let δ be a positive number $\leqq \delta_1$ such that $0 < |x - a| < \delta$ implies $|\phi(x)| < \epsilon/P$. Then $0 < |x - a| < \delta$ implies

$$|\phi(x)\psi(x)| < (\epsilon/P)\cdot P = \epsilon,$$

and the proof of the theorem is complete.

Theorem VI. *Under the hypotheses of* Theorem III *and the additional hypothesis that* $\lim g(x) \neq 0$, *the limit of the quotient is the quotient of the limits:*

$$\lim \frac{f(x)}{g(x)} = \frac{\lim f(x)}{\lim g(x)}.$$

Theorem VII. *If* $f(x) \leqq g(x)$ *and if* $\lim f(x)$ *and* $\lim g(x)$ *exist (finite, or* $+\infty$, *or* $-\infty$ *), then* $\lim f(x) \leqq \lim g(x)$.

208. EXERCISES

In Exercises 1-7, prove the indicated limit theorem for the specified behavior of the independent variable.

1. Theorem I, § 207; $x \to a$, finite or infinite limit.

2. Theorem II, § 207; $x \to \infty$.

3. Theorem III, § 207; $x \to a+$.

4. Theorem III, § 207; $x \to +\infty$.

5. Theorem IV, § 207; $x \to a-$.

6. Theorem V, § 207; $x \to -\infty$.

7. Theorem VII, § 207; $x \to a$.

8. Prove that if $\lim_{x \to a} \phi(x) = 0$, and if $\psi(x)$ is bounded in some deleted neighborhood of a (that is, if there exist positive numbers P and η such that $|\psi(x)| \leqq P$ for $0 < |x - a| < \eta$), then $\lim_{x \to a} \phi(x)\psi(x) = 0$. Find $\lim_{x \to 0} x \sin \frac{1}{x}$ (cf. Example 2, § 403).

9. Prove that if $\lim_{x \to a} f(x)$ exists and is positive (negative), then $f(x)$ is positive (negative) in some deleted neighborhood of a. Prove, in fact, that if $\lim_{x \to a} f(x) = m \neq 0$, then for all x within some deleted neighborhood of a, $f(x) > \frac{1}{2}m$ if $m > 0$ and $f(x) < \frac{1}{2}m$ if $m < 0$. Consequently show that the reciprocal of a function is bounded in some deleted neighborhood of any point at which the function has a nonzero limit. Show that this last statement is true even if the nonzero limit is infinite. *Hint:* In case $\lim_{x \to a} f(x) = m > 0$, let δ be a positive number such that $0 < |x - a| < \delta$ implies $|f(x) - m| < \frac{1}{2}m$, so that $m - f(x) < \frac{1}{2}m$.

10. Prove Theorem VI, § 207, for the case $x \to a$. (Cf. Exs. 8 and 9.)

11. Prove Theorem VI, § 207, for the case $x \to +\infty$. (Cf. Exs. 8-10.)

12. Prove that if $f(x) \leqq g(x) \leqq h(x)$ and if $\lim f(x)$ and $\lim h(x)$ are finite and equal (for the same behavior of the independent variable subject to the restrictions of the first paragraph of § 207), then $\lim g(x)$ exists and is equal to their common value. Extend this result to include infinite limits.

In Exercises 13-20, prove the given statement.

13. $\lim_{x \to a} f(x)$ exists and is finite if and only if $\lim_{x \to a+} f(x)$ and $\lim_{x \to a-} f(x)$ exist and are finite and equal.

14. $\lim_{x \to a} f(x)$ exists (in the finite or infinite sense) if and only if $\lim_{x \to a+} f(x)$ and $\lim_{x \to a-} f(x)$ exist and are equal.

15. Theorems III and V, § 207, hold for any finite number of functions.

16. If k is a constant and $\lim f(x)$ exists and is finite, then $\lim k f(x)$ exists and is equal to $k \lim f(x)$, whatever the behavior of the independent variable x, subject to the restrictions of the first paragraph of § 207.

17. $\lim_{x \to a} x = a$.

18. If n is a positive integer, $\lim_{x \to a} x^n = a^n$. *Hint:* Use Theorem V, § 207, and Ex. 17.

19. If $f(x)$ is a polynomial,
$$f(x) = a_0 x^n + a_1 x^{n-1} + \cdots + a_{n-1}x + a_n,$$
then $\lim_{x \to a} f(x) = f(a)$.

20. If $f(x)$ is a rational function,
$$f(x) = g(x)/h(x),$$
where $g(x)$ and $h(x)$ are polynomials, and if $h(a) \neq 0$, then $\lim_{x \to a} f(x) = f(a)$.

In Exercises 21-26, find the indicated limit.

21. $\lim_{x \to 3} (2x^2 - 5x + 1)$. $= 4$

22. $\lim_{x \to -2} \dfrac{3x^2 - 5}{2x + 17}$. $1/13$

23. $\lim_{x \to 2} \dfrac{3x^2 - x - 10}{x^2 + 5x - 14}$.   *Hint:* Reduce to lowest terms. $\dfrac{11}{9}$

24. $\lim_{x \to -3} \dfrac{x^3 + 27}{x^4 - 81}$.   (Cf. Ex. 23.) $\frac{1}{4}$

25. $\lim_{x \to a} \dfrac{x^3 - a^3}{x - a}$.   (Cf. Ex. 23.) $3a^2$

26. $\lim_{x \to a} \dfrac{x^m - a^m}{x - a}$, where m is an integer.   (Cf. Ex. 23, above, and Ex. 9,
§ 107.)

In Exercises 27-30, give a precise definition for the given limit statement.

27. $\lim_{x \to a+} f(x) = -\infty$.

28. $\lim_{x \to -\infty} f(x) = +\infty$.

29. $\lim_{x \to \infty} f(x) = \infty$.

30. $\lim_{x \to a-} f(x) = \infty$.

31. Prove that $\lim_{x \to 0} \dfrac{1}{x} = \infty$ and $\lim_{x \to \infty} \dfrac{1}{x} = 0$.   More generally, assuming $f(x)$ to be nonzero except possibly for the limiting value of the independent variable, prove that $\lim f(x) = 0$ if and only if $\lim \dfrac{1}{f(x)} = \infty$.   Discuss Theorem VI, § 207, if $\lim f(x) \neq 0$ and $\lim g(x) = 0$.   (Cf. Theorem XI, § 204.)

32. Prove that $\lim_{x \to 0+} \dfrac{1}{x} = +\infty$.   More generally, assuming $f(x)$ to be positive except possibly for the limiting value of the independent variable, prove that $\lim f(x) = +\infty$ if and only if $\lim \dfrac{1}{f(x)} = 0$.

In Exercises 33 and 34, assuming the standard facts regarding trigonometric functions (cf. §§ 603-604 for analytic definitions of the trigonometric functions), find the specified limits, or establish their nonexistence.

33. (a) $\lim_{x \to \frac{1}{2}\pi+} \tan x$;   (b) $\lim_{x \to \frac{1}{2}\pi-} \tan x$;

(c) $\lim_{x \to \frac{1}{2}\pi} \tan x$;   (d) $\lim_{x \to 0+} \cot x$;

(e) $\lim_{x \to 0-} \cot x$;   (f) $\lim_{x \to 0} \cot x$.

34. (a) $\lim_{x \to +\infty} \sin x$;   (b) $\lim_{x \to -\infty} \cos x^2$;

(c) $\lim\limits_{x\to\infty} \dfrac{\sin x}{x}$;

(d) $\lim\limits_{x\to+\infty} \dfrac{\sec x}{x}$;

(e) $\lim\limits_{x\to-\infty} \dfrac{x - \cos x}{x}$;

(f) $\lim\limits_{x\to\infty} \dfrac{x \sin x}{x^2 - 4}$.

35. Let $f(x)$ be a rational function

$$f(x) = \frac{a_0 x^m + a_1 x^{m-1} + \cdots + a_{m-1}x + a_m}{b_0 x^n + b_1 x^{n-1} + \cdots + b_{n-1}x + b_n},$$

where $a_0 \neq 0$ and $b_0 \neq 0$. Show that $\lim\limits_{x\to\infty} f(x)$ is equal to 0 if $m < n$, to a_0/b_0 if $m = n$, and to ∞ if $m > n$. In particular, show that if $f(x)$ is any nonconstant polynomial, $\lim\limits_{x\to\infty} f(x) = \infty$. *Hint:* Divide every term in both numerator and denominator by the highest power of x present.

36. Discuss the result of Exercise 35 for the case $m > n$ if (i) $x \to +\infty$; (ii) $x \to -\infty$; (iii) $x \to \infty$ and m and n are either both even or both odd. Consider in particular the special case where $f(x)$ is a polynomial.

In Exercises 37-42, find the indicated limit. (Cf. Exs. 35-36.)

37. $\lim\limits_{x\to\infty} \dfrac{5x^2 - 3x + 1}{6x^2 + 5}$.

38. $\lim\limits_{x\to+\infty} (2x^5 - 350x^2 - 10{,}000)$.

39. $\lim\limits_{x\to\infty} (-6x^4 - 9x^3 + x)$.

40. $\lim\limits_{x\to\infty} \dfrac{2x^3 - 5}{3x + 7}$.

41. $\lim\limits_{x\to+\infty} \dfrac{150x + 2000}{x^2 + 3}$.

42. $\lim\limits_{x\to-\infty} \dfrac{8x^3 + 13x + 6}{5x^2 + 11}$.

In Exercises 43-50, interpret and prove each relation. For these exercises p designates a positive number, n a negative number, m a nonzero number, and q any number. *Hint for* Ex. 43: This means: If $\lim f(x) = p$ and $\lim g(x) = +\infty$, then $\lim f(x) g(x) = +\infty$. For simplicity let $x \to a$.

43. $p \cdot (+\infty) = +\infty$.

44. $n \cdot (+\infty) = -\infty$.

45. $q - (-\infty) = +\infty$.

46. $q + (\infty) = \infty$.

47. $(-\infty) - q = -\infty$.

48. $(+\infty) + (+\infty) = +\infty$.

49. $\dfrac{0}{\infty} = \dfrac{m}{\infty} = 0$.

50. $\dfrac{\infty}{0} = \dfrac{m}{0} = \infty$.

In Exercises 51-56, show by examples that the given expression is indeterminate. (See Hint for Ex. 43.)

51. $\infty + \infty$.

52. $(+\infty) - (+\infty)$.

Hint for Ex. 52: Consider the examples (i) $x - x$ and (ii) $x^2 - x$ as $x \to +\infty$.

53. $(+\infty) + (\infty)$.

54. $0 \cdot \infty$.

55. $\dfrac{0}{0}$.

56. $\dfrac{\infty}{\infty}$.

★★**57.** Give an example of a function $f(x)$ satisfying the following three conditions: $\lim\limits_{x\to0} |f(x)| = 1$, $\lim\limits_{x\to0-} f(x) = -1$, $\lim\limits_{x\to0+} f(x)$ does not exist. (Cf. Ex. 39, § 216.)

★★**58.** Give an example of a function $f(x)$ satisfying the following three conditions: $\lim\limits_{x\to0+} f(x) = \infty$, $\lim\limits_{x\to0+} f(x) \neq +\infty$, $\lim\limits_{x\to0+} f(x) \neq -\infty$. (Cf. Ex. 57.)

In Exercises 59-64, find the required limit, prove that it is the limit by direct use of Definition I, § 206, and obtain explicitly a function $\delta(\epsilon)$ as demanded by that definition. (Cf. Exs. 32-37, § 216.)

★**59.** $\lim\limits_{x\to2} 3x$.

★**60.** $\lim\limits_{x\to-3} x^2$.

★**61.** $\lim\limits_{x\to4} (3x^2 - 5x)$.

★**62.** $\lim\limits_{x\to-5} \dfrac{1}{x}$.

★**63.** $\lim\limits_{x\to1} \dfrac{4x^2 - 1}{5x + 2}$.

★**64.** $\lim\limits_{x\to2} \dfrac{3x}{4x - 7}$.

In Exercises 65-70, find the required limit, prove that it is the limit by direct use of Definition II or Definition III, § 206, and obtain explicitly a function $N(\epsilon)$ or $\delta(B)$ as demanded by the definition.

★**65.** $\lim\limits_{x\to+\infty} \dfrac{5}{x}$.

★**66.** $\lim\limits_{x\to-\infty} \dfrac{1}{x^2}$.

★**67.** $\lim\limits_{x\to+\infty} \dfrac{3x - 2}{x + 5}$.

★**68.** $\lim\limits_{x\to+\infty} \dfrac{5x^2 + 1}{3x^2}$.

★**69.** $\lim\limits_{x\to0} \dfrac{1}{x^2}$.

★**70.** $\lim\limits_{x\to1} \dfrac{2x - 5}{x^3 - 2x^2 + x}$.

209. CONTINUITY

Continuity of a function at a point a can be defined either in terms of limits (Definition I, below), or directly by use of the type of δ-ϵ formulation in which the original limit concepts are framed (Definition II, below). When continuity is couched in terms of limits, we shall make the same implicit assumption that was stated in the first paragraph of § 206, namely, that every neighborhood of the point a contains at least one point x different from a for which the function $f(x)$ is defined. (Cf. Note 2, below.)

Definition I. *A function $f(x)$ is **continuous** at $x = a$ if and only if the following three conditions are satisfied:*

(*i*) *$f(a)$ exists; that is, $f(x)$ is defined at $x = a$;*

(*ii*) *$\lim\limits_{x\to a} f(x)$ exists and is finite;*

(*iii*) *$\lim\limits_{x\to a} f(x) = f(a)$.*

By inspection of the definition of $\lim\limits_{x\to1} f(x)$, it is possible (cf. Ex. 11, § 212) to establish the equivalence of this definition and the following (in case the implicit assumption of the first paragraph, above, is satisfied).

Definition II. *A function $f(x)$ is* **continuous** *at $x = a$ if and only if it is defined at $x = a$ and corresponding to an arbitrary positive number ϵ, there exists a positive number $\delta = \delta(\epsilon)$ such that $|x - a| < \delta$ implies*

$$|f(x) - f(a)| < \epsilon,$$

for values of x for which $f(x)$ is defined.

NOTE 1. Definition I is sometimes called the *limit definition of continuity* and Definition II the *δ-ϵ definition of continuity.*

NOTE 2. The δ-ϵ definition is applicable even when the function is not defined at points neighboring $x = a$ (except at a itself). In this case a is an *isolated point* of the domain of definition, and $f(x)$ is continuous there, although $\lim\limits_{x \to a} f(x)$ has no meaning.

NOTE 3. Each of the following limit statements is a formulation of continuity of $f(x)$ at $x = a$ (Ex. 3, § 212):

(1) $\qquad\qquad f(a + h) - f(a) \to 0 \quad$ as $\quad h \to 0$;

(2) $\qquad\qquad$ if $\quad \Delta y \equiv f(a + \Delta x) - f(a), \quad$ then

$$\Delta y \to 0 \quad \text{as} \quad \Delta x \to 0.$$

A function is said to be **continuous on a set** if and only if it is continuous at every point of that set. In case a function is continuous at every point of its domain of definition it is simply called **continuous,** without further modifying words.

Continuity from the right, or **right-hand continuity,** is defined by replacing, in Definition I, $\lim\limits_{x \to a} f(x)$ by $\lim\limits_{x \to a+} f(x)$. Similarly, **continuity from the left,** or **left-hand continuity,** is obtained by replacing $\lim\limits_{x \to a} f(x)$ by $\lim\limits_{x \to a-} f(x)$. Thus $f(x)$ is continuous from the right at $x = a$ if and only if $f(a+) = f(a)$, and $f(x)$ is continuous from the left if and only if $f(a-) = f(a)$, it being assumed that the expressions written down exist.

A useful relation between continuity and limits is stated in the following theorem:

Theorem. *If $f(x)$ is continuous at $x = a$ and if $\phi(t)$ has the limit a, as t approaches some limit (finite or infinite, one-sided or not), then*

$$f(\phi(t)) \to f(a).$$

In short, the limit of the function is the function of the limit:

$$\lim f(\phi(t)) = f(\lim \phi(t)).$$

Proof. We shall prove the theorem for the single case $t \to +\infty$. (Cf. Exs. 12-13, § 212.) Accordingly, let ϵ be an arbitrary positive number, and let δ be a positive number such that $|x - a| < \delta$ implies

$$|f(x) - f(a)| < \epsilon.$$

Then choose N so large that $t > N$ implies $|\phi(t) - a| < \delta$. Combining these two implications by setting $x = \phi(t)$ we have the result: $t > N$ implies $|f(\phi(t)) - f(a)| < \epsilon$.   This final implication is the one sought.

Example 1.   A function whose domain of definition is a closed interval $[a, b]$ is continuous there if and only if it is continuous at each interior point, continuous from the right at $x = a$, and continuous from the left at $x = b$. (See Fig. 205.)

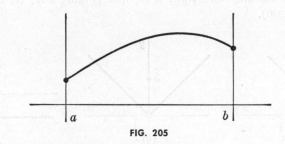

FIG. 205

Example 2.   The function $[x]$ (Example 5, § 201) is continuous except when x is an integer.   It is everywhere continuous from the right.   (See Fig. 206.)

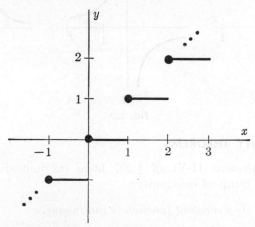

FIG. 206

210. TYPES OF DISCONTINUITY

The principal types of discontinuity are the following four:

(i) *The limit of the function exists, but the function either is not defined at the point or has a value different from the limit there.*   (Figure 207, (a) and (b); cf. Example 1, § 206.)   Such a discontinuity is called a **removable discontinuity** because if the function is redefined to have the value $f(a) \equiv \lim_{x \to a} f(x)$ at $x = a$, it becomes continuous there.

(*ii*) *The two one-sided limits exist and are finite, but are not equal.* An example is the signum function (Figure 207, (*c*); cf. Example 1, § 206). Such a discontinuity is called a **jump discontinuity.**

(*iii*) *At least one one-sided limit fails to exist.* An example is $\sin \dfrac{1}{x}$ (Figure 207, (*d*); cf. Example 1, § 206).

(*iv*) *At least one one-sided limit is infinite* (Figure 207, (*e*) and (*f*); cf. Example 1, § 206).

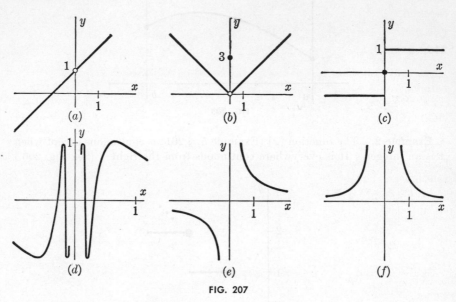

FIG. 207

211. CONTINUITY THEOREMS

The limit theorems II–VI of § 207 have (as immediate corollaries) counterparts in terms of continuity:

Theorem I. *Any constant function is continuous.*

Theorem II. *If* $f(x)$ *and* $g(x)$ *are continuous at* $x = a$, *then their sum* $f(x) + g(x)$ *is also continuous at* $x = a$. *In short, the sum of two continuous functions is a continuous function. This rule applies to any finite number of functions.*

Theorem III. *Under the hypotheses of* Theorem II, $f(x) - g(x)$ *is continuous at* $x = a$: *the difference of two continuous functions is a continuous function.*

Theorem IV. *Under the hypotheses of* Theorem II, $f(x)\, g(x)$ *is continuous at* $x = a$: *the product of two continuous functions is a continuous function. This rule applies to any finite number of functions.*

Theorem V. *Under the hypotheses of* Theorem II *and the additional hypothesis that* $g(a) \neq 0$, $f(x)/g(x)$ *is continuous at* $x = a$: *the quotient of two continuous functions is continuous where the denominator does not vanish.*

A direct consequence of the Theorem of § 209 is the following:

Theorem VI. *A continuous function of a continuous function is a continuous function. More precisely, if* $f(x)$ *is continuous at* $x = a$, *if* $g(y)$ *is continuous at* $y = b = f(a)$, *and if* $h(x) \equiv g(f(x))$, *then* $h(x)$ *is a continuous function of* x *at* $x = a$.

212. EXERCISES

1. Prove that any polynomial is continuous for all values of the independent variable. (Cf. Ex. 19, § 208.)

2. Prove that any rational function is continuous except where the denominator vanishes. (Cf. Ex. 20, § 208.)

3. Prove the statements in Note 3, § 209.

4. Redefine the signum function (Example 1, § 206) at $x = 0$ so that it becomes everywhere continuous from the right; so that it becomes everywhere continuous from the left.

5. Establish continuity at $x = 0$ for each of the two functions:

(a) $f(x) \equiv x \sin \dfrac{1}{x}$ if $x \neq 0$, $f(0) \equiv 0$; (b) $g(x) \equiv x^2 \sin \dfrac{1}{x}$ if $x \neq 0$, $\equiv 0$ if $x = 0$.

(Cf. Ex. 8, § 208. Also see Examples 2 and 3, § 403, for graphs and further discussion.)

6. Define the function $x \cos \dfrac{1}{x}$ at $x = 0$ so that it becomes everywhere continuous.

In Exercises 7-10, state the type of discontinuity at $x = 0$.

7. $f(x) \equiv x^2 - 8x$ if $x \neq 0$, $f(0) \equiv 6$.

8. $f(x) \equiv x^3 \cos \dfrac{1}{x^2}$ if $x \neq 0$, undefined if $x = 0$.

9. $f(x) \equiv \dfrac{1}{x}$ if $x > 0$, $f(x) \equiv 0$ if $x \leq 0$.

10. $f(x) \equiv x + 1$ if $x > 0$, $f(x) \equiv -x - 1$ if $x < 0$, $f(0) \equiv 0$.

11. Prove the equivalence of the two definitions of continuity, § 209, under the assumptions of the first paragraph of that section.

12. Prove the Theorem of § 209 (a) for the case $t \to c$; (b) for the case $t \to c-$.

13. Give an example to show that the Theorem of § 209 is false if the continuity assumption is omitted.

14. Prove that the **negation of continuity** of a function at a point of its domain can be expressed: $f(x)$ *is discontinuous at* $x = a$ *if and only if there is a positive number* ϵ *having the property that corresponding to an arbitrary positive number* δ *(however small), there exists a number* x *such that* $|x - a| < \delta$ *and* $|f(x) - f(a)| \geq \epsilon$.

15. Show that the function defined for all real numbers, $f(x) \equiv 1$ if x is rational, $f(x) \equiv 0$ if x is irrational, is everywhere discontinuous. (Cf. Example 6, § 201.)

16. Prove that $|x|$ is everywhere continuous.

★**17.** Prove that $|f(x)|$ is continuous wherever $f(x)$ is. Give an example of a function defined for all real numbers which is never continuous but whose absolute value is always continuous. *Hint:* Consider a function like that of Ex. 15, with values ± 1.

18. Prove that if $f(x)$ is continuous and positive at $x = a$, then there is a neighborhood of a in which $f(x)$ is positive. Prove that, in fact, there exist a positive number ϵ and a neighborhood of a such that in this neighborhood $f(x) > \epsilon$. State and prove corresponding facts if $f(a)$ is negative. *Hint:* Cf. Ex. 9, § 208.

★**19.** Prove that if $f(x)$ is continuous at $x = a$, and if $\epsilon > 0$ is given, then there exists a neighborhood of a such that for any two points in this neighborhood the values of $f(x)$ differ by less than ϵ.

★★**20.** Show that the function with domain the closed interval $[0, 1]$, $f(x) \equiv x$ if x is rational, $f(x) \equiv 1 - x$ if x is irrational, is continuous only for $x = \frac{1}{2}$.

★★**21.** Show that the following example is a counterexample to the following False Theorem, which strives to generalize the Theorem of § 209, and Theorem VI, § 211: If $\lim \phi(t) = a$, where a is finite and t approaches some limit, and if $\lim_{x \to a} f(x) = b$, where b is finite, then $\lim f(\phi(t)) = b$, as t approaches its limit.
Counterexample: $\phi(t) \equiv 0$ for all t, $f(x) \equiv 0$ if $x \neq 0$, $f(0) \equiv 1$; $t \to 0$, $x \to 0$. Prove that this False Theorem becomes a True Theorem with the additional hypothesis that $\phi(t)$ is never equal to a, except possibly for the limiting value of t.

213. MORE THEOREMS ON CONTINUOUS FUNCTIONS

We list below a few important theorems on continuous functions, whose proofs depend on certain rather sophisticated ideas discussed in Chapter 3, which is starred for possible omission or postponement. The proofs of these particular theorems are given in § 306.

Theorem I. *A function continuous on a closed interval is bounded there. That is, if $f(x)$ is continuous on $[a, b]$, there exists a number B such that $a \leqq x \leqq b$ implies $|f(x)| \leqq B$.*

Theorem II. *A function continuous on a closed interval has a maximum and a minimum there. That is, if $f(x)$ is continuous on $[a, b]$, there exist points x_1 and x_2 in $[a, b]$ such that $a \leqq x \leqq b$ implies $f(x_1) \leqq f(x) \leqq f(x_2)$.*

Theorem III. *If $f(x)$ is continuous on the closed interval $[a, b]$ and if $f(a)$ and $f(b)$ have opposite signs, there is a point x_0 between a and b for which $f(x_0) = 0$.*

Theorem IV. *A function continuous on an interval assumes (as a value) every number between any two of its values.*   (Cf. Ex. 47, § 408.)

NOTE. For other properties of a function continuous on a closed interval, see § 307 and § 501.

214. EXISTENCE OF $\sqrt{2}$ AND OTHER ROOTS

In Chapter 1 (Ex. 8, § 109) $\sqrt{2}$ was mentioned as an example of an irrational number, but proof of its existence was deferred. We are able now, with the aid of the last theorem of the preceding section, to give a simple proof that there exists a positive number whose square is 2. The idea is to consider the function $f(x) \equiv x^2$, which is continuous everywhere (Ex. 1, § 212) and, in particular, on the closed interval from $x = 0$ to $x = 2$. Since the values of the function at the end-points of this interval are $0^2 = 0$ and $2^2 = 4$, and since the number 2 is between these two extreme values, there must be a (positive) number between these end-points for which the value of the function is 2. That is, there is a positive number whose square is 2. The following theorem generalizes this result, and establishes the uniqueness of positive nth roots:

Theorem. *If p is a positive number and n is a positive integer, there exists a unique positive number x such that $x^n = p$. This number is called the **nth root of p** and is written $x = \sqrt[n]{p}$.*

Proof. We establish uniqueness first. If $x^n = y^n = p$, where x and y are positive, then (Ex. 9, § 107) $x^n - y^n = (x - y)(x^{n-1} + x^{n-2}y + \cdots + y^{n-1}) = 0$. Since the second factor is positive (Ex. 8, § 107) the first factor must vanish (Ex. 14, § 103): $x - y = 0$, or $x = y$.

For the proof of existence, we note first that since $x^n \geq x$ for $x \geq 1$, $\lim_{x \to +\infty} x^n = +\infty$. Therefore there exists a number b such that $b^n > p$. The number p is thus between the extreme values assumed by x^n on the closed interval $[0, b]$, and therefore, since x^n is continuous, this function must assume the value p at some point x between 0 and b: $x^n = p$.

215. MONOTONIC FUNCTIONS AND THEIR INVERSES

Definition. *A function $f(x)$ is **monotonically increasing (decreasing)**, written $f(x) \uparrow (\downarrow)$, on a set A if and only if whenever a and b are elements of A and $a < b$, then $f(a) \leq f(b)$ $(f(a) \geq f(b))$. In either case it is called **monotonic**. Whenever $a < b$ implies $f(a) < f(b)$ $(f(a) > f(b))$, $f(x)$ is called **strictly increasing (decreasing)**, and in either case **strictly monotonic**.*   (Cf. Fig. 208.)

Theorem XIV, § 204, states facts about monotonic sequences. If we permit the inclusion of infinite limits we can drop the assumption of boundedness and state that any monotonic sequence has a limit (cf. the Note, § 204).   In Exercise 27, § 216, the student is asked to generalize this fact and prove that a monotonic function $f(x)$ always has one-sided limits. Consequently the only type of discontinuity that a monotonic function can have (at a point where it is defined) is a finite jump (Ex. 28, § 216).

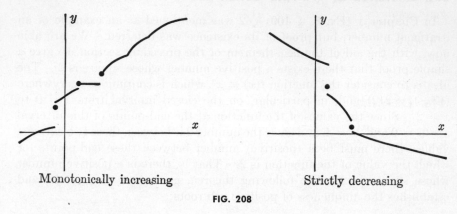

Monotonically increasing   Strictly decreasing

FIG. 208

Consider now the case of a function that is continuous and strictly monotonic on a closed interval $[a, b]$.   For definiteness assume that $f(x)$ is strictly *increasing* there, and let $c \equiv f(a)$ and $d \equiv f(b)$.   Then $c < d$, and (Theorem IV, § 213) $f(x)$ assumes in the interval $[a, b]$ every value between c and d.   Furthermore, it cannot assume the same value twice, for if $\alpha < \beta$, then $f(\alpha) < f(\beta)$.   (Cf. Fig. 209.)   The function $f(x)$, there-

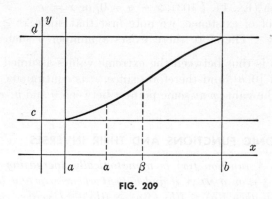

FIG. 209

fore, establishes a one-to-one correspondence between the points of the two closed intervals $[a, b]$ and $[c, d]$.   Thus to each point y of the closed interval $[c, d]$ corresponds a unique point x of $[a, b]$ such that $y = f(x)$. Since y determines x uniquely, x can be considered as a single-valued function of y, $x = \phi(y)$, and is called the **inverse function** of $y = f(x)$, the latter being referred to, then, as the **direct function.** The nth roots obtained in the preceding section are inverse functions: if $y = f(x) = x^n$, then $x = \phi(y) = \sqrt[n]{y}$. We now state an important fact regarding the continuity of inverse functions. The proof is given in § 306.

Theorem. *If $y = f(x)$ is continuous and strictly monotonic on a closed interval $[a, b]$, its inverse function $x = \phi(y)$ is continuous and strictly monotonic on the corresponding closed interval $[c, d]$.*

Corollary. *The function $y = \sqrt[n]{x}$, where n is a positive integer, is a continuous and strictly increasing function of x for $x \geqq 0$.* (Cf. Ex. 18, § 216.)

216. EXERCISES

1. Show that the equation $x^4 + 2x - 11 = 0$ has a real root. Prove that if $f(x)$ is a real polynomial (real coefficients) of odd degree, the equation $f(x) = 0$ has a real root.

2. Prove that the maximum (minimum) value of a function on a closed interval is unique, but show by examples that the point ξ at which $f(x)$ is a maximum (minimum) may or may not be unique.

3. Prove that $\sqrt{f(x)}$ is continuous wherever $f(x)$ is continuous and positive, and that $\sqrt[3]{f(x)}$ is continuous wherever $f(x)$ is continuous.

4. Assuming continuity and other standard properties of $\sin x$ and $\cos x$ (cf. §§ 603-604), discuss continuity of each function.

$$(a) \ \sqrt{1 + \sin x}; \qquad\qquad (b) \ \frac{1}{\sqrt{1 - \sin x}};$$

$$(c) \ \sqrt[3]{\cos x^2}; \qquad\qquad (d) \ \frac{1}{\sqrt[3]{1 + \cos^2 x - \sin^2 x}}.$$

In Exercises 5-10, discuss the discontinuities of each function, and draw a graph in each case. The bracket function $[x]$ is defined in Example 5, § 201. (Also cf. Exs. 7-10, § 203.)

5. $[-x]$.   **6.** $[x] + [-x]$.

7. $[\sqrt{x}]$.   **8.** $[x^2]$.

9. $[x] + \sqrt{x - [x]}$.   **10.** $[x] + (x - [x])^2$.

11. Prove the two laws of radicals:

$$(i) \ \sqrt[n]{ab} = \sqrt[n]{a} \ \sqrt[n]{b},$$

$$(ii) \ \sqrt[n]{\frac{a}{b}} = \frac{\sqrt[n]{a}}{\sqrt[n]{b}}, \ b \neq 0,$$

where n is a positive integer, and in case n is even a and b are nonnegative.

12. Prove that $\lim\limits_{x \to +\infty} \sqrt[n]{x} = +\infty$, where n is a positive integer.

★13. Prove that $\lim_{x \to +\infty} \sqrt{x} (\sqrt{x+a} - \sqrt{x}) = \frac{1}{2}a$. *Hint:* Multiply by $(\sqrt{x+a} + \sqrt{x})/(\sqrt{x+a} + \sqrt{x})$.

★14. Let $f(x)$ be a polynomial of degree m and leading coefficient $a_0 > 0$, and let $g(x)$ be a polynomial of degree n and leading coefficient $b_0 > 0$, and let k be a positive integer. Prove that the limit

$$\lim_{x \to +\infty} \sqrt[k]{f(x)} / \sqrt[k]{g(x)}$$

is equal to 0 if $m < n$, to $\sqrt[k]{a_0/b_0}$ if $m = n$, and to $+\infty$ if $m > n$. (Cf. Ex. 35, § 208.)

★15. Give an example of a function which is continuous and bounded on the open interval $(0, 1)$, but which has neither maximum nor minimum there.

★16. Give an example of a function which is defined and single-valued on the closed interval $[0, 1]$, but which is not bounded there.

★17. Give an example of a function which is defined, single-valued, and bounded on the closed interval $[0, 1]$, but which has neither maximum nor minimum there.

★18. Prove that $\sqrt[n]{x}$ is an increasing function of n for any fixed x between 0 and 1, and a decreasing function of n for any fixed $x > 1$. *Hint:* Show that the desired order relation between $\sqrt[n]{x}$ and $\sqrt[n+1]{x}$ follows from Ex. 10, § 107, by taking $n(n + 1)$th powers.

★19. Prove that if $x > 0$ then $\lim_{n \to +\infty} \sqrt[n]{x} = 1$. *Hint:* Assume for definiteness that $0 < x < 1$. Then (Ex. 18) $\sqrt[n]{x} \uparrow$ as $n \uparrow$. Since $\sqrt[n]{x} < 1$ for all n, $\lim_{n \to +\infty} \sqrt[n]{x} = L$ exists (Theorem XIV, § 204) and $L \leq 1$. If $L < 1$, then $\sqrt[n]{x} \leq L$ for all n, and $x \leq L^n$ for all n. Use Theorem XIII, § 204.

★20. Define $\sqrt[2n-1]{x}$ for all x, and show that $\lim_{n \to +\infty} \sqrt[2n-1]{x} = \operatorname{sgn} x$ (cf. Example 1 (*c*), § 206).

★21. If r is a positive rational number, represented as the quotient of two positive integers, $r = p/q$, prove that the two definitions of x^r, where $x \geq 0$, are equivalent: $x^r \equiv \sqrt[q]{x^p}$; $x^r \equiv (\sqrt[q]{x})^p$. Also show that either definition is independent of the representation of r as a quotient of positive integers. Discuss the function $f(x) \equiv x^r$ as a strictly increasing continuous function of x for $x \geq 0$.

★★22. Define x^r, where $x > 0$ and r is any rational number, and establish the laws of exponents of Exercises 17-21, § 107, for rational exponents. (Cf. Ex. 7, § 109, and Exs. 11 and 21, above.)

★★23. Discuss the function $f(x) \equiv x^r$, where r is any rational number and $x > 0$, as a continuous monotonic function of x. Find $\lim_{x \to 0+} f(x)$ and $\lim_{x \to +\infty} f(x)$. (Cf. Ex. 21.)

★24. If $f(x)$ is continuous on $[a, b]$, if $a \leq c < d \leq b$, and $K = f(c) + f(d)$, prove that there exists a number ξ between a and b such that $K = 2f(\xi)$. More generally, if m and n are positive numbers, show that $mf(c) + nf(d) = (m + n) f(\xi)$, for some ξ between a and b. Finally, extend this result to the formula

$$m_1 f(c_1) + \cdots + m_k f(c_k) = (m_1 + \cdots + m_k) f(\xi).$$

Hint: Show that $\dfrac{m}{m + n} f(c) + \dfrac{n}{m + n} f(d)$ is between $f(c)$ and $f(d)$, and use Theorem IV, § 213.

★★**25.** Discuss the function $h(r) \equiv x^r$, where r is any rational number and $x > 0$, as a monotonic function of r. Show that for $0 < x < 1$, $h(r) \downarrow$ as $r \uparrow$ and that for $x > 1$, $h(r) \uparrow$ as $r \uparrow$. Find $\lim\limits_{r \to +\infty} h(r)$ and $\lim\limits_{r \to -\infty} h(r)$. (Cf. Ex. 18.)

★★**26.** Prove that the function $h(r)$ of Exercise 25 is continuous, if only rational values of r are considered. *Hint:* Write $x^r - x^{r_0} = x^{r_0}(x^{r-r_0} - 1)$, and use Exs. 19 and 25.

★**27.** Prove that a monotonic function always has one-sided limits (finite or infinite).

★**28.** Prove that the only discontinuities that a monotonic function can have at points where it is defined are finite jumps. (Cf. Ex. 27.)

★**29.** Prove that the set of points of discontinuity of a monotonic function is either finite or denumerable. (Cf. Ex. 12, § 113. Also cf. Ex. 25, § 717.) *Hint:* There are at most two values of x at which $y = f(x)$ can become infinite. Any other point of discontinuity, on the x-axis, corresponds to a finite interval of jump on the y-axis, and to distinct points of jump discontinuity correspond open intervals having no point in common. In each of these intervals of jump lies a rational number $((v),$ § 112$)$, and the rational numbers are denumerable (Ex. 14, § 113).

★**30.** Prove that any monotonic function can be redefined at the points of discontinuity at which it is defined so that it becomes everywhere continuous from the right (or from the left).

★**31.** Prove the following converse of the statement of § 215 that a continuous strictly monotonic function has a single-valued inverse: If $f(x)$ is continuous on a closed interval $[a, b]$ and if $f(x)$ does not assume there any value twice (that is, at distinct points of $[a, b]$ $f(x)$ has distinct values), then $f(x)$ is strictly monotonic there.

In Exercises 32–37, find a specific function $\delta = \delta(\epsilon)$ as specified by Definition II, § 209, for the given function at the prescribed point. (Cf. Exs. 59–64, § 208.)

★**32.** $\sqrt{x}$, $a = 3$. *Hint:* If $x > 0$,

$$|\sqrt{x} - \sqrt{3}| = \left| \frac{\sqrt{x} - \sqrt{3}}{1} \cdot \frac{\sqrt{x} + \sqrt{3}}{\sqrt{x} + \sqrt{3}} \right| = \frac{|x - 3|}{\sqrt{x} + \sqrt{3}} < |x - 3|.$$

★**33.** $\sqrt{x^2 - 4}$, $a = 2$.   ★**34.** $\sqrt{3x^2 - x}$, $a = -1$.

★**35.** $\sqrt[3]{x}$, $a = 5$. *Hint:* If $x > 0$,

$$|\sqrt[3]{x} - \sqrt[3]{5}| = \left| \frac{\sqrt[3]{x} - \sqrt[3]{5}}{1} \cdot \frac{\sqrt[3]{x^2} + \sqrt[3]{5x} + \sqrt[3]{25}}{\sqrt[3]{x^2} + \sqrt[3]{5x} + \sqrt[3]{25}} \right| < |x - 5|.$$

★**36.** $\dfrac{1}{\sqrt{x}}$, $a = 6$.   ★**37.** $\dfrac{1}{\sqrt[3]{x}}$, $a = 1$.

★★**38.** If a is a fixed positive rational number prove that the set of all numbers of the form $r + s\sqrt{a}$, where r and s are arbitrary rational numbers, form a field (cf. Ex. 8, § 113).

★★39. Prove that each example demanded by Exercises 57 and 58, § 208, must be discontinuous and that, in fact, it must have infinitely many points of discontinuity.

★★40. Prove that $\lim\limits_{n \to +\infty} \left(1 + \dfrac{1}{n}\right)^n$ exists and is between 2 and 3. (This is one definition of e. For another treatment see §§ 601-602.) *Hint:* First express the binomial expansion of $a_n \equiv \left(1 + \dfrac{1}{n}\right)^n$ in the form

$$1 + 1 + \frac{1}{2!}\left(1 - \frac{1}{n}\right) + \frac{1}{3!}\left(1 - \frac{1}{n}\right)\left(1 - \frac{2}{n}\right) + \cdots,$$

and thereby show that $a_n \uparrow$ and, furthermore, that

$$a_n < 1 + 1 + \frac{1}{2} + \frac{1}{2^2} + \frac{1}{2^3} + \cdots + \frac{1}{2^{n-1}}.$$

3

★Some Theoretical Considerations

~~~~~~

★301. A FUNDAMENTAL THEOREM ON BOUNDED SEQUENCES †

One of the properties of the real number system that was assumed as an axiom in Chapter 1 is that of *completeness*. A useful consequence (which is actually one of several alternative formulations of the concept of completeness) is stated in the following theorem:

Theorem. Fundamental Theorem on Bounded Sequences. *Every bounded sequence (of real numbers) contains a convergent subsequence.*

In order to prove this theorem we observe first that we already know (Theorem XIV, § 204) that every bounded *monotonic* sequence converges. Therefore the proof will be complete as soon as we establish the following lemma:

Lemma I. *Every sequence (of real numbers) contains a monotonic subsequence.*

Before proceeding with the details of the proof of this lemma we discuss briefly the idea of *largest term* of a sequence, and give a few illustrative examples.

By a **largest term** of a sequence $a_1, a_2, a_3, \cdots$ we mean any term a_k with the property $a_k \geq a_n$ for every positive integer n. The examples below show that a sequence may not have a largest term, and that if it does have a largest term it may have several. In case a sequence has a largest term, there must be a *first* largest term (first in the order of the terms according to the subscripts). This particular largest term will be called for convenience **the largest term.**

Example 1. The sequence $0, 1, 0, 1, \cdots$ contains the two monotonic constant subsequences $0, 0, 0, \cdots$ and $1, 1, 1, \cdots$. It has a largest term $a_k = 1$,

† Unless otherwise qualified the word *sequence* should be interpreted in this chapter to mean *infinite sequence of real numbers*.

61

where k may be any even positive integer. *The* largest term of the sequence is the second.

Example 2.   The sequence 1, -1, 2, -2, 3, -3, $\cdots$ contains the monotonic subsequences 1, 2, 3, $\cdots$ and -1, -2, -3, $\cdots$.   It has no largest term, but the subsequence -1, -2, -3, $\cdots$ has the largest term -1.

Example 3.   The sequence 1, -1, $\frac{1}{2}$, $-\frac{1}{2}$, $\frac{1}{3}$, $-\frac{1}{3}$, $\cdots$ contains the monotonic subsequences 1, $\frac{1}{2}$, $\frac{1}{3}$, $\cdots$ and -1, $-\frac{1}{2}$, $-\frac{1}{3}$, $\cdots$, and has the largest term 1. The subsequence -1, $-\frac{1}{2}$, $-\frac{1}{3}$, $\cdots$ has no largest term.

Example 4.   The sequence 1, $\frac{1}{2}$, $\frac{2}{3}$, $\frac{3}{4}$, $\frac{4}{5}$, $\cdots$ contains the monotonic subsequence $\frac{1}{2}$, $\frac{2}{3}$, $\frac{3}{4}$, $\cdots$.   The sequence has the largest term 1, but no monotonic subsequence has a largest term.

As an aid in the proof of Lemma I we establish a simple auxiliary lemma:

Lemma II.   *If a sequence S has a largest term equal to x, and if a subsequence T of S has a largest term equal to y, then $x \geqq y$.*

Proof of Lemma II.   Let $S = \{a_n\}$.   Since T is a subsequence of S, y is equal to some term a_n of S.   If a_k is the largest term of S, then $a_k \geqq a_n$, or $x \geqq y$.

We are now ready to prove Lemma I:

Proof of Lemma I.   Let $S = a_1, a_2, a_3, \cdots$ be a given sequence of real numbers, and let certain subsequences of S be denoted as follows: $S_0 \equiv S$, $S_1 \equiv a_2, a_3, a_4, \cdots$, $S_2 \equiv a_3, a_4, a_5, \cdot \cdot$, etc.   There are two cases to consider:

Case I.   *Every sequence S_0, S_1, S_2, $\cdots$ contains a largest term.*   Denote by a_{n_1} the largest term of S_0, by a_{n_2} the largest term of S_{n_1}, by a_{n_3} the largest term of S_{n_2}, etc.   By construction, $n_1 < n_2 < n_3 \cdots$, so that a_{n_1}, a_{n_2}, a_{n_3}, $\cdots$ is a subsequence of S, and by Lemma II it is a monotonically decreasing subsequence.

Case II.   *There exists a sequence S_N containing no largest term.*   Then every term of S_N is followed ultimately by some larger term (for otherwise there would be some term of S_N which could be exceeded only by its predecessors, of which there are at most a finite number, so that S_N would have a largest term).   We can therefore obtain inductively an increasing subsequence of S by letting $a_{n_1} \equiv a_{N+1}$, $a_{n_2} \equiv$ the first term following a_{n_1} that is greater than a_{n_1}, $a_{n_3} \equiv$ the first term following a_{n_2} that is greater than a_{n_2}, etc.   This completes the proof of Lemma I, and therefore that of the Fundamental Theorem.

★302. THE CAUCHY CRITERION FOR CONVERGENCE OF A SEQUENCE

Convergence of a sequence means that there is some number (the limit of the sequence) that has a particular property, formulated in terms of ϵ and N.   In order to test the convergence of a given sequence, then, it might seem that one is forced to obtain its limit first. That this is not *always* the case was seen in Theorem XIV, § 204, where the convergence of a *monotonic* sequence is guaranteed by the simple condition of *boundedness*. A natural question to ask now is whether there is some way of testing an *arbitrary* sequence for convergence without knowing in advance what its limit is. It is the purpose of this section to answer this question by means of the celebrated Cauchy Criterion which, in a crude way, says that the terms of a sequence get arbitrarily close to something fixed, for sufficiently large subscripts, if and only if they get arbitrarily close to each other, for sufficiently large subscripts.

Definition. *If $\{a_n\}$ is a sequence (of real numbers), the notation* $\lim\limits_{m,n\to+\infty} (a_m - a_n) = 0$ *means that corresponding to an arbitrary positive number ϵ there exists a number N such that $m > N$ and $n > N$ together imply* $|a_m - a_n| < \epsilon$. *A sequence $\{a_n\}$ satisfying the condition* $\lim\limits_{m,n\to+\infty} (a_m - a_n) = 0$ *is called a* **Cauchy sequence.**

Theorem. Cauchy Criterion. *A sequence (of real numbers) converges if and only if it is a Cauchy sequence.*

Proof. The "only if" part of the proof is simple. Assume that the sequence $\{a_n\}$ converges, and let its limit be a: $a_n \to a$. We wish to show that $\lim\limits_{m,n\to+\infty} (a_m - a_n) = 0$. Corresponding to a preassigned $\epsilon \geqq 0$, let N be a number such that $n > N$ implies $|a_n - a| < \frac{1}{2}\epsilon$. Then if m and n are both greater than N, we have simultaneously

$$|a_m - a| < \tfrac{1}{2}\epsilon \quad \text{and} \quad |a_n - a| < \tfrac{1}{2}\epsilon,$$

so that by the triangle inequality (§ 110)

$$|a_m - a_n| = |(a_m - a) - (a_n - a)| \leqq |a_m - a| + |a_n - a| < \epsilon.$$

For the "if" half of the proof we assume that a sequence $\{a_n\}$ satisfies the Cauchy condition, and prove that it converges. The first step is to show that it is bounded. To establish boundedness we choose N so that $n > N$ implies $|a_n - a_{N+1}| < 1$. (This is the Cauchy Criterion with $\epsilon = 1$ and $m = N + 1$.) Then, by the triangle inequality, for $n > N$,

$$|a_n| = |(a_n - a_{N+1}) + a_{N+1}| \leqq |a_n - a_{N+1}| + |a_{N+1}| < |a_{N+1}| + 1.$$

Since the terms of the sequence are bounded for all $n > N$, and since there are only a finite number of terms with subscripts less than N, the entire sequence is bounded. According to the Fundamental Theorem (§ 301), then, there must be a convergent subsequence $\{a_{n_k}\}$. Let the limit of this subsequence be a. We shall show that $a_n \to a$. Let ϵ be an arbitrary positive number. Then, by the Cauchy condition, there exists a number N such that for $m > N$ and $n > N$, $|a_m - a_n| < \frac{1}{2}\epsilon$. Let n be an *arbitrary* positive integer greater than N. We shall show that $|a_n - a| < \epsilon$. By the triangle inequality,

$$|a_n - a| \leq |a_n - a_{n_k}| + |a_{n_k} - a|.$$

This inequality holds for all positive integers k and, in particular, for values of k so large that (i) $n_k > N$ and (ii) $|a_{n_k} - a| < \frac{1}{2}\epsilon$. If we choose any such value for k, the inequality above implies $|a_n - a| < \frac{1}{2}\epsilon + \frac{1}{2}\epsilon = \epsilon$, and the proof is complete.

NOTE. Without the Axiom of Completeness, the Cauchy condition is not a criterion for convergence. For example, in the system of rational numbers, where the Axiom of Completeness fails (Ex. 2, § 116), a sequence of rational numbers converging to the irrational number $\sqrt{2}$ (Ex. 15, § 205) satisfies the Cauchy condition, but does not converge *in the system of rational numbers.*

At this point, the student may wish to do a few of the Exercises of § 305. Some that are suitable for performance now are Exercises 1-6 and 15-22.

★303. SEQUENTIAL CRITERIA FOR CONTINUITY AND EXISTENCE OF LIMITS

For future purposes it will be convenient to have a necessary and sufficient condition for continuity of a function at a point, in a form that involves only sequences of numbers, and a similar condition for existence of limits. (Cf. the Theorem, § 209.)

Theorem I. *A necessary and sufficient condition for a function $f(x)$ to be continuous at $x = a$ is that whenever $\{x_n\}$ is a sequence of numbers which converges to a (and for which $f(x)$ is defined), then $\{f(x_n)\}$ is a sequence of numbers converging to $f(a)$; in short, that $x_n \to a$ implies $f(x_n) \to f(a)$.*

Proof. We first establish necessity. Assume that $f(x)$ is continuous at $x = a$, and let $x_n \to a$. We wish to show that $f(x_n) \to f(a)$. Let $\epsilon > 0$ be given. Then there exists a positive number δ such that $|x - a| < \delta$ implies $|f(x) - f(a)| < \epsilon$ (for values of x for which $f(x)$ is defined). Since $x_n \to a$, there exists a number N such that, for $n > N$, $|x_n - a| < \delta$. Therefore, for $n > N$, $|f(x_n) - f(a)| < \epsilon$. This establishes the desired convergence.

Next we prove sufficiency, by assuming that $f(x)$ is discontinuous at $x = a$, and showing that we can then obtain a sequence $\{x_n\}$ converging to a such that the sequence $\{f(x_n)\}$ does not converge to $f(a)$. By Exercise 14, § 212, the discontinuity of $f(x)$ at $x = a$ means that there exists a positive number ϵ such that however small the positive number δ may be, there exists a number x such that $|x - a| < \delta$ and $|f(x) - f(a)| \geq \epsilon$. We construct the sequence $\{x_n\}$ by requiring that x_n satisfy the two inequalities $|x_n - a| < 1/n$ and $|f(x_n) - f(a)| \geq \epsilon$. The former guarantees the convergence of $\{x_n\}$ to a, while the latter forbids the convergence of $\{f(x_n)\}$ to $f(a)$.   This completes the proof of Theorem I.

The formulation and the proof of a sequential criterion for the existence of a limit of a function are similar to those for continuity.   The statement in the following theorem does not specify the manner in which the independent variable approaches its limit, since the result is independent of the behavior of the independent variable, subject to the restrictions of the first paragraph of § 207.   The details of the proof, with hints, are left to the student in Exercises 8 and 9, § 305.

Theorem II.   *The limit,* $\lim f(x)$, *of the function* $f(x)$ *exists (finite or infinite) if and only if, for every sequence* $\{x_n\}$ *of numbers having the same limit as* x *but never equal to this limit (and for which* $f(x)$ *is defined), the sequence* $\{f(x_n)\}$ *has a limit (finite or infinite); in short, if and only if* $x_n \to \lim x$, $x_n \neq \lim x$ *imply* $f(x_n) \to$ *limit.*

As might be expected, the Cauchy Criterion for convergence of a sequence has its application to the question of the existence of a limit of a function.   With the same understanding regarding the behavior of the independent variable as was assumed for Theorem II, we have as an immediate corollary of that theorem the following:

Theorem III.   *The limit,* $\lim f(x)$, *of the function* $f(x)$ *exists and is finite if and only if, for every sequence* $\{x_n\}$ *of numbers approaching the same limit as* x *but never equal to this limit (and for which* $f(x)$ *is defined), the sequence* $\{f(x_n)\}$ *is a Cauchy sequence; in short, if and only if* $x_n \to \lim x$, $x_n \neq \lim x$ *imply* $\{f(x_n)\}$ *is a Cauchy sequence.*

★304. THE CAUCHY CRITERION FOR FUNCTIONS

The Cauchy Criterion for sequences gives a test for the convergence of a sequence that does not involve explicit evaluation of the limit of the sequence.   Similar tests can be formulated for the existence of finite limits for more general functions, where explicit evaluation of the limits is not a part of the test.   Such criteria are of great theoretical importance and practical utility whenever direct evaluation of a limit is difficult.   Owing to the latitude in the behavior granted the independent variable, we have selected for specific formulation in this section only two particular cases, and the proof of one.   The remaining proof and other special cases are treated in the exercises of § 305.

Theorem I.   *Assume that every deleted neighborhood of the point* a *contains at least one point of the domain of definition of the function* $f(x)$. *Then the limit* $\lim_{x \to a} f(x)$ *exists and is finite if and only if corresponding to an arbitrary* *positive number ϵ there exists a positive number δ such that $0 < |x' - a| < \delta$ and $0 < |x'' - a| < \delta$ imply $|f(x') - f(x'')| < \epsilon$, for values of x' and x'' for which $f(x)$ is defined.*

Proof. "*Only if*": Assume $\lim\limits_{x \to a} f(x) = L$ and let $\epsilon > 0$. Then there exists $\delta > 0$ such that $0 < |x - a| < \delta$ implies $|f(x) - L| < \frac{1}{2}\epsilon$. If x' and x'' are any two numbers such that $0 < |x' - a| < \delta$ and $0 < |x'' - a| < \delta$, the triangle inequality gives

$$|f(x') - f(x'')| = |(f(x') - L) - (f(x'') - L)|$$
$$\leq |f(x') - L| + |f(x'') - L| < \tfrac{1}{2}\epsilon + \tfrac{1}{2}\epsilon = \epsilon.$$

"*If*": Let $\{x_n\}$ be an arbitrary sequence of numbers (for which $f(x)$ is defined) such that $x_n \to a$ and $x_n \neq a$. By Theorem III, § 303, we need only show that the sequence $\{f(x_n)\}$ is a Cauchy sequence:

$$\lim_{m,n \to +\infty} [f(x_m) - f(x_n)] = 0.$$

If ϵ is a preassigned positive number, let δ be a positive number having the assumed property that $0 < |x' - a| < \delta$ and $0 < |x'' - a| < \delta$ imply $|f(x') - f(x'')| < \epsilon$. Since $x_n \to a$ and $x_n \neq a$, there exists a number N such that $n > N$ implies $0 < |x_n - a| < \delta$. Accordingly, if $m > N$ and $n > N$, we have simultaneously $0 < |x_m - a| < \delta$ and $0 < |x_n - a| < \delta$, so that $|f(x_m) - f(x_n)| < \epsilon$. Thus the sequence $\{f(x_n)\}$ is a Cauchy sequence, and the proof is complete.

Theorem II. *The limit $\lim\limits_{x \to +\infty} f(x)$ exists and is finite if and only if corresponding to an arbitrary positive number ϵ there exists a number N such that $x' > N$ and $x'' > N$ imply $|f(x') - f(x'')| < \epsilon$ (for values of x' and x'' for which $f(x)$ is defined).*

★305. EXERCISES

★1. Prove that a sequence $\{a_n\}$ (of real numbers) converges if and only if corresponding to an arbitrary positive number ϵ there exists a positive integer N such that for all positive integers p and q, $|a_{N+p} - a_{N+q}| < \epsilon$.

★2. Prove that a sequence $\{a_n\}$ (of real numbers) converges if and only if corresponding to an arbitrary positive number ϵ there exists a number N such that $n > N$ implies $|a_n - a_N| < \epsilon$.

★3. Prove that a sequence $\{a_n\}$ (of real numbers) converges if and only if corresponding to an arbitrary positive number ϵ there exists a positive integer N such that for all positive integers p, $|a_{N+p} - a_N| < \epsilon$.

★4. Prove that the condition $\lim\limits_{n \to +\infty} (a_{n+p} - a_n) = 0$ for every positive integer p is necessary but not sufficient for the convergence of the sequence $\{a_n\}$. *Hint:* Consider a sequence suggested by the terms $1, 2, 2\frac{1}{2}, 3, 3\frac{1}{3}, 3\frac{2}{3}, 4, 4\frac{1}{4}, 4\frac{1}{2}, 4\frac{3}{4}, 5, 5\frac{1}{5}, \cdots$.

★**5.** Find the error in the "theorem" and "proof": *If $a_n \to a$, then $a_n = a$ for sufficiently large n.* *Proof.* Any convergent sequence is a Cauchy sequence. Therefore, if $\epsilon > 0$ there exists a positive integer N such that for all positive integers m and n, with $m > N$, $|a_m - a_{N+n}| < \epsilon$. But this means that $\lim_{n \to +\infty} a_{N+n} = a_m$, which in turn implies that $\lim_{n \to +\infty} a_n = a = a_m$ for all $m > N$.

★**6.** If $\{b_n\}$ is a convergent sequence and if $\{a_n\}$ is a sequence such that $|a_m - a_n| \leqq |b_m - b_n|$ for all positive integers m and n, prove that $\{a_n\}$ converges.

★**7.** If $f(x)$ and $g(x)$ are functions defined for $x > 0$, if $\lim_{x \to 0+} g(x)$ exists and is finite, and if $|f(b) - f(a)| \leqq |g(b) - g(a)|$ for all positive numbers a and b, prove that $\lim_{x \to 0+} f(x)$ exists and is finite.

★**8.** Prove Theorem II, § 303, for the case $x \to a$. *Hint:* First show that if $x_n \to a$, $x_n \neq a$ imply that the sequence $\{f(x_n)\}$ has a limit then this limit is unique, by considering, for any two sequences $\{x_n\}$ and $\{x_n'\}$ which converge to a, the compound sequence $x_1, x_1', x_2, x_2', x_3, x_3', \cdots$. For the case $f(x_n) \to +\infty$, assume that $\lim_{x \to a} f(x) \neq +\infty$, and show that there must exist a constant B and a sequence $\{x_n\}$ such that $0 < |x_n - a| < 1/n$ and $f(x_n) \leqq B$. For other cases of $\lim_{x \to a} f(x_n)$, proceed similarly.

★**9.** Prove Theorem II, § 303, for the case $x \to a+$; $x \to a-$; $x \to +\infty$; $x \to -\infty$; $x \to \infty$. (Cf. Ex. 8.)

★**10.** Assuming only Theorem I, § 303, and the limit theorems for sequences (§ 204), prove the continuity theorems of § 211. *Hint for Theorem IV:* Let $\{x_n\}$ be an arbitrary sequence converging to a. Then $f(x_n) \to f(a)$ and $g(x_n) \to g(a)$, and therefore $f(x_n)g(x_n) \to f(a)g(a)$.

★**11.** Assuming only Theorem II, § 303, and the limit theorems for sequences (§ 204), prove the limit theorems of § 207. (Cf. Ex. 10.)

★**12.** Reformulate and prove Theorem I, § 304, for the case $x \to a+$; for the case $x \to a-$.

★**13.** Prove Theorem II, § 304.

★**14.** Reformulate and prove Theorem II, § 304, for the case $x \to -\infty$; for the case $x \to \infty$.

★**15.** Let $\{a_n\}$ be a sequence of real numbers, and let A_n be the least upper bound of the set $\{a_n, a_{n+1}, a_{n+2}, \cdots\}$ ($A_n \equiv +\infty$ if this set is not bounded above). Prove that either $A_n = +\infty$ for every n, or A_n is a monotonically decreasing sequence of real numbers, and that therefore $\lim_{n \to +\infty} A_n$ exists ($+\infty$, finite, or $-\infty$). Prove a similar result for the sequence $\{B_n\}$, where B_n is the greatest lower bound of the set $\{a_n, a_{n+1}, a_{n+2}, \cdots\}$.

★**16.** The **limit superior** and the **limit inferior** of a sequence $\{a_n\}$, denoted $\overline{\lim}_{n \to +\infty} a_n$, or $\limsup_{n \to +\infty} a_n$, and $\underline{\lim}_{n \to +\infty} a_n$, or $\liminf_{n \to +\infty} a_n$, respectively, are defined as the limits of the sequences $\{A_n\}$ and $\{B_n\}$, respectively, of Exercise 15. Justify the following formulations:

$$\varlimsup_{n \to +\infty} a_n \equiv \lim_{n \to +\infty} A_n = \inf_{n=1}^{+\infty} \left[\sup_{m=n}^{+\infty} (a_m) \right],$$

$$\varliminf_{n \to +\infty} a_n \equiv \lim_{n \to +\infty} B_n = \sup_{n=1}^{+\infty} \left[\inf_{m=n}^{+\infty} (a_m) \right].$$

(Cf. § 114.)

★**17.** Prove that a number L is the limit superior of a sequence $\{a_n\}$ if and only if it has the following two properties, where ϵ is an arbitrary preassigned positive number:

(*i*) The inequality $a_n < L + \epsilon$ holds for all but a finite number of terms.

(*ii*) The inequality $a_n > L - \epsilon$ holds for infinitely many terms.

State and prove a similar result for the limit inferior.

Prove that the limit superior and limit inferior of a bounded sequence are limit points of that sequence (cf. Exs. 24-26, § 205), and that any other limit point of the sequence is between these two.   Extend this result to unbounded sequences.   (Cf. Exs. 15-16, and Ex. 29, § 312.)

★**18.** Prove that for any sequence $\{a_n\}$, bounded or not, $\varliminf\limits_{n \to +\infty} a_n \leqq \varlimsup\limits_{n \to +\infty} a_n$.

Prove that a sequence converges if and only if its limit superior and limit inferior are finite and equal, and that in the case of convergence, $\lim\limits_{n \to +\infty} a_n = \varliminf\limits_{n \to +\infty} a_n =$

$\varlimsup\limits_{n \to +\infty} a_n$.   Extend these results to include infinite cases.   (Cf. Exs. 15-17,)

In Exercises 19-22, find the limit superior and the limit inferior.   (Cf. Exs. 15-18.)

★**19.** $0, 1, 0, 1, 0, 1, \cdots$.

★**20.** $1, -2, 3, -4, \cdots, (-1)^{n+1} n, \cdots$.

★**21.** $\frac{2}{3}, \frac{1}{3}, \frac{3}{4}, \frac{1}{4}, \frac{4}{5}, \frac{1}{5}, \frac{5}{6}, \frac{1}{6}, \cdots$.

★**22.** $\frac{3}{2}, -\frac{1}{2}, \frac{4}{3}, -\frac{1}{3}, \frac{5}{4}, -\frac{1}{4}, \frac{6}{5}, -\frac{1}{5}, \cdots$.

★**23.** Let $f(x)$ be a real-valued function, defined for at least some values of x neighboring the point $x = a$ (except possibly at a itself).   If δ is an arbitrary positive number, let $\phi(\delta)$ and $\psi(\delta)$ be the least upper bound and the greatest lower bound, respectively, of the values of $f(x)$ for all x such that $0 < |x - a| < \delta$ (and for which $f(x)$ is defined).   Prove that, in a sense that includes infinite values (cf. Ex. 15), $\phi(\delta)$ and $\psi(\delta)$ are monotonic functions and therefore have limits as $\delta \to 0+$.   (Cf. § 215.)

★**24.** The limit superior and the limit inferior of a function $f(x)$ at a point $x = a$, denoted $\varlimsup\limits_{x \to a} f(x)$, or $\limsup\limits_{x \to a} f(x)$, and $\varliminf\limits_{x \to a} f(x)$, or $\liminf\limits_{x \to a} f(x)$, respectively, are defined as the limits of the functions $\phi(\delta)$ and $\psi(\delta)$, respectively, of Exercise 23.   Justify the following formulations:

$$\varlimsup_{x \to a} f(x) \equiv \lim_{\delta \to 0+} \phi(\delta) = \inf_{\delta > 0} \left[\sup_{0 < |x-a| < \delta} f(x) \right].$$

$$\varliminf_{x \to a} f(x) \equiv \lim_{\delta \to 0+} \psi(\delta) = \sup_{\delta > 0} \left[\inf_{0 < |x-a| < \delta} f(x) \right].$$

★**25.** Prove that a number L is the limit superior of a function $f(x)$ at $x = a$ if and only if it has the following two properties. where ϵ is an arbitrary preassigned positive number:

(i) The inequality $f(x) < L + \epsilon$ holds for all x in some deleted neighborhood of $a : 0 < |x - a| < \delta$.

(ii) The inequality $f(x) > L - \epsilon$ holds for some x in every deleted neighborhood of $a : 0 < |x - a| < \delta$.

State and prove a similar result for the limit inferior.   (Cf. Exs. 23-24.)

★**26.** Prove that for any function $f(x)$, $\varliminf_{x\to a} f(x) \leq \varlimsup_{x\to a} f(x)$ (cf. Ex. 18).   Prove that $\lim_{x\to a} f(x)$ exists if and only if $\varliminf_{x\to a} f(x) = \varlimsup_{x\to a} f(x)$, and in case of equality,

$$\lim_{x\to a} f(x) = \varliminf_{x\to a} f(x) = \varlimsup_{x\to a} f(x).   \text{(Cf. Exs. 23-25.)}$$

★**27.** Formulate definitions and state and prove results corresponding to those of Exercises 23-26 for the case $x \to a+$; $x \to a-$.

★**28.** Formulate definitions and state and prove results corresponding to those of Exercises 23-26 for the case $x \to +\infty$; $x \to -\infty$; $x \to \infty$.

In Exercises 29-34, find the limit superior and the limit inferior.   Draw a graph.   (Cf. Exs. 23-28.)

★**29.** $x \sin x$, as $x \to +\infty$.

★**30.** $\cos \dfrac{1}{x}$, as $x \to 0$.

★**31.** $\dfrac{x + 1}{x} \sin x$, as $x \to +\infty$.

★**32.** $\dfrac{x + 1}{x} \sin x$, as $x \to -\infty$.

★**33.** $\dfrac{x - 1}{x} \cos x$, as $x \to +\infty$.

★**34.** $(x^2 + 1) \sin \dfrac{1}{x}$, as $x \to 0+$.

★★**35.** A function $f(x)$ is **upper semicontinuous** at a point $x = a$ if and only if $\varlimsup_{x\to a} f(x) = f(a)$, and is **lower semicontinuous** there if and only if $\varliminf_{x\to a} f(x) = f(a)$. Prove that a function is continuous at a point if and only if it is both upper and lower semicontinuous at the point.

★★**36.** Prove that a monotonically increasing function defined in a neighborhood of a point a is upper semicontinuous at that point if and only if it is continuous from the right at $x = a$.   (Cf. Ex. 35.)

★306. PROOFS OF SOME THEOREMS ON CONTINUOUS FUNCTIONS

The first four sections of this chapter provide us with the means of proving the theorems on continuous functions given in §§ 213 and 215.   Some important generalizations of these theorems are obtained in § 311.

Proof of Theorem I, § 213.   In order to prove that a function continuous on a closed interval is bounded there, we assume the contrary and seek a contradiction.   Let $f(x)$ be continuous on $[a, b]$, and assume it is unbounded there. Under these conditions, for any positive integer n there is a point x_n of the interval $[a, b]$ such that $|f(x_n)| > n$. By the Fundamental Theorem on bounded sequences (§ 301), since the sequence $\{x_n\}$ is bounded, it contains a convergent subsequence $\{x_{n_k}\}$, converging to some point x_0, $x_{n_k} \to x_0$. By Exercise 13, § 205, $a \leqq x_{n_k} \leqq b$ implies $a \leqq x_0 \leqq b$, so that x_0 also belongs to the closed interval $[a, b]$. Since $f(x)$ is continuous at x_0, $f(x_{n_k}) \to f(x_0)$ (Theorem I, § 303). But this means that the sequence $\{f(x_{n_k})\}$ is bounded, a statement inconsistent with the inequality

$$|f(x_{n_k})| > n_k.$$

This contradiction establishes Theorem I, § 213.

Proof of Theorem II, § 213. Let $f(x)$ be continuous on the closed interval $[a, b]$. We shall show that it has a maximum value there (the proof for a minimum value is similar). By the preceding theorem, $f(x)$ is bounded on $[a, b]$. Let M be the least upper bound of its values there. We wish to show that there is some number x_0 such that $f(x_0) = M$. By the definition of M, there are values of $f(x)$ arbitrarily close to M. For each positive integer n, let x_n be a point in the interval $[a, b]$ such that $|f(x_n) - M| < \dfrac{1}{n}$. Then $\lim\limits_{n \to +\infty} f(x_n) = M$. Furthermore, since the sequence $\{x_n\}$ is bounded, it contains a convergent subsequence $\{x_{n_k}\}$ (by the Fundamental Theorem of § 301) converging to some point x_0 of the closed interval (cf. proof of Theorem I, § 213), $x_{n_k} \to x_0$. Since $f(x)$ is continuous at x_0, $f(x_{n_k}) \to f(x_0)$ (Theorem I, § 303). Since $\{f(x_{n_k})\}$ is a subsequence of the sequence $\{f(x_n)\}$ and $f(x_n) \to M$, $f(x_{n_k}) \to M$ (Theorem IV, § 204). Finally, by the uniqueness of the limit of the convergent sequence $f(x_{n_k})$ (Theorem II, § 204), $f(x_0) = M$, and the proof is complete.

Proof of Theorem III, § 213. Assume for definiteness that $f(a) < 0$ and $f(b) > 0$. We wish to find a number x_0 between a and b such that $f(x_0) = 0$. Let A be the set of points x of the interval $[a, b]$ where $f(x) < 0$ (this set contains at least the point a and is bounded above by b) and *define* x_0 to be the least upper bound of the set A: $x_0 \equiv \sup (A)$. We shall prove that $f(x_0) = 0$ by showing that *each* of the inequalities $f(x_0) < 0$ and $f(x_0) > 0$ is impossible. First assume that $f(x_0) < 0$. By Exercise 18, § 212, any function negative and continuous at a point is negative (where defined) in some neighborhood of that point. If $f(x_0) < 0$, therefore, there must exist some neighborhood of x_0 throughout which $f(x) < 0$, or since $x_0 < b$, this means that $f(x) < 0$ for some values of x *greater* than x_0, in contradiction to the fact that x_0 is an upper bound of A. Finally, by the same argument, if $f(x_0) > 0$ then $f(x) > 0$ for values of x throughout some neighborhood of x_0, so that some number *less* than x_0 is an upper bound of A. This fact is inconsistent with the definition of x_0 as the *least* upper bound of A. The only alternative left is the one sought: $f(x_0) = 0$.

Proof of Theorem IV, § 213. Assume that c lies between the two numbers $f(a)$ and $f(b)$, and consider the function $g(x) \equiv f(x) - c$. Since $g(x)$ is continuous throughout the closed interval $[a, b]$ and has opposite signs at a and b, there must exist, by the theorem just established, a number x_0 between a and b at which $g(x)$ vanishes, so that $g(x_0) = f(x_0) - c = 0$, or $f(x_0) = c$.

Proof of the Theorem of § 215. The only part of the proof that presents any difficulty is the continuity of the inverse function. We shall seek a contradiction to the assumption that $x = \phi(y)$ is discontinuous at some point y_0 of the interval $[c,d]$. Accordingly, by Exercise 14, § 212, there must be a positive number ϵ such that however small the positive number δ may be, there exists a number y of the interval $[c, d]$ such that $|y - y_0| < \delta$ and $|\phi(y) - \phi(y_0)| \geq \epsilon$. We construct the sequence $\{y_n\}$ such that if $x_n \equiv \phi(y_n)$ and $x_0 \equiv \phi(y_0)$, then $|y_n - y_0| < 1/n$ and $|x_n - x_0| \geq \epsilon$. The former inequality guarantees the convergence of $\{y_n\}$ to y_0. The boundedness of the sequence $\{x_n\}$ (each x_n belongs to the interval $[a, b]$), by the Fundamental Theorem of § 301, ensures the convergence of some subsequence $\{x_{n_k}\}$ to some number x_0' of the interval $[a, b]$ (cf. proof of Theorem I, § 213). The inequality $|x_n - x_0| \geq \epsilon$ implies $|x_{n_k} - x_0| \geq \epsilon$, for all k, so that the subsequence $\{x_{n_k}\}$ cannot converge to x_0. In other words, $x_0' \neq x_0$. On the other hand, the direct function $y = f(x)$ is assumed to be continuous at x_0', so that $x_{n_k} \to x_0'$ implies $y_{n_k} = f(x_{n_k}) \to f(x_0')$. But $y_n \to y_0 = f(x_0)$ implies $y_{n_k} \to f(x_0)$ (Theorem IV, § 204). Finally, the uniqueness of limits (Theorem II, § 204) means that $f(x_0) = f(x_0')$, in contradiction to the assumption that $f(x)$ is strictly monotonic.

★307. UNIFORM CONTINUITY

The function $\dfrac{1}{x}$ is continuous in the open interval $(0,1)$ (Ex. 2, § 212). Let us consider this statement from the point of view of the δ-ϵ definition of continuity. Let x_0 be a point in $(0, 1)$, and let ϵ be a preassigned positive number. We wish to find δ as a function of ϵ so that $|x - x_0| < \delta$ implies $\left|\dfrac{1}{x} - \dfrac{1}{x_0}\right| < \epsilon$. In other words, by making the numerator of the fraction $\dfrac{|x - x_0|}{|x| \cdot x_0}$ small, we wish to ensure the smallness of the fraction itself. It is clear, however, that mere smallness of the numerator alone is not going to be enough. If the denominator is also small, the fraction is not restricted. The trick (cf. Exs. 59-64, § 208) is to pin down the denominator first by not permitting x to come too close to 0, and then to tackle the numerator. Without going through any of the details, however, it can be seen by inspection of Figure 301 that δ is going to depend quite essentially not only on ϵ but on the point x_0 as well.   If x_0 is near 1, and an ϵ is given, we can be fairly generous in the size of δ.   However, if x_0 is near 0, and the same ϵ is given, the δ required must be considerably smaller.

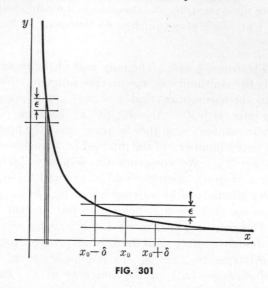

FIG. 301

In some cases it is possible, for a given interval or other set, and for a given ϵ, to choose δ so that the inequalities concerned will hold for all points of the set *without varying the number δ*.   When this state exists we have a sort of *uniformity* to the amount of squeezing on $|x - x_0|$ that has to be imposed.   This leads to the definition:

Definition.   *A function $f(x)$, defined on a set A, is* **uniformly continuous** *on the set A if and only if corresponding to an arbitrary positive number ϵ there exists a positive number $\delta = \delta(\epsilon)$ such that for any x' and x'' belonging to A, $|x' - x''| < \delta$ implies $|f(x') - f(x'')| < \epsilon$.*

Let us contrast the definitions of continuity and uniform continuity. The most obvious distinction is that continuity is defined *at a point*, whereas uniform continuity is defined *on a set*.   These concepts are also distinguished by the order in which things happen.   In the case of continuity we have (1) the point x_0, (2) the positive number ϵ, and (3) the positive number δ, which depends on both x_0 and ϵ.   In the case of uniform continuity we have (1) the positive number ϵ, (2) the positive number δ, which depends only on ϵ, and (3) the points x' and x''.

In spite of these contrasts, there are certain relations between the two ideas.   The simplest one is stated in the following theorem, whose proof is requested in Exercise 1, § 308.

Theorem I. *A function uniformly continuous on a set is continuous at each point of that set. In brief, uniform continuity implies continuity.*

The converse, as we have seen by an example, is false. The function $\dfrac{1}{x}$ is continuous at each point of the open interval $(0, 1)$, but it is not uniformly continuous on that set. However, it is an important fact that for *closed intervals* there is a valid converse, as given in Theorem II below. (For a more general theorem see Theorem IV, § 311.) As an aid in the proof of Theorem II, we first formulate the *negation* of uniform continuity. The student is asked in Exercise 2, § 308, to validate this formulation. (Cf. Ex. 14, § 212.)

Negation of Uniform Continuity. *A function $f(x)$, defined on a set A, fails to be uniformly continuous on A if and only if there exists a positive number ϵ having the property that for any positive number δ there exist points x' and x'' of A such that $|x' - x''| < \delta$ and $|f(x') - f(x'')| \geqq \epsilon$.*

Theorem II. *A function continuous on a closed interval is uniformly continuous there.*

Proof. Assume that $f(x)$ is continuous on the closed interval I but fails to be uniformly continuous there. Then (by the Negation above) for any positive integer n there exist $\epsilon > 0$ and points x_n' and x_n'' of I such that $|x_n' - x_n''| < \dfrac{1}{n}$ and $|f(x_n') - f(x_n'')| \geqq \epsilon$. The bounded sequence $\{x_n'\}$ contains a convergent subsequence $\{x_{n_k}'\}$, converging to some point x_0 of I (cf. proof of Theorem I, § 213, given in § 306). We show that the corresponding sequence $\{x_{n_k}''\}$ also converges to x_0 by use of the triangle inequality:

$$|x_{n_k}'' - x_0| = |(x_{n_k}'' - x_{n_k}') + (x_{n_k}' - x_0)|$$
$$\leqq |x_{n_k}'' - x_{n_k}'| + |x_{n_k}' - x_0| < 1/n_k + |x_{n_k}' - x_0|.$$

As k becomes infinite each of the last two terms approaches zero, and therefore so does the quantity $|x_{n_k}'' - x_0|$. By continuity of $f(x)$ at x_0, $\lim\limits_{k \to +\infty} f(x_{n_k}') = \lim\limits_{k \to +\infty} f(x_{n_k}'') = f(x_0)$, and therefore $\lim\limits_{k \to +\infty} [f(x_{n_k}') - f(x_{n_k}'')]$ $= 0$. This last statement is inconsistent with the inequality $|f(x_{n_k}') - f(x_{n_k}'')| \geqq \epsilon$, which must hold for all values of k, and the proof is complete.

★308. EXERCISES

★**1.** Prove Theorem I, § 307.

★**2.** Establish the Negation of Uniform Continuity, § 307.

In Exercises 3–8, find an explicit function $\delta = \delta(\epsilon)$ in conformity with the definition of uniform continuity.

★3. $y = x^2$, for $0 \leqq x \leqq 1$.   *Hint:*
$$|x''^2 - x'^2| = |x'' - x'| \cdot |x'' + x'| \leqq 2|x'' - x'|.$$

★4. $y = x^2$, for $0 \leqq x \leqq 2$.

★5. $y = \sqrt{x}$, for $1 \leqq x \leqq 2$.   *Hint:* $\sqrt{x''} - \sqrt{x'} = \dfrac{x'' - x'}{\sqrt{x''} + \sqrt{x'}}.$

★6. $y = \sqrt{x}$, for $0 \leqq x \leqq 1$.   *Hint:*
$$\sqrt{x''} + \sqrt{x'} \geqq \sqrt{|x'' - x'|}   \text{(cf. Ex. 5).}$$

★7. $y = \dfrac{1}{x}$, for $x \geqq 1$.

★8. $y = \sqrt{1 - x^2}$, for $|x| \leqq 1$.   *Hint:* For $0 \leqq x' < x'' \leqq 1$,
$$\sqrt{1 - x'^2} - \sqrt{1 - x''^2} = \frac{(x'' + x')(x'' - x')}{\sqrt{1 + x'}\sqrt{1 - x'} + \sqrt{1 + x''}\sqrt{1 - x''}}$$
$$\leqq \frac{2(x'' - x')}{\sqrt{1 - x'} + \sqrt{1 - x''}} \leqq \frac{2(x'' - x')}{\sqrt{(1 - x') - (1 - x'')}}   \text{(cf. Ex. 6).}$$

In Exercises 9-12, use the Negation of § 307 to show that the given function is not uniformly continuous on the given interval.   (Cf. Exs. 13-14.)

★9. $\dfrac{1}{x}$, $0 < x < 1$.

★10. x^2, $x \geqq 1$.

★11. $\sin \dfrac{1}{x}$, $0 < x < 1$.

★12. $x \sin x$, $x > 0$.

In Exercises 13-14, find an explicit function $\delta = \delta(\epsilon, x_0)$, in conformity with the δ-ϵ definition of continuity, for the given function at a given point x_0 of the specified interval.   Observe that δ depends essentially on x_0.   (Cf. Exs. 9-10; also Exs. 59-64, § 208.)

★13. $\dfrac{1}{x}$, $0 < x < 1$.

★14. x^2, $x \geqq 1$.

★15. If $f(x)$ is uniformly continuous on an open interval (a, b), prove that the two limits $f(a+)$ and $f(b-)$ exist and are finite.   *Hint:* Use the Cauchy Criterion for functions.

★16. Prove the following converse to Exercise 15: If $f(x)$ is continuous on an open interval (a, b) and if the two limits $f(a+)$ and $f(b-)$ exist and are finite, then $f(x)$ is uniformly continuous on (a, b).   *Hint:* Extend $f(x)$ to a function continuous on the closed interval $[a, b]$.

★★309. POINT SETS: OPEN, CLOSED, COMPACT, CONNECTED SETS

Many of the results obtained in the preceding portions of this chapter are special cases of more general theorems which can be formulated for Euclidean spaces of any number of dimensions.   In the remaining sections of this chapter we shall establish some of these general theorems for the particular one-dimensional space of real numbers.   The statements of the theorems and the concepts and techniques involved are of such a nature that their analogues in higher dimensional spaces are immediately available, with only a few minor adjustments in basic definitions. In this chapter the single word *set* means *set of real numbers*, and the word *point* means *real number*.

Definition I. *If A is a set, the* **complement** *of A, written A', is the set of all real numbers that are not members of A.*

Examples. If $A \equiv (-\infty, 23]$, then $A' = (23, +\infty)$. If $A \equiv [1, 3)$, then A' consists of all real numbers less than 1, or greater than or equal to 3.

Definition II. *A set A is* **open** *if and only if every member of A has some neighborhood contained entirely in A.*

Examples. The set $A \equiv (2, 7)$ is open, because if $2 < x < 7$ and ϵ is a positive number less than both $7 - x$ and $x - 2$, then the open interval $(x - \epsilon, x + \epsilon)$ is a neighborhood of x lying within A. More generally, any open interval, finite or infinite, is open (Ex. 1, § 312). The set $B \equiv (-1, 8]$ is not open, since every neighborhood of the point 8 extends to the right, outside the set B.

Definition III. *A point p is a* **limit point** *of a set A if and only if every deleted neighborhood of p contains at least one point of A.*

Note 1. If p is a limit point of a set A we say that the set A has p as a limit point, whether p is a member of A or not. For example, the two sets $B \equiv [2, 5]$ and $C \equiv (2, 5)$ both have 5 as a limit point, but only B contains 5 as a member.

Note 2. If p is a limit point of a set A, every neighborhood of p contains *infinitely many* points of A (Ex. 2, § 312).

Definition IV. *A set A is* **closed** *if and only if it contains all of its limit points.*

Examples. The set $A \equiv [1, 6]$ is closed. More generally, any finite closed interval is closed, and the infinite intervals $[a, +\infty)$ and $(-\infty, b]$ are closed (Ex. 5, § 312). The set $B \equiv (3, 5]$ is not closed, since the point 3 is a limit point of B but not a member of B. It is neither open nor closed. The set C of all integers is a closed set since it has *no* limit points and therefore contains all of its limit points. For the same reason any *finite* set is closed. The set D of all rational numbers is not closed since every real number, rational or irrational, is a limit point of D. It is neither open nor closed.

Note 3. The **empty set**, denoted $\emptyset$, is both open and closed by double default. Since it has no points, every member of $\emptyset$ has every property, including that of having a neighborhood contained in $\emptyset$, so that $\emptyset$ is open; and since $\emptyset$ has no points it has no limit points and is therefore closed. The entire space S of real numbers is also both open and closed. The student is asked to show in Exercise 11, § 312, that $\emptyset$ and S are the *only* sets of real numbers that are both open and closed. Any set with at least one member is called **nonempty**.

Definition V.   *A set A is **compact** if and only if it is closed and bounded.*†

Examples.   Any finite closed interval is compact.   Any finite set is compact.   The set consisting of the reciprocals of the positive integers together with the number 0 is compact.   The set of all integers is not compact because it is unbounded.   The open interval (0, 1) is not compact because it is not closed.

The preceding examples show that a set may be neither open nor closed (a half-open interval and the set of rational numbers are two instances). On the other hand, as explained in the Note above, a set may be both open and closed.   One might wonder whether there is any relation between these two concepts of openness and closedness.   The following theorem gives the answer.

Theorem I.   *A set is open if and only if its complement is closed.   Equivalently, a set is closed if and only if its complement is open.*

Proof.   *"Only if"*: Let A be an open set.   We wish to show that the complement A' contains all of its limit points.   Assume that x is a limit point of A' that does *not* belong to A'.   Then x belongs to A.   Since A is open, x has a neighborhood lying entirely in A and therefore containing *no* points of A'.   Therefore x is not a limit point of A'.   Contradiction.

"If": Let A' be a closed set.   We wish to prove that A is open.   Let x be any point of A.   Then x is *not* a limit point of A'.   Therefore x has a neighborhood that contains no points of A' and thus lies entirely in A. Therefore A is open, and the proof is complete.

A useful relation between least upper bounds (or greatest lower bounds) and limit points is the following, whose proof is requested in Exercise 8, § 312:

Theorem II.   *If p is the least upper bound (or the greatest lower bound) of a set A and if p is not a member of A, then p is a limit point of A.*

An immediate consequence (Ex. 9, § 312) is the following:

Theorem III.   *Every compact set of real numbers has a greatest member and a least member.*

Definition VI.   *Two sets are **disjoint** if and only if they have no point in common.*

† This formulation of compactness is suitable for finite dimensional Euclidean spaces, but not for general topological or metric spaces.   For a treatment of metric spaces the reader is referred to M. H. A. Newman, *Elements of the Topology of Plane Sets of Points* (Cambridge, Cambridge University Press, 1939).

Examples. The intervals (0, 1) and (1, 2) are disjoint. The intervals (0, 1] and (1, 2] are disjoint. The intervals [0, 1] and [1, 2] are not disjoint, since they have the point 1 in common.

Definition VII. *Two sets are* **separated** *if and only if they are disjoint and neither contains a limit point of the other.*

Examples. The intervals (0, 1) and (1, 2) are separated. The intervals (0, 1] and (1, 2] are not separated, since the point 1 belongs to (0, 1] and is a limit point of (1, 2]. The intervals [0, 1] and [1, 2] are not separated, since they are not disjoint. The set of rational numbers and the set of irrational numbers are disjoint, but are about as far from being separated as two disjoint sets of real numbers can be!

Definition VIII. *A set A is said to be* **split into two parts** *B and C if and only if B and C are disjoint and every point of A belongs either to B or to C.*

Definition IX. *A set A is* **connected** *if and only if it cannot be split into two separated nonempty parts.*

The following theorem shows that for real numbers, connectedness is not a sufficiently rich concept to excite anyone. Our reason for presenting the subject here is that connectedness, along with openness, closedness, and compactness, is a very significant idea in the theory of spaces of more than one dimension. In the study of functions of several variables it is important to know the substance of the theorem that we now state and prove.

Theorem IV. *A nonempty set of real numbers is connected if and only if it is an interval or consists of one point.*

Proof. The "only if" half of this proof is fairly easy. Let A be any connected set consisting of more than one point. We divide the proof that A is an interval into two parts, the second of which is left to the student, with hints (Ex. 10, § 312): (i) if a and b are any two points belonging to A, then any point between a and b must also belong to A; (ii) any set having the property just specified in (i) is an interval. To prove (i), we seek a contradiction to the assumption that there exist two points a and b ($a < b$) which are members of A and a third point c between a and b ($a < c < b$) which is not a member of A. The point c provides a splitting of A into two parts (one consisting of all points of A less than c and the other consisting of all points of A greater than c) neither of which contains a limit point of the other. Since the set A is assumed to be connected, the desired contradiction has been obtained.

The "if" half is more difficult. We wish to show that every interval is connected. Let us assume the contrary, and let A be an interval which is not connected, and let A consist of the two nonempty parts B and C neither of which contains a limit point of the other. Let b be any point in B and c any point in C and assume for definiteness that $b < c$. Since A is an interval, every point between b and c must belong either to B or to C. Denote by D the set of points of the closed interval $[b, c]$ which belong to B, and let $d \equiv \sup (D)$. There are two cases: (i) d belongs to B. In this case $d < c$ since c belongs to C, and every point of the half-open interval $(d, c]$ belongs to C (by the definition of d). But d, being a limit point of $(d, c]$ must thereby be a limit point of C. But a member of B cannot be a limit point of C! (ii) d belongs to C. In this case d must be a limit point of D (Theorem II), and therefore of B. But a member of C cannot be a limit point of B! In either case we obtain a contradiction, and the theorem is proved.

★★310. POINT SETS AND SEQUENCES

Much of our earlier work has been based on sequential arguments resting ultimately on the Fundamental Theorem for sequences. In order to exploit the techniques already used, we obtain in this section some useful facts about certain types of sets, phrased in terms of sequences. It turns out that the key concept that permits the useful extension of the Fundamental Theorem for sequences to more general sets than intervals is *compactness*. This is shown in Theorem IV of this section.

Definition. *A sequence $\{a_n\}$ of points is called a **sequence of distinct points** if and only if no two terms are equal; that is, if and only if $m \neq n$ implies $a_m \neq a_n$.*

Theorem I. *If a sequence $\{a_n\}$ (of real numbers) has a finite limit a, then either all but a finite number of the terms are equal to a or there exists a subsequence of distinct terms converging to a.*

Proof. Assume that $a_n \to a$ and that for every N there exists an $n > N$ such that $a_n \neq a$. The subsequence sought can be obtained inductively. Let a_{n_1} be the first term different from a. Take $\epsilon = |a_{n_1} - a| > 0$ and let a_{n_2} be the first term a_n satisfying the inequalities $0 < |a_n - a| < \epsilon = |a_{n_1} - a|$, let a_{n_3} be the first term a_n satisfying the inequalities

$$0 < |a_n - a| < |a_{n_2} - a|, \text{ etc.}$$

By construction, $n_1 < n_2 < n_3 < \cdots$, so that $\{a_{n_k}\}$ is a subsequence, and no two terms are equal.

Theorem II. *A point p is a limit point of a set A if and only if there exists a sequence $\{a_n\}$ of distinct points of A converging to p.*

Proof. If $\{a_n\}$ is a sequence of distinct points of A converging to p, then every neighborhood of p contains all points of the sequence from some index on, and therefore infinitely many points of A, so that p is a limit point of A. On the other hand, if p is a limit point of A, we can find, for each positive integer n, a point p_n of A such that $0 < |p_n - p| < 1/n$. The sequence $\{p_n\}$ therefore converges to p, and since none of the terms are equal to p it contains (by Theorem I) a subsequence $\{p_{n_k}\}$ no two terms of which are equal, such that $p_{n_k} \to p$. Let $a_k \equiv p_{n_k}$.

Theorem III. *A set A of real numbers is closed if and only if the limit of every convergent sequence $\{a_n\}$ of points of A is a point of A.*

Proof. "If": Assume that the limit of every convergent sequence of points of A is a point of A and let p be a limit point of A. We wish to show that p is a point of A. Since p is a limit point of A, Theorem II guarantees the existence of a sequence of points of A converging to p, so that p must belong to A.

"Only if": Let A be a closed set, and let $\{a_n\}$ be a sequence of points of A converging to the point a. We wish to show that a belongs to A. According to Theorem I there are two possibilities. Either $a_n = a$ for all but a finite number of n (in which case a must belong to A) or the sequence $\{a_n\}$ contains a subsequence of distinct terms (in which case, by Theorem II, a must be a limit point of A). In either case, since A contains all of its limit points, a must belong to A.

Theorem IV. *A set A of real numbers is compact if and only if every sequence $\{a_n\}$ of points of A contains a subsequence converging to a point of A.*

Proof. "*If*": Assume that every sequence $\{a_n\}$ of points of A contains a convergent subsequence whose limit belongs to A. We wish to show that A is bounded and closed. If A were unbounded there would exist a sequence $\{a_n\}$ of points of A such that $|a_n| > n$, so that no subsequence could converge to *any* point. If A were not closed, there would exist (by Theorem III) a sequence $\{a_n\}$ of points of A converging to a point p not a member of A. Since every subsequence would also converge to p, no subsequence could converge to a point of A. These contradictions show that A must be both bounded and closed, and therefore compact.

"*Only if*": Assume that A is compact and let $\{a_n\}$ be an arbitrary sequence of points of A. Since A is bounded, $\{a_n\}$ contains a convergent subsequence $\{a_{n_k}\}$, and since A is closed, by Theorem III the limit of this subsequence must belong to A.

★★311. SOME GENERAL THEOREMS

With the aid of the theorems on sets and sequences given in the preceding section, we can now establish four of the most important general theorems on continuous functions. We remind the reader that in this chapter only real-valued functions of a real variable are considered, but the theorems are stated in general terms, so that they may be taken without change for more general use.   Joining *compactness* as a key concept, now, is *connectedness*.

Theorem I.   *A function continuous on a compact domain has a compact range.*

Proof.   Let the function be $y = f(x)$, with compact domain A and range B.   If B is *not* compact, there is a sequence $\{b_n\}$ of points of B such that $\{b_n\}$ contains no subsequence converging to a point of B (Theorem IV, § 310).   For each n, let a_n be a point of A such that $b_n = f(a_n)$.   Since A is assumed to be compact, the sequence $\{a_n\}$ contains a subsequence $\{a_{n_k}\}$ converging to some point a of A.   But from the continuity of $f(x)$ at $x = a$ we can infer that $a_{n_k} \to a$ implies $f(a_{n_k}) \to f(a)$ (Theorem I, § 303).   In other words, the subsequence $\{b_{n_k}\}$ of the sequence $\{b_n\}$ converges to the point $b \equiv f(a)$ of B.   This contradiction completes the proof.

Since any compact set is bounded and since any compact set of real numbers has a greatest member and a least member (Theorem III, § 309), we have immediately the following two corollaries, of which the first two theorems of § 213 are special cases where the domain is a closed interval:

Corollary I.   *A function continuous on a compact domain is bounded there.*

Corollary II.   *A real-valued function continuous on a compact domain has a maximum value and a minimum value there.*

Theorem II.   *A function continuous on a connected domain has a connected range.*

Proof.   Let the function be $y = f(x)$, with connected domain A and range B.   If B is *not* connected, then B can be split into two disjoint nonempty parts, B_1 and B_2, neither of which contains a limit point of the other.   Denote by A_1 the points x of A such that $f(x)$ is a point of B_1, and by A_2 the points x of A such that $f(x)$ is a point of B_2.   Then A is split into the two disjoint nonempty subsets, A_1 and A_2.   Since A is connected, one of these sets must contain a limit point of the other.   For definiteness, assume that p belongs to A_1 and is a limit point of A_2, and let $\{a_n\}$ be a sequence of points of A_2 such that $a_n \to p$.   Since $f(x)$ is assumed to be continuous at $x = p$, $a_n \to p$ implies $f(a_n) \to f(p)$.   But this means that a sequence of points of B_2 converges to a point of B_1, in contradiction to the assumption that *no* point of B_1 is a limit point of B_2, and the proof is complete.

Since any connected set of real numbers is an interval or a one-point set, we have the following corollary, of which Theorems III and IV, § 213, are special cases where the domain is an interval:

Corollary. *A real-valued function continuous on a connected domain assumes (as a value) every number between any two of its values.*

The Theorem of § 215 on the continuity of the inverse function of a strictly monotonic function finds its generalization again based on compactness, with the monotonic property replaced by the mere existence of a single-valued inverse:

Theorem III. *If a function $y = f(x)$ is continuous on a compact domain A and never assumes the same value at distinct points of A, then the inverse function $x = \phi(y)$ is continuous on the range B of $f(x)$.*

Proof. We observe first that since $f(x)$ always has distinct values at distinct points of A, $f(x)$ establishes a one-to-one correspondence between the points of A and the points of B, so that the inverse function $x = \phi(y)$ exists on B. To establish continuity of $\phi(y)$ we wish to show that $b_n \to b$ (where b_n and b are points of B) implies $a_n \to a$, where $a_n \equiv \phi(b_n)$ and $a \equiv \phi(b)$ (a_n and a are points of A). Let us assume that $a_n \nrightarrow a$, so that there exists a neighborhood of a outside of which lie infinitely many terms of the sequence $\{a_n\}$. Since these infinitely many terms form a subsequence of $\{a_n\}$, and since A is assumed to be compact, there must be a subsequence of this subsequence which converges to some point of A (Theorem IV, § 310) different from a. Denote by $\{a_{n_k}\}$ this new convergent subsequence, and denote by a' its limit: $a' \equiv \lim\limits_{k \to +\infty} a_{n_k}$, where $a' \neq a$. Since $f(x)$ is assumed to be continuous at a', $a_{n_k} \to a'$ implies $f(a_{n_k}) = b_{n_k} \to f(a')$. On the other hand, $b_n \to b$ implies $b_{n_k} \to b = f(a)$. By the uniqueness of the limit of a sequence (Theorem II, § 204), as applied to the subsequence $\{b_{n_k}\}$, we infer that $f(a) = f(a')$, in contradiction to our assumption that $f(x)$ never assumes the same value at distinct points.

Finally, the proof given in § 307 that a function continuous on a closed interval is uniformly continuous there generalizes with only trivial notational changes (Ex. 23, § 312) to a function continuous on any compact set:

Theorem IV. *A function continuous on a compact domain is uniformly continuous there.*

★★312. EXERCISES

★★1. Prove that any open interval, finite or infinite, is open. Give some examples of open sets (of real numbers) that are not intervals.

★★2. Prove the statement of Note 2, § 309.

★★3. Prove that every nonempty open set (of real numbers) contains both rational and irrational numbers. Show, in fact, that it contains infinitely many of each type.

★★4. Find an example of a pair of nonempty open sets (of real numbers) such that every member of each set is exceeded by some member of the other.

★★5. Prove that any finite closed interval and the infinite intervals $[a, +\infty)$ and $(-\infty, b]$ are closed.

★★6. Give some more examples of closed sets.

★★7. Give some more examples of sets (of real numbers) that are neither open nor closed.

★★8. Prove Theorem II, § 309.

★★9. Prove Theorem III, § 309.

★★10. Prove that if A is a set of real numbers containing more than one point, with the property that whenever two points belong to A every point between these two also belongs to A, then A is an interval (finite or infinite). *Hint:* If A is bounded, show that any point c between inf (A) and sup (A) is flanked by two members, a and b, of A: $a < c < b$. If A is unbounded proceed similarly.

★★11. Prove that the only sets of real numbers both open and closed are the empty set and the entire space S. *Hint:* Assume that A is a nonempty, open, and closed set of real numbers not containing all real numbers. Then its complement $B \equiv A'$ is also nonempty, open, and closed. But this means that the connected set S is split into two nonempty separated parts, A and B.

★★12. Prove that if A and B are two nonempty disjoint open sets (of real numbers) there exist numbers a, b, and c, where c is between a and b, such that a belongs to A, b belongs to B, and c belongs to neither A nor B. *Hint:* Show that the contrary assumption implies that the set C made up of all of the points of A together with all of the points of B is connected (cf. Exs. 10-11).

★★13. Prove the **Bolzano-Weierstrass Theorem**: *Any infinite bounded set of real numbers has a limit point.* *Hint:* If A is an infinite bounded set, let $\{a_n\}$ be a sequence of distinct points of A, and let $\{a_{n_k}\}$ be a convergent subsequence of $\{a_n\}$ converging to a point p. Show that p is a limit point of A.

★★14. Give some examples of bounded sets (of real numbers) that have no limit points.

★★15. Give some examples of infinite sets that have no limit points.

★★16. Give some examples of sets having the property that each point of the set is a limit point of the set.

★★17. If A is an arbitrary set of real numbers, prove that the set B of all limit points of A is closed.

★★18. The **closure** of a set A, denoted $\bar{A}$, is the set made up by adjoining to A all limit points of A. Prove that $\bar{A}$ is always closed.

★★19. The **distance between a point** p **and a nonempty set** A, written $\delta(p, A)$, is defined to be the greatest lower bound of the set of distances $|p - a|$ between p and arbitrary points a of A. Prove that the distance between p and A is 0 if and only if p is either a point of A or a limit point of A. Prove that if p is not a point of a nonempty closed set A, then $\delta(p, A) > 0$.

★★20. Prove that if p is a point that is not a member of a nonempty closed set A, then there is a point a of A such that $\delta(p, A) = |p - a|$. (Cf. Ex. 19.)
Hint: Let $\{a_n\}$ be a sequence of points of A such that $|p - a_n| < \delta(p, A) + \dfrac{1}{n}$ for every positive integer n, and let $a_{n_k} \to a$.

★★21. The **distance between two nonempty sets** A and B, written $\delta(A, B)$, is defined to be the greatest lower bound of the set of distances $|a - b|$ between arbitrary points a of A and b of B. Prove that $\delta(A, B) \geqq 0$, and is always zero unless A and B are disjoint. Show that $\delta(A, B)$ may be zero if A and B are disjoint, and even if A and B are disjoint closed sets. *Hint:* Consider the example: A is the set of positive integers and B is the set of numbers of the form $n + \dfrac{1}{n}$, where n is a positive integer.

★★**22.** Prove that if A and B are nonempty disjoint closed sets at least one of which is bounded (compact), then there exist points a of A and b of B such that $\delta(A, B) = |a - b|$. Hence prove that $\delta(A, B) > 0$. (Cf. Exs. 20-21.) *Hint:* Assume that A is compact, and choose points a_n of A and b_n of B such that $|a_n - b_n| < \delta(A, B) + \dfrac{1}{n}$. Let $a_{n_k} \to a$, and choose a convergent subsequence of $\{b_{n_k}\}$.

★★**23.** Prove Theorem IV, § 311.

★★**24.** Let $f(x)$ be continuous for all real numbers x, and let c be a constant. Prove that the following sets are open: (*i*) all x such that $f(x) > c$; (*ii*) all x such that $f(x) < c$. Prove that the following sets are closed: (*iii*) all x such that $f(x) \geqq c$; (*iv*) all x such that $f(x) \leqq c$; (*v*) all x such that $f(x) = c$. If $f(x)$ is bounded, must any of these sets be bounded? (Prove or give a counterexample.)

★★**25.** Give an example of a function, defined for all real numbers x, such that the set of all points of continuity is (*i*) open but not closed; (*ii*) closed but not open; (*iii*) neither open nor closed.

★★**26.** A sequence $\{A_n\}$ of sets is called **monotonically decreasing** if and only if every set A_n of the sequence contains its successor A_{n+1}. This property is symbolized $A_n \downarrow$. (A **constant sequence**, where $A_n \equiv A$, for all n, is an extreme example.) Prove the theorem: *If $\{A_n\}$ is a monotonically decreasing sequence of nonempty compact sets there exists a point x common to every set of the sequence.* The **nested intervals theorem** is the special case of this theorem where every compact set A_n is a (finite) closed interval. *Hint:* For every positive integer n let a_n be a point of A_n, and let $a_{n_k} \to x$. For any N, a_{n_k} belongs to A_N for sufficiently large k, so that x also belongs to A_N.

★★**27.** Show that the theorem of Exercise 26 is false if the assumption of compactness is replaced by either boundedness or closedness alone. *Hint:* Consider the sequences $\left\{\left(0, \dfrac{1}{n}\right)\right\}$ and $\{[n, +\infty)\}$.

★★**28.** A collection of open sets is said to **cover** a set A if and only if *every* point of A is a member of *some* open set of the collection. Such a collection of open sets is called an **open covering** of A. An open covering of a set A is said to be **reducible to a finite covering** if and only if there exists some finite subcollection of the open sets of the covering which also covers A. Prove the **Heine-Borel Theorem**: *Any open covering of a compact set is reducible to a finite covering.* *Hint:* First prove the theorem for the special case where the compact set is a (finite) closed interval I, as follows: Assume that F is a collection of open sets (each *member* of F is an open set) which covers I and which is not reducible to a finite covering of I. Consider the two closed intervals into which I is divided by its midpoint. At least one of these two subintervals cannot be covered by any finite collection of sets of F. Call this closed subinterval I_2, and relabel $I = I_1$. Let I_3 be a closed half of I_2 that is not covered by any finite collection of sets of F, and repeat the process to obtain a decreasing sequence $\{I_n\}$ of closed intervals whose lengths tend toward zero. If x is a point common to every interval I_n (Ex. 26), let B be an open set of the family F which contains x. Then B contains a neighborhood $(x - \epsilon, x + \epsilon)$ of x which, in turn, must contain one of the intervals I_n. But this means that I_n is covered by a finite collection of sets of F, namely, the single set B. This contradiction establishes the special case. Now let A be an arbitrary compact set and let F be an arbitrary open covering of A. Let I be a closed interval containing A, and adjoin to the family F the open set A' (A' is the complement of A). This larger collection is an open covering of I, and accordingly is reducible to a finite covering of I, by the first part of the proof. Those sets of F which belong to this finite covering of I cover A.

★★**29.** A *limit point* of a sequence $\{a_n\}$ was defined in Exercise 20, § 205, to be a number x to which some subsequence converges. Prove that the set of all limit points of a given sequence is closed, and that the set of all limit points of a bounded sequence is compact. Hence show that any bounded sequence has a largest limit point and a smallest limit point. Prove that these are the limit superior and limit inferior, respectively, of the sequence. (Cf. Exs. 16-17, § 305.) Extend these results to unbounded sequences.

★★**30.** Let A be a set contained in the domain of definition of a bounded function $f(x)$. The **oscillation** of $f(x)$ on the set A, $\omega(A)$, is defined to be the difference between the least upper bound of its values there and the greatest lower bound of its values there,

$$\omega(A) \equiv \sup_{x \text{ in } A} (f(x)) - \inf_{x \text{ in } A} (f(x)).$$

Prove that if A is contained in B, then $\omega(A) \leqq \omega(B)$. Hence show that if $\delta > 0$, and if $A_\delta \equiv (x_0 - \delta, x_0 + \delta)$, then $\omega(A_\delta)$ is a monotonically increasing function of δ, so that $\lim_{\delta \to 0+} \omega(A_\delta)$ exists (cf. § 215). Make appropriate modifications to take care of the possibility that A or A_δ may be only partly contained in the domain of definition of $f(x)$.

★★**31.** Let $f(x)$ be defined on a closed interval I. The **oscillation** $\omega(x_0)$ of $f(x)$ **at a point** x_0 of I is defined to be the limit of the function $\omega(A_\delta)$ of Exercise 30:

$$\omega(x_0) \equiv \lim_{\delta \to 0+} \omega(A_\delta).$$

Prove that $\omega(x_0) \geqq 0$ and that $f(x)$ is continuous at $x = x_0$ if and only if $\omega(x_0) = 0$.

★★**32.** Let $f(x)$ be defined on a closed interval I. If $\epsilon > 0$, let D_ϵ be the set of all points x such that $\omega(x) \geqq \epsilon$. Prove that D_ϵ is closed. (Cf. Ex. 31.) *Hint:* If $\omega(x_0) < \epsilon$, let $\eta \equiv \epsilon - \omega(x_0)$ and show that there exists a neighborhood N of x_0 for which $\omega(I) < \omega(x_0) + \eta$, so that for x in N, $\omega(x) < \omega(x_0) + \eta = \epsilon$.

★★**33.** Let $f(x)$ be defined on a closed interval I, and consider the sequence of closed sets $D_1, D_{\frac{1}{2}}, D_{\frac{1}{3}}, \cdots, D_{\frac{1}{n}}, \cdots$ (cf. Ex. 32). Prove that each of these sets is contained in its successor, and that the set of points x such that x is a member of some $D_{\frac{1}{n}}$ is precisely the set D of points of discontinuity of $f(x)$.

4

Differentiation

401. INTRODUCTION

This and the following chapter contain a review and an amplification of certain topics from a first course in Calculus. Some of the theorems that are usually stated without proof in a first introduction are established here. Other results are extended beyond the scope of a first course. On the other hand, many definitions and theorems with which the student can be assumed to be familiar are repeated here for the sake of completeness, without the full discussion and motivation which they deserve when first encountered. For illustrative material we have felt free to use calculus formulas which either are assumed to be well known or are established in later sections. For example, the trigonometric, exponential, and logarithmic functions provide useful examples and exercises for these chapters, but their analytic treatment is deferred to Chapter 6. The only inverse trigonometric functions used in this book are the inverse sine and inverse tangent, denoted Arcsin x and Arctan x, respectively, with values restricted to the principal value ranges $-\frac{\pi}{2} \leqq \text{Arcsin } x \leqq \frac{\pi}{2}$ and $-\frac{\pi}{2} < \text{Arctan } x < \frac{\pi}{2}$ (the upper case A indicates principal values).

402. THE DERIVATIVE

We shall consider only single-valued real-valued functions of a real variable defined in a neighborhood of the particular value of the independent variable concerned (or possibly just for values of the independent variable neighboring the particular value on one side).

Definition. *A function $y = f(x)$ is said to have a derivative or be **differentiable** at a point x if and only if the following limit exists and is finite; the function $f'(x)$ defined by the limit is called its **derivative**:*

$$(1) \qquad \frac{dy}{dx} \equiv f'(x) \equiv \lim_{h \to 0} \frac{f(x + h) - f(x)}{h}.$$

85

NOTE. On occasion it is convenient to speak of an infinite derivative in the sense that the limit in the definition above is either $+\infty$ or $-\infty$. For simplicity we shall adopt the convention that the word *derivative* refers to a finite quantity unless it is preceded by the word *infinite*.

Let us observe first that any differentiable function is continuous. More precisely, if $f(x)$ has a (finite) derivative at $x = x_0$, it is continuous there. We show this by taking limits of both members of the equation

$$f(x_0 + h) - f(x_0) = h \cdot \frac{f(x_0 + h) - f(x_0)}{h},$$

as $h \to 0$, the limit of the right-hand member being $0 \cdot f'(x_0) = 0$ (cf. Theorem V, § 207, and Note 3, § 209). The finiteness of the derivative is essential. For example, the signum function (Example 1, § 206) has an infinite derivative at $x = 0$, but is not continuous there.

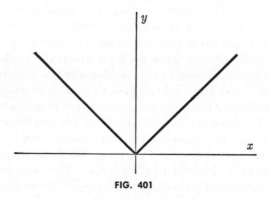

FIG. 401

The converse of the statement of the preceding paragraph is false. A continuous function need not have a derivative at every point. For example, the function $|x|$ (Fig. 401) is everywhere continuous, but has no derivative at $x = 0$. Example 2, § 403, contains a more pathological function. Even more startling is the renowned example of Weierstrass of a function which is everywhere continuous and nowhere differentiable. Although we shall not present this particular example in this book, every student at the level of Advanced Calculus should know of its existence. A discussion is given in E. W. Hobson, *The Theory of Functions of a Real Variable* (Washington, Harren Press, 1950). Another example of a continuous nondifferentiable function is presented in Exercise 41, § 908.

With the notation $\Delta y \equiv f(x + \Delta x) - f(x)$, the definition of a derivative takes the form

$$(2) \qquad \frac{dy}{dx} \equiv \lim_{\Delta x \to 0} \frac{\Delta y}{\Delta x}.$$

This fact can be written $\lim_{\Delta x \to 0} \left(\frac{\Delta y}{\Delta x} - \frac{dy}{dx} \right) = 0$. In other words, the expression

(3) $$\epsilon \equiv \frac{\Delta y}{\Delta x} - \frac{dy}{dx},$$

as a function of Δx, is an infinitesimal (that is, its limit as $\Delta x \to 0$ is 0). With the aid of this infinitesimal, equation (3) can be rewritten in either of the following two ways:

(3) $$\frac{\Delta y}{\Delta x} = \frac{dy}{dx} + \epsilon,$$

(4) $$\Delta y = \frac{dy}{dx} \Delta x + \epsilon \Delta x.$$

Under the assumption that the difference Δx between the values of the independent variable is numerically small, equation (3) states that the difference quotient $\Delta y/\Delta x$ differs but slightly from the derivative, and equation (4) states that the difference Δy can be approximated closely by an expression involving the derivative. Use of this fact is made in § 411.

The derivations of the formulas for the derivative of a constant function and of the sum, product, and quotient of functions will be omitted since they are available in any Calculus text. Two standard formulas, however, are often not completely proved in a first course, and we supply their proofs now. The first is the *chain rule* for differentiation of a *composite function* (a function of a function).

Theorem I. Chain Rule. *If y is a differentiable function of u and if u is a differentiable function of x, then y, as a function of x, is differentiable and*

(5) $$\frac{dy}{dx} = \frac{dy}{du} \cdot \frac{du}{dx}.$$

Proof. Let $u \equiv f(x)$ be differentiable at $x = x_0$, $y \equiv g(u)$ be differentiable at $u = u_0 = f(x_0)$, and let $h(x) \equiv g(f(x))$. With the customary notation,

$$\Delta u = f(x_0 + \Delta x) - f(x_0) = f(x_0 + \Delta x) - u_0$$
$$\Delta y = g(u_0 + \Delta u) - g(u_0)$$
$$= g(f(x_0 + \Delta x)) - g(f(x_0)) = h(x_0 + \Delta x) - h(x_0).$$

The usual simple device to make formula (5) seem plausible is the following: Write

(6) $$\frac{\Delta y}{\Delta x} = \frac{\Delta y}{\Delta u} \frac{\Delta u}{\Delta x}$$

and take limits as $\Delta x \to 0$. Since u is a continuous function of x at $x = x_0$, $\Delta x \to 0$ implies $\Delta u \to 0$ (Note 3, § 209), and the desired formula is obtained:

$$\lim_{\Delta x \to 0} \frac{\Delta y}{\Delta x} = \lim_{\Delta u \to 0} \frac{\Delta y}{\Delta u} \cdot \lim_{\Delta x \to 0} \frac{\Delta u}{\Delta x}$$

—unless in this process Δu vanishes and makes equation (6) meaningless!

To avoid this difficulty we define a new function of the independent variable Δu:

$$(7) \qquad \epsilon(\Delta u) \equiv \begin{cases} \dfrac{\Delta y}{\Delta u} - \dfrac{dy}{du}, \text{ if } \Delta u \neq 0, \\ 0 \quad\;\;, \text{ if } \Delta u = 0. \end{cases}$$

Then $\lim\limits_{\Delta x \to 0} \epsilon(\Delta u) = \lim\limits_{\Delta u \to 0} \epsilon(\Delta u) = \dfrac{dy}{du} - \dfrac{dy}{du} = 0.$

From the formulation (7), if $\Delta u \neq 0$,

$$(8) \qquad \Delta y = \frac{dy}{du} \cdot \Delta u + \epsilon(\Delta u) \cdot \Delta u.$$

In fact, equation (8) holds whether Δu is zero or not! All that remains is to divide by Δx (which is *nonzero*) and take limits:

$$\lim_{\Delta x \to 0} \frac{\Delta y}{\Delta x} = \frac{dy}{du} \cdot \lim_{\Delta x \to 0} \frac{\Delta u}{\Delta x} + \lim_{\Delta x \to 0} \epsilon(\Delta u) \cdot \lim_{\Delta x \to 0} \frac{\Delta u}{\Delta x},$$

or
$$\frac{dy}{dx} = \frac{dy}{du} \cdot \frac{du}{dx} + 0 \cdot \frac{du}{dx}.$$

Theorem II. *If $y = f(x)$ is strictly monotonic (§ 215) and differentiable in an interval, and if $f'(x) \neq 0$ in this interval, then the inverse function $x = \phi(y)$ is strictly monotonic and differentiable in the corresponding interval, and*

$$\frac{dx}{dy} = \frac{1}{\dfrac{dy}{dx}}.$$

Proof. By the Theorem of § 215, $\phi(y)$ is a continuous function, and therefore $\Delta x \to 0$ if and only if $\Delta y \to 0$ (Note 3, § 209). By Theorem VI, § 207, therefore,

$$\lim_{\Delta y \to 0} \frac{\Delta x}{\Delta y} = \lim_{\Delta x \to 0} \frac{1}{\dfrac{\Delta y}{\Delta x}} = \frac{1}{\lim\limits_{\Delta x \to 0} \dfrac{\Delta y}{\Delta x}},$$

and the proof is complete.

It will be assumed that the reader is familiar with the definitions and notations for derivatives of higher order than the first.

403. ONE-SIDED DERIVATIVES

It is frequently important to consider one-sided limits in relation to derivatives. There are three principal ways in which this can be done. We give the three definitions here and call for examples and properties in the exercises of § 404. It happens that in many applications the most useful of these three definitions is the second, and accordingly we reserve the term *right-hand* or *left-hand derivative* for that concept rather than for the first, for which it might at first seem more natural.   For Definitions I and III we create names for distinguishing purposes.

Definition I.   *The **derivative from the right** (**left**) of a function $f(x)$ at the point $x = a$ is the one-sided limit*

$$\lim_{h\to 0+} \frac{f(a+h) - f(a)}{h} \quad \left(\lim_{h\to 0-} \frac{f(a+h) - f(a)}{h}\right).$$

Definition II.   *The **right-hand** (**left-hand**) **derivative** of a function $f(x)$ at the point $x = a$ is the one-sided limit*

$$\lim_{h\to 0+} \frac{f(a+h) - f(a+)}{h} \quad \left(\lim_{h\to 0-} \frac{f(a+h) - f(a-)}{h}\right),$$

where $f(a+) \equiv \lim_{x\to a+} f(x) \ \left(f(a-) \equiv \lim_{x\to a-} f(x)\right).$

Definition III.   *The **right-hand** (**left-hand**) **limit of the derivative** of a function $f(x)$ at the point $x = a$ is the one-sided limit*

$$f'(a+) \equiv \lim_{x\to a+} f'(x) \ \left(f'(a-) \equiv \lim_{x\to a-} f'(x)\right).$$

A function has a derivative at a point if and only if it has equal derivatives from the right and from the left at the point (cf. Ex. 14, § 208). The function $|x|$ (Fig. 401) is an example of a function which has unequal derivatives from the right and from the left.   Definitions I, II, and III are related as follows: In case of one-sided continuity, Definitions I and II coincide, and hence if the limit in Definition I exists and is finite, the limit in Definition II exists and is equal to it.   If the limit in Definition III exists and is finite, it can be proved (Ex. 54, § 408) that the limit in Definition II exists and is equal to it.   Therefore, in case of differentiability, Definitions I and II are consistent with each other and with the Definition of § 402, and in case of continuity of the derivative all four definitions (Definitions I, II, and III of this section and the Definition of § 402) are consistent.

Example 1.   The signum function (Example 1, § 206) has infinite derivatives from the right and from the left at $x = 0$.   (Fig. 402.)   Its right-hand and left-hand derivatives and the right-hand and left-hand limits of the derivative are all zero.

Example 2.   The function defined by $y \equiv x \sin \dfrac{1}{x}$ if $x \neq 0$ and $y \equiv 0$ if $x = 0$ is everywhere continuous, even at the point $x = 0$ (cf. Ex. 8, § 208), but it has no derivative of any kind at $x = 0$.   (Fig. 403.)   Relative to the point $a = 0$, the fraction $\dfrac{\Delta y}{\Delta x}$ oscillates infinitely many times between $+1$ and -1 as $\Delta x \to 0$. For the manner in which Definition III applies to this function, cf. Example 3.

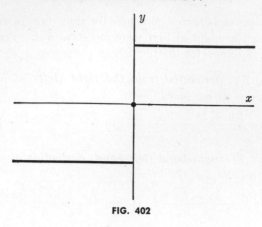

FIG. 402

Example 3. The function defined by $y \equiv x^2 \sin \dfrac{1}{x}$ if $x \neq 0$ and $y \equiv 0$ if $x = 0$ *has a derivative for every value of* x. When $x = 0$ this derivative has the

value $f'(0) = \lim\limits_{\Delta x \to 0} \dfrac{\Delta y}{\Delta x} = \lim\limits_{\Delta x \to 0} \dfrac{\Delta x^2 \sin\left(\dfrac{1}{\Delta x}\right)}{\Delta x} = \lim\limits_{\Delta x \to 0} \Delta x \sin\left(\dfrac{1}{\Delta x}\right) = 0$ (cf. Ex. 8, § 208). However, the derivative $f'(x)$ *is not continuous at* $x = 0$ and, in fact, its one-sided limits as $x \to 0$ (Definition III) both fail to exist! To show this, we differentiate $y = x^2 \sin \dfrac{1}{x}$ according to formula: $\dfrac{dy}{dx} = 2x \sin \dfrac{1}{x} - \cos \dfrac{1}{x}$, when $x \neq 0$. The first term of this expression tends to zero as $x \to 0$, but the second term approaches no limit. Therefore $\dfrac{dy}{dx}$ can approach no limit. (Why?) Cf. Exs. 47-49, § 408. (See Fig. 404.)

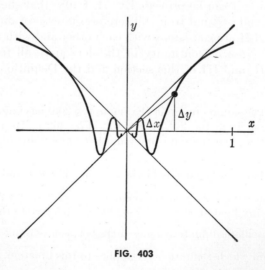

FIG. 403

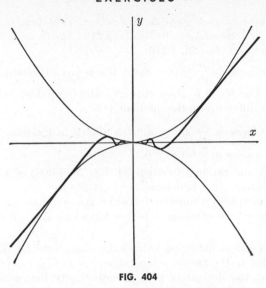

FIG. 404

404. EXERCISES

In Exercises 1-6, differentiate the given function by direct use of the Definition of § 402 (without appeal to any differentiation formulas).

1. $y = x^2 - 4x + 7$.

2. $y = x^3$.

3. $y = \dfrac{1}{x^2}$.

4. $y = \dfrac{3x + 2}{5x - 4}$.

5. $y = \sqrt{x}$.

Hint: Multiply numerator and denominator of $(\sqrt{x + h} - \sqrt{x})/h$ by a quantity which rationalizes the numerator.

6. $y = \sqrt[3]{x}$.

Hint: Multiply numerator and denominator of $(\sqrt[3]{x + h} - \sqrt[3]{x})/h$ by a quantity (consisting of three terms) which rationalizes the numerator.

7. Prove that if $f(x)$ is defined in a neighborhood of $x = \xi$, and if $f'(\xi)$ exists and is positive (negative), then within some neighborhood of ξ, $f(x) < f(\xi)$ for $x < \xi$ and $f(x) > f(\xi)$ for $x > \xi$ ($f(x) > f(\xi)$ for $x < \xi$ and $f(x) < f(\xi)$ for $x > \xi$).

Hint: If $\lim\limits_{\Delta x \to 0} \dfrac{f(\xi + \Delta x) - f(\xi)}{\Delta x} > 0$, then by Ex. 9, § 208, there exists a deleted neighborhood of 0 such that for any Δx within this deleted neighborhood $\dfrac{f(\xi + \Delta x) - f(\xi)}{\Delta x} > 0$.

8. Derive the formula $\dfrac{d}{dx}(x^n) = nx^{n-1}$, if n is a positive integer.

★9. Derive the formula $\dfrac{d}{dx}(x^n) = nx^{n-1}$, if n is a positive rational number and x is positive (without assuming in the process that x^n is differentiable). *Hint:* With standard notation, $y \equiv x^{p/q}$, $y^q = x^p$, and $(y + \Delta y)^q = (x + \Delta x)^p$, so that

$y^q + qy^{q-1} \Delta y + \cdots = x^p + px^{p-1} \Delta x + \cdots$. Cancel first terms, divide by Δx, and let $\Delta x \to 0$. Since $\Delta y \to 0$ (Ex. 21, § 216), the formula follows by algebraic simplification (cf. Ex. 22, § 216).

★10. Derive the formula $\dfrac{d}{dx}(x^n) = nx^{n-1}$, if n is any rational number and x is positive. *Hint:* Use Ex. 9 to show that x^n is differentiable. If n is negative, let $m \equiv -n$ and differentiate the quotient $1/x^m$.

NOTE 1.   The formula $\dfrac{d}{dx}(x^n) = nx^{n-1}$ is shown in Exercise 7, § 602, to be valid for all real values of n for $x > 0$.

11. Prove that any rational function (cf. Ex. 20, § 208) of a single variable is differentiable wherever it is defined.

12. Give an example of a function for which $\Delta x \to 0$ does not imply $\Delta y \to 0$. Give an example of a continuous function for which $\Delta y \to 0$ does not imply $\Delta x \to 0$.

13. By mathematical induction extend the chain rule for differentiating a composite function to the case of n functions: $y = f_1(f_2(f_3 \cdots (f_n(x)) \cdots))$.

14. Prove that the derivative of a monotonically increasing (decreasing) differentiable function $f(x)$ satisfies the inequality $f'(x) \geqq 0 \,(\leqq 0)$. Does strict increase (decrease) imply a strict inequality?

In Exercises 15-20, discuss differentiability of the given function $f(x)$ (where $f(0) \equiv 0$). Is the derivative continuous wherever it is defined?

15. $x^2 \operatorname{sgn} x$ (cf. Example 1, § 206).   **16.** $x \cos \dfrac{1}{x}$.

17. $x^2 \cos \dfrac{1}{x}$.   **18.** $x^2 \sin \dfrac{1}{x^2}$.

★19. $x^{\frac{4}{3}} \sin \dfrac{1}{x}$.   **★20.** $x^{\frac{5}{3}} \cos \dfrac{1}{\sqrt[3]{x}}$.

★21. Discuss differentiability of the function $f(x) \equiv 0$ if $x \leqq 0$, $f(x) \equiv x^n$ if $x > 0$. For what values of n does $f'(x)$ exist for all values of x? For what values of n is $f'(x)$ continuous for all values of x?

★22. If $f(x)$ is the function of Exercise 21, for what values of n does the kth derivative of $f(x)$ exist for all values of x? For what values of n is the kth derivative continuous for all values of x?

★23. If $f(x) \equiv x^n \sin \dfrac{1}{x}$ for $x > 0$ and $f(0) \equiv 0$, find $f'(x)$. For what values of n does $f'(x)$ exist for all nonnegative values of x? For what values of n is $f'(x)$ continuous for all nonnegative values of x?

★24. If $f(x) \equiv x^n \sin \dfrac{1}{x}$ for $x > 0$ and $f(0) \equiv 0$, find $f''(x)$. For what values of n does $f''(x)$ exist for all nonnegative values of x? For what values of n is $f''(x)$ continuous for all nonnegative values of x?

NOTE 2.   For the function $e^{-\frac{1}{x^2}}$, which behaves in a curious fashion near the origin, see Exercise 52, § 419.

★25. By mathematical induction establish **Leibnitz's Rule:** *If* u *and* v *are functions of* x, *each of which possesses derivatives of order* n, *then the product also does and*

$$\frac{d^n}{dx^n}(uv) = \frac{d^n u}{dx^n} \cdot v + \binom{n}{1}\frac{d^{n-1}u}{dx^{n-1}} \cdot \frac{dv}{dx} + \binom{n}{2}\frac{d^{n-2}u}{dx^{n-2}} \cdot \frac{d^2 v}{dx^2} + \cdots + \frac{d^n v}{dx^n},$$

where the coefficients are the binomial coefficients (Ex. 35, § 107).

★26. If y is a function of u, and u is a function of x, each possessing derivatives of as high an order as desired, establish the following formulas for higher order derivatives of y with respect to x:

$$\frac{d^2 y}{dx^2} = \frac{d^2 y}{du^2}\left(\frac{du}{dx}\right)^2 + \frac{dy}{du}\frac{d^2 u}{dx^2},$$

$$\frac{d^3 y}{dx^3} = \frac{d^3 y}{du^3}\left(\frac{du}{dx}\right)^3 + 3\frac{d^2 y}{du^2}\frac{du}{dx}\frac{d^2 u}{dx^2} + \frac{dy}{du}\frac{d^3 u}{dx^3},$$

$$\frac{d^4 y}{dx^4} = \frac{d^4 y}{du^4}\left(\frac{du}{dx}\right)^4 + 6\frac{d^3 y}{dx^3}\left(\frac{du}{dx}\right)^2\frac{d^2 u}{dx^2} + 3\frac{d^2 y}{du^2}\left(\frac{d^2 u}{dx^2}\right)^2$$

$$+ 4\frac{d^2 y}{du^2}\frac{du}{dx}\frac{d^3 u}{dx^3} + \frac{dy}{du}\frac{d^4 u}{dx^4}.$$

405. ROLLE'S THEOREM AND THE LAW OF THE MEAN

From the fact that a function continuous on a closed interval has a maximum value there (Theorem II, § 213) stem many of the most important propositions of pure and applied mathematics. In this section we initiate a sequence of these theorems.

Theorem I. *If* $f(x)$ *is continuous on the closed interval* $[a, b]$ *and differentiable in the open interval* (a, b), *and if* $f(x)$ *assumes either its maximum or minimum value for the closed interval* $[a, b]$ *at an interior point* ξ *of the interval, then* $f'(\xi) = 0$.

Proof. Assume the hypotheses of the theorem and, for definiteness, let $f(\xi)$ be the *maximum* value of $f(x)$ for the interval $[a, b]$, where $a < \xi < b$. (The student should supply the details for the case where $f(\xi)$ is the *minimum* value of $f(x)$.) Consider the difference quotient

$$(1) \qquad \frac{\Delta y}{\Delta x} \equiv \frac{f(\xi + \Delta x) - f(\xi)}{\Delta x}$$

for values of Δx so small numerically that $\xi + \Delta x$ is also in the open interval (a, b). Since $f(\xi)$ is the maximum value of $f(x)$, $f(\xi) \geqq f(\xi + \Delta x)$, and $\Delta y \leqq 0$. Therefore $\Delta y / \Delta x \geqq 0$ for $\Delta x < 0$ and $\Delta y / \Delta x \leqq 0$ for $\Delta x > 0$. Hence (in the limit) the derivative from the left at ξ is nonnegative and the derivative from the right at ξ is nonpositive. By hypothesis these one-sided derivatives are equal, and must therefore both equal zero.

Theorem II. Rolle's Theorem. *If* $f(x)$ *is continuous on the closed interval* $[a, b]$, *if* $f(a) = f(b) = 0$, *and if* $f(x)$ *is differentiable in the open*

interval (a, b), *then there is some point* ξ *of the open interval* (a, b) *such that*
$f'(\xi) = 0$.

Proof. If $f(x)$ vanishes identically the conclusion is trivial. If $f(x)$ is somewhere positive it attains its maximum value at some interior point, and if it is somewhere negative it attains its minimum value at some interior point. In either case, the conclusion follows from Theorem I.

The geometric interpretation of Rolle's Theorem (Fig. 405) is that the graph of the function $f(x)$ has a horizontal tangent for at least one intermediate point.

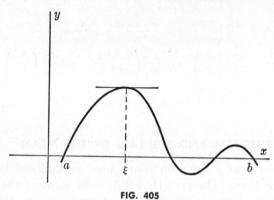

FIG. 405

Theorem III. Law of the Mean (Mean Value Theorem for Derivatives). *If $f(x)$ is continuous on the closed interval $[a, b]$, and if $f(x)$ is differentiable in the open interval (a, b), then there is some point ξ of the open interval (a, b) such that*

(2) $$f'(\xi) = \frac{f(b) - f(a)}{b - a}.$$

Proof. The geometric interpretation is suggested in Figure 406: the tangent line to the graph of the function $f(x)$, at some appropriate point between a and b, is parallel to the secant line between the points with abscissas a and b. The figure also suggests a proof. Let $K \equiv \dfrac{f(b) - f(a)}{b - a}$ be the slope of the secant line, so that

(3) $$f(b) = f(a) + K(b - a).$$

The equation of this secant line (the straight line through the point $(b, f(b))$ with slope K) can be written in the form

(4) $$y = f(b) - K(b - x).$$

For an arbitrary x on the closed interval $[a, b]$, since the curve has the equation $y = f(x)$, the vertical distance from the curve to the secant (ϕ in Figure 406) is given by the expression

(5) $$\phi(x) \equiv f(b) - f(x) - K(b - x).$$

It is a simple matter to verify that the function $\phi(x)$ defined by (5) satisfies the conditions of Rolle's Theorem (check the details), so that the conclusion is valid. That is, there exists a number ξ of the open interval (a, b)

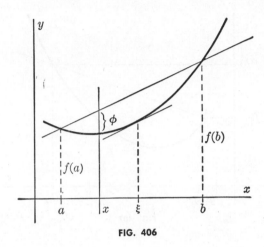

FIG. 406

where the derivative $\phi'(x) = -f'(x) + K$ vanishes, and we have the conclusion sought:

$$f'(\xi) = K = \frac{f(b) - f(a)}{b - a}.$$

A more general form of the Law of the Mean which is useful in evaluating indeterminate forms (§§ 413-416) is given in the following theorem. The proof is requested in Exercise 14, § 408, where hints are given.

Theorem IV. Generalized Law of the Mean (Generalized Mean Value Theorem for Derivatives). *If $f(x)$ and $g(x)$ are continuous on the closed interval $[a, b]$, if $f(x)$ and $g(x)$ are differentiable in the open interval (a, b), and if $g'(x)$ does not vanish in the open interval (a, b), then there is some point ξ of the open interval (a, b) such that*

(6) $$\frac{f'(\xi)}{g'(\xi)} = \frac{f(b) - f(a)}{g(b) - g(a)}.$$

The geometric interpretation is similar to that for the preceding Law of the Mean. The curve this time is given parametrically, where for convenience we relabel the independent variable with the letter t. The coordinates of a point (x, y) on the curve are given in terms of the parameter t by the functions $x = g(t)$ and $y = f(t)$, where $a \leq t \leq b$ (Fig. 407). In this case, by a formula from Calculus (cf. Ex. 46, § 408), the slope of the tangent at the point where $t = \xi$ is the left-hand member of (6), while the slope of the secant joining the points corresponding to $t = a$ and $t = b$ is the right-hand member of (6).

We conclude this section with some Notes, whose proofs are requested in the Exercises of § 408.

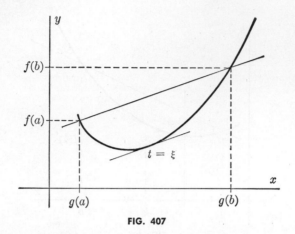

FIG. 407

NOTE 1.   Rolle's Theorem and the Law of the Mean remain valid if $f'(x)$ is permitted to be either positively or negatively infinite in the open interval (a, b).   (Ex. 11, § 408.)

NOTE 2.   Formulas (2) and (6) are valid, under corresponding assumptions, in case $a > b$.   (Ex. 12, § 408.)

NOTE 3.   If $f(x)$ is differentiable in a neighborhood of $x = a$, then for any x in this neighborhood there exists a point ξ between a and x ($\xi = a$ if $x = a$) such that

(7) $$f(x) = f(a) + f'(\xi)(x - a).$$

(Ex. 13, § 408.)

NOTE 4.   If $f(x)$ is differentiable in a neighborhood of $x = a$, and if h is sufficiently small numerically, then there exists a number θ such that $0 < \theta < 1$ and

(8) $$f(a + h) = f(a) + f'(a + \theta h)h.$$

(Ex. 13, § 408.)

Example 1.   Use the Law of the Mean to establish the inequality $\sin x < x$, for $x > 0$.

Solution.   If $a = 0$, $h = x$, and $f(x) = \sin x$, the equation $f(a + h) = f(a) + f'(a + \theta h) \cdot h$ becomes $\sin x = \cos (\theta x) \cdot x$.   If $0 < x \leq 1$, then $0 < \theta x < 1$ and $\cos (\theta x) < 1$, so that $\sin x < x$.   If $x > 1$, $\sin x \leq 1 < x$.

Example 2.   Use the Law of the Mean to establish the inequalities

(9) $$\frac{h}{1 + h} < \ln (1 + h) < h,$$

if $h > -1$ and $h \neq 0$.

Solution. If $a = 1$, and $f(x) = \ln x$, the equation $f(a + h) = f(a) + f'(a + \theta h) \cdot h$ becomes $\ln (1 + h) = \dfrac{h}{1 + \theta h}$. If $h > 0$, the inequalities $0 < \theta < 1$ imply $1 < 1 + \theta h < 1 + h$, and hence $\dfrac{1}{1 + h} < \dfrac{1}{1 + \theta h} < 1$, whence (9) follows. If $-1 < h < 0$, the inequalities $0 < \theta < 1$ imply $1 > 1 + \theta h > 1 + h > 0$, and hence $\dfrac{1}{1 + h} > \dfrac{1}{1 + \theta h} > 1$, whence (9) follows.

406. CONSEQUENCES OF THE LAW OF THE MEAN

It is a trivial fact that a constant function has a derivative that is identically zero. The converse, though less trivial, is also true.

Theorem I. *A function with an identically vanishing derivative throughout an interval must be constant in that interval.*

Proof. If $f(x)$ is differentiable and nonconstant in an interval, there are two points, a and b, of that interval where $f(a) \neq f(b)$. By the Law of the Mean there must be a point ξ between a and b such that

$$f'(\xi) = [f(b) - f(a)]/(b - a) \neq 0,$$

in contradiction to the basic assumption.

Theorem II. *Two differentiable functions whose derivatives are equal throughout an interval must differ by a constant in that interval.*

Proof. This is an immediate consequence of Theorem I, since the difference of the two functions has an identically vanishing derivative and must therefore be a constant.

A direct consequence of the definition of a derivative is that monotonic differentiable functions have derivatives of an appropriate sign (Ex. 14, § 404). A converse is stated in the following theorem:

Theorem III. *If $f(x)$ is continuous over an interval and differentiable in the interior, and if $f(x) \geq 0 \ (\leq 0)$ there, then $f(x)$ is monotonically increasing (decreasing) on the interval. If furthermore $f'(x) > 0 \ (< 0)$, then $f(x)$ is strictly increasing (decreasing).*

Proof. Let x_1 and x_2 be points of the interval such that $x_1 < x_2$. Then, by the Law of the Mean, there is a number x_3 between x_1 and x_2 such that $f(x_2) - f(x_1) = f'(x_3)(x_2 - x_1)$. The resulting inequalities give the desired conclusions.

An important relation between monotonicity of a function and the nonvanishing of its derivative is contained in the following theorem:

Theorem IV. *A function continuous over an interval and having a nonzero derivative throughout at least the interior of that interval is strictly mono-*

tonic (over the interval), and its derivative is of constant sign (wherever it is defined in the interval).

Proof. By Theorem III, it is sufficient to show that the derivative is of constant sign. Accordingly, we seek a contradiction to the assumption that there exist two points, a and b ($a < b$), of an interval throughout which the function $f(x)$ has a nonzero derivative, and such that $f'(a)$ and $f'(b)$ have *opposite* signs. On the closed interval $[a, b]$ the continuous function $f(x)$ has a maximum value at some point ξ of $[a, b]$ and a minimum value at some point η of $[a, b]$, where $\xi \neq \eta$ (why must ξ and η be distinct?). By Theorem I, § 405, neither ξ nor η can be an interior point of $[a, b]$. Therefore either $\xi = a$ and $\eta = b$ or $\xi = b$ and $\eta = a$. However, if $\xi = a$ and $\eta = b$, $f'(a) \leq 0$ and $f'(b) \leq 0$ (why?), whereas if $\xi = b$ and $\eta = a$, $f'(a) \geq 0$ and $f'(b) \geq 0$. Either conclusion is a contradiction to the assumption that $f'(a)$ and $f'(b)$ have opposite signs.

Corollary. *If a function has a nonzero derivative over an interval, the inverse function exists and is differentiable, and consequently the formula* $\dfrac{dx}{dy} = 1 / \dfrac{dy}{dx}$ *is valid whenever its right-hand member exists over an interval.*

407. THE EXTENDED LAW OF THE MEAN

In order to motivate an extension of the Law of the Mean to include higher order derivatives, we consider heuristically the problem of trying to approximate a given function $f(x)$ in a neighborhood of a point $x = a$ by means of a polynomial $p(x)$. The higher the degree of $p(x)$, the better we should expect to be able to approximate $f(x)$ (assuming, as we shall for this introductory discussion, that $f(x)$ not only is continuous but has derivatives of as high an order as we wish to consider, for x in the neighborhood of a). If $p(x)$ is a constant (degree zero), a reasonable value for this constant, if it is to approximate $f(x)$ for x near a, is clearly $f(a)$. If $p(x)$ is a polynomial of (at most) the first degree, it should certainly approximate $f(x)$ if its graph is the line tangent to the graph of $y = f(x)$ at the point $(a, f(a))$, that is, if $p(a) = f(a)$ and $p'(a) = f'(a)$. In this case, $p(x)$ has the form

$$(1) \qquad p(x) = f(a) + f'(a)(x - a).$$

More generally, let us approximate $f(x)$ in the neighborhood of $x = a$ by a polynomial $p(x)$ of degree $\leq n$ with the property that $p(a) = f(a)$, $p'(a) = f'(a)$, $\cdots$, $p^{(n)}(a) = f^{(n)}(a)$. We first express $p(x)$ by means of the substitution of $a + (x - a)$ for x, and subsequent expansion, in the form

$$(2) \qquad p(x) = p_0 + p_1(x - a) + \cdots + p_n(x - a)^n$$

Successive differentiation and substitution in the equations $p(a) = f(a)$, $p'(a) = f'(a)$, $\cdots$, $p^{(n)}(a) = f^{(n)}(a)$ lead to an evaluation of the coefficients in (2) in terms of the function $f(x)$, and hence to the following expression for $p(x)$ (check the details):

$$(3) \quad p(x) = f(a) + f'(a)(x - a) + \frac{f''(a)}{2!}(x - a)^2 + \cdots + \frac{f^{(n)}(a)}{n!}(x - a)^n.$$

The Law of the Mean, in the form

$$(4) \qquad f(x) = f(a) + f'(\xi)(x - a),$$

states that $f(x)$ can be represented by an expression which resembles the approximating polynomial (1) of (at most) the first degree, differing from it only by the substitution of ξ for a in the coefficient of the last term. It is not altogether unreasonable to expect that $f(x)$ can be represented more generally by an expression which resembles the approximating polynomial (3) of degree $\leq n$, differing from it only by the substitution of ξ for a in the coefficient of the last term. Our objective in this section is to show that this is indeed the case.

Theorem. Extended Law of the Mean (Mean Value Theorem). *If $f(x), f'(x), \cdots, f^{(n-1)}(x)$ are continuous on the closed interval $[a, b]$, and if $f^{(n)}(x)$ exists in the open interval (a, b), then there is some point ξ of the open interval (a, b) such that*

$$(5) \quad f(b) = f(a) + f'(a)(b - a) + \frac{f''(a)}{2!}(b - a)^2 + \cdots$$

$$+ \frac{f^{(n-1)}(a)}{(n-1)!}(b - a)^{n-1} + \frac{f^{(n)}(\xi)}{n!}(b - a)^n.$$

Proof. The methods used in establishing the Law of the Mean in § 405 can be extended to the present theorem. Let the constant K be defined by the equation

$$(6) \quad f(b) = f(a) + f'(a)(b - a) + \frac{f''(a)}{2!}(b - a)^2 + \cdots$$

$$+ \frac{f^{(n-1)}(a)}{(n-1)!}(b - a)^{n-1} + \frac{K}{n!}(b - a)^n,$$

and define a function $\phi(x)$ by replacing a by x in (6), and rearranging terms:

$$(7) \quad \phi(x) \equiv f(b) - f(x) - f'(x)(b - x) - \frac{f''(x)}{2!}(b - x)^2 - \cdots$$

$$- \frac{f^{(n-1)}(x)}{(n-1)!}(b - x)^{n-1} - \frac{K}{n!}(b - x)^n.$$

This function $\phi(x)$, for the interval $[a, b]$, satisfies the conditions of Rolle's Theorem (check this), and therefore its derivative must vanish for some point ξ of the open interval (a, b):

(8) $$\phi'(\xi) = 0.$$

Routine differentiation of (7) gives

(9) $\quad \phi'(x) = -f'(x) + f'(x) - f''(x)(b - x) + f''(x)(b - x) - \cdots$
$$- \frac{f^{(n)}(x)}{(n - 1)!} (b - x)^{n-1} + \frac{K}{(n - 1)!} (b - x)^{n-1},$$

in a form where all of the terms except the last two cancel in pairs. Equation (8) becomes, therefore, on simplification:

(10) $$K = f^{(n)}(\xi),$$

and the proof is complete.

Notes similar to those of § 405 apply to this section.

NOTE 1. The Extended Law of the Mean remains valid if $f^{(n)}(x)$ is permitted to be either positively or negatively infinite in the open interval (a, b). (Ex. 15, § 408.)

NOTE 2. Formula (5) is valid, under corresponding assumptions, in case $a > b$. (Ex. 16, § 408.)

NOTE 3. If $f^{(n)}(x)$ exists at every point of an interval I (open, closed, or half-open) that contains the point $x = a$, then for any x belonging to I there exists a point ξ between a and x ($\xi = a$ if $x = a$) such that

(11) $\quad f(x) = f(a) + f'(a)(x - a) + \dfrac{f''(a)}{2!} (x - a)^2 + \cdots$
$$+ \frac{f^{(n-1)}(a)}{(n - 1)!} (x - a)^{n-1} + \frac{f^{(n)}(\xi)}{n!} (x - a)^n.$$

(Ex. 17, § 408.)

NOTE 4. If $f^{(n)}(x)$ exists at every point of an interval I (open, closed, or half-open) that contains the point $x = a$, then for any h such that $a + h$ belongs to I there exists a number θ such that $0 < \theta < 1$ and

(12) $\quad f(a + h) = f(a) + f'(a)h + \dfrac{f''(a)}{2!} h^2 + \cdots$
$$+ \frac{f^{(n-1)}(a)}{(n - 1)!} h^{n-1} + \frac{f^{(n)}(a + \theta h)}{n!} h^n.$$

(Ex. 17, § 408.)

408. EXERCISES

In Exercises 1-2, find a value for ξ as prescribed by Rolle's Theorem. Draw a figure.

1. $f(x) \equiv \cos x$, for $\frac{1}{2}\pi \leqq x \leqq \frac{7}{2}\pi$.

2. $f(x) \equiv x^3 - 6x^2 + 6x - 1$, for $\frac{1}{2}(5 - \sqrt{21}) \leqq x \leqq 1$.

In Exercises 3-4, find a value for ξ as prescribed by the Law of the Mean, (2), § 405. Draw a figure.

3. $f(x) \equiv \ln x$, for $1 \leqq x \leqq e$.

4. $f(x) \equiv px^2 + qx + r$, for $a \leqq x \leqq b$.

In Exercises 5-6, find a value for θ as prescribed by the Law of the Mean, (8), § 405.   Draw a figure.

5. $f(x) \equiv \ln x$, for $a = e$, $h = 1 - e$.
6. $f(x) \equiv px^2 + qx + r$, a and h arbitrary.

In Exercises 7-8, find a value for ξ as prescribed by the Generalized Law of the Mean, (6), § 405.   Draw a figure.

7. $f(x) \equiv 2x + 5$, $g(x) \equiv x^2$, for $0 < b \leqq x \leqq a$.
8. $f(x) \equiv x^3$, $g(x) \equiv x^2$, for $1 \leqq x \leqq 3$.

In Exercises 9-10, find a value for ξ as prescribed by the Extended Law of the Mean, (5), § 407.

9. $f(x) \equiv \dfrac{1}{1 - x}$, $a = 0$, arbitrary n, and $b < 1$.
10. $f(x) \equiv \ln x$, $a = 1$, $b = 3$, $n = 3$.

11. Prove Note 1, § 405.   Explain why the function $x^{\frac{2}{3}}$ on the closed interval $[-1, 1]$ is excluded.
12. Prove Note 2, § 405.
13. Prove Notes 3 and 4, § 405.
14. Prove Theorem IV, § 405.   *Hint:* First show that $g(b) \neq g(a)$, by using Rolle's Theorem with the function $h(x) \equiv g(x) - g(a)$.   Then let
$$K \equiv (f(b) - f(a))/(g(b) - g(a))$$
and define the function $\phi(x) \equiv f(b) - f(a) - K[g(b) - g(a)]$.   Proceed as with the proof of the Law of the Mean.
15. Prove Note 1, § 407.
16. Prove Note 2, § 407.
17. Prove Notes 3 and 4, § 407.
18. The functions $f(x) \equiv \dfrac{1}{x}$ and $g(x) \equiv \dfrac{1}{x} + \operatorname{sgn} x$ (Example 1, § 206) have identical derivatives, but do not differ by a constant.   Explain how this is possible in the presence of Theorem II, § 406.

In Exercises 19-30, use the Law of the Mean to establish the given inequalities.   (Assume the standard properties of the transcendental functions.   Cf. §§ 428-431.)

19. $\tan x > x$ for $0 < x < \frac{1}{2}\pi$.
20. $|\sin a - \sin b| \leqq |a - b|$.   (Cf. Ex. 44.)
21. $\dfrac{b - a}{b} < \ln \dfrac{b}{a} < \dfrac{b - a}{a}$, for $0 < a < b$.
22. $\sqrt{1 + h} < 1 + \frac{1}{2}h$, for $-1 < h < 0$ or $h > 0$.   More generally, for these values of h and $0 < p < 1$, $(1 + h)^p < 1 + ph$.   (Cf. Exs. 38-41.)
23. $(1 + h)^p > 1 + ph$, for $-1 < h < 0$ or $h > 0$, and $p > 1$ or $p < 0$.   (Cf. Exs. 38-41.)
24. $\dfrac{h}{1 + h^2} < \operatorname{Arctan} h < h$, for $h > 0$.

25. $x < \text{Arcsin } x < \dfrac{x}{\sqrt{1 - x^2}}$, for $0 < x < 1$.

26. $\text{Arctan } (1 + h) \leqq \dfrac{\pi}{4} + \dfrac{h}{2}$, for $h > -1$.

27. $\left| \dfrac{\cos ax - \cos bx}{x} \right| \leqq |a - b|$, for $x \neq 0$.

28. $\dfrac{\sin px}{x} < p$, for $p > 0$ and $x > 0$.

29. $e^a(b - a) < e^b - e^a < e^b(b - a)$, for $a < b$.

30. $ae^{-ax} < \dfrac{1 - e^{-ax}}{x} < a$, for $a > 0$ and $x > 0$.

In Exercises 31-34, use the Extended Law of the Mean to establish the given inequalities.

31. $\cos x \geqq 1 - \dfrac{x^2}{2}$.

32. $\cos x > 1 - \dfrac{x^2}{2}$, for $x \neq 0$.

33. $x - \dfrac{x^3}{6} < \sin x < x$, for $x > 0$.

34. $1 + x + \dfrac{x^2}{2} < e^x < 1 + x + \dfrac{x^2}{2} e^x$, for $x > 0$.

★35. Use the trigonometric identity

$$\cos u - \cos v = -2 \sin \tfrac{1}{2}(u + v) \sin \tfrac{1}{2}(u - v)$$

to establish the inequality

$$\cos a - \cos b < \frac{b^2 - a^2}{2}, \quad \text{for} \quad 0 \leqq a < b.$$

Prove that

$$\frac{\cos ax - \cos bx}{x^2} < \frac{b^2 - a^2}{2}, \quad \text{for} \quad 0 \leqq a < b, \quad x \neq 0.$$

★36. Prove that $\dfrac{2}{\pi} < \dfrac{\sin x}{x} < 1$, for $0 < x < \dfrac{\pi}{2}$. *Hint:* For the first inequality, show that $\sin x/x$ is a decreasing function.

★37. Prove that $\dfrac{4}{\pi} > \dfrac{\tan x}{x} > 1$, for $0 < x < \dfrac{\pi}{4}$. (Cf. Ex. 36.)

38. Use the Law of the Mean to establish the following inequalities, for the designated ranges of p, assuming in each case that $x > 0$ and $x \neq 1$:

$$p(x - 1)x^{p-1} < x^p - 1 < p(x - 1), \quad \text{for} \quad 0 < p < 1,$$
$$p(x - 1)x^{p-1} > x^p - 1 > p(x - 1), \quad \text{for} \quad p < 0 \quad \text{or} \quad p > 1.$$

★39. By solving the left-hand inequalities of Exercise 38 for x^p, establish the following inequalities for the designated ranges of p and $h \equiv x - 1 \cdot$

$$\frac{1 + h}{1 + h - ph} < (1 + h)^p < 1 + ph,$$

$$\text{for } 0 < p < 1 \text{ and either } -1 < h < 0 \text{ or } h > 0.$$

$$\frac{1 + h}{1 + h - ph} > (1 + h)^p > 1 + ph,$$

$$\text{for } p > 1 \text{ and either } -1 < h < 0 \text{ or } 0 < h < \frac{1}{p-1},$$

$$\text{or for } p < 0 \text{ and either } h > 0 \text{ or } \frac{-1}{1-p} < h < 0.$$

Conclude that for any real number p, the expression $(1 + h)^p$, for sufficiently small $|h|$, is between the two numbers $(1 + h)/(1 + h - ph)$ and $1 + ph$ (being equal to them if they are equal). (Cf. Exs. 22-23.)

★**40.** Show that if n is an integer greater than 1, and if either $h > 0$ or $-1 < h < 0$, then

$$\frac{1 + h}{1 + h - \dfrac{h}{n}} < \sqrt[n]{1 + h} < 1 + \frac{h}{n}.$$

(Cf. Ex. 39.)

★**41.** Show that if n is an integer greater than 1, and if either $h > 0$ or $-\frac{2}{3} < h < 0$, then

$$\frac{1 + h}{1 + h + \dfrac{h}{n}} > \frac{1 + h - \dfrac{h}{n}}{1 + h} > \frac{1}{\sqrt[n]{1 + h}} > \frac{1}{1 + \dfrac{h}{n}} > 1 - \frac{h}{n}.$$

(Cf. Exs. 39-40.)

★**42.** Let $f(x)$ be differentiable, with $f'(x) \geqq 0$ $(f'(x) \leqq 0)$, on an interval, and assume that on no subinterval does $f'(x)$ vanish identically. Prove that $f(x)$ is strictly increasing (decreasing) on the interval.

★**43.** Establish the inequality $\sin x < x$, for $x > 0$ (Example 1, § 405) by applying Exercise 42 to the function $x - \sin x$. Similarly, establish the inequality $\tan x > x$ for $0 < x < \dfrac{\pi}{2}$ (Ex. 19).

★**44.** Let $f(x)$ be differentiable, with $f'(x) \geqq k$ $(f'(x) \leqq k)$, on an interval and assume that on no subinterval does $f'(x)$ equal k identically. Prove that for the graph of $y = f(x)$, on the given interval, every secant line has slope $> k$ $(< k)$. As a consequence, show that if $a \neq b$,

$$|\sin a - \sin b| < |a - b|,$$
$$|\cos a - \cos b| < |a - b|.$$

Hint: Let $g(x) \equiv f(x) - kx$, and use Exercise 42.

45. Prove that a function differentiable at every point of an interval is monotonic there if and only if its derivative does not change sign there.

46. Let $x = g(t)$ and $y = f(t)$ be continuous over a closed interval $a \leqq t \leqq b$ and differentiable in the interior, and assume that $g'(t)$ does not vanish there. Prove that y, as a function of x, is continuous over a corresponding interval and differentiable in the interior, and that for any interior point

$$\frac{dy}{dx} = \frac{f'(t)}{g'(t)}.$$

Interpret the results geometrically.

★**47.** It was shown in Example 3, § 403, that although a function may be differentiable for all values of the independent variable, its derivative may not be continuous. In spite of this fact, a derivative shares with continuous functions the intermediate value property of Theorem IV, § 213. Prove the theorem: *If $f(x)$ is the derivative of some function $g(x)$, on an interval, then $f(x)$ assumes (as a value) every number between any two of its values.* *Hint:* Let c and d be any two distinct values of $f(x)$, let r be any number between c and d, and apply Theorem IV, § 406, to the function $f(x) \equiv g(x) - rx$.

★**48.** Show by the example $f(x) \equiv x^2 \sin \dfrac{1}{x^2}$ ($f(0) \equiv 0$) that derivatives do not always share with continuous functions the property of being bounded on closed intervals (Theorem I, § 213). That is, exhibit a closed interval at every point of which $f(x)$ is differentiable but on which $f'(x)$ is unbounded.

★**49.** Prove that among the discontinuities discussed in § 210 for functions in general, *derivatives* can have discontinuities only of type (*iii*), where *not both* one-sided limits exist. In other words, show that the kinds of discontinuities exhibited by the derivatives of the functions of Example 3, § 403, and Exercise 48 are the rule and not the exception. *Hint:* If $\lim\limits_{x \to c+} f'(x)$ exists and $\neq f'(c)$, there exist positive numbers ϵ and δ such that $c < x < c + \delta$ implies $|f'(x) - f'(c)| \geq \epsilon$. Use Ex. 47.

★**50.** Show by the example $f(x) \equiv x + 2x^2 \sin (1/x)(f(0) \equiv 0)$ that the hypotheses (*i*) $f'(x)$ exists in a neighborhood of the point $x = a$, and (*ii*) $f'(a) > 0$, do not imply that there exists some neighborhood of $x = a$ throughout which $f(x)$ is increasing.

★**51.** The **Wronskian determinant** of two differentiable functions, $f(x)$ and $g(x)$, is defined:

$$W(f, g) \equiv \begin{vmatrix} f(x) & g(x) \\ f'(x) & g'(x) \end{vmatrix}.$$

Prove that if the Wronskian of f and g never vanishes over an interval, then between any two roots of the equation $f(x) = 0$ $(g(x) = 0)$ there must exist at least one root of the equation $g(x) = 0$ $(f(x) = 0)$. (Example: $f(x) = \sin x$, $g(x) = \cos x$.) *Hint:* Observe first that $f(x)$ and $g(x)$ never vanish simultaneously. Let a and b $(a < b)$ be two roots of $f(x)$ and assume that $g(x)$ does not vanish for $a < x < b$. Apply Rolle's Theorem to the quotient $f(x)/g(x)$, to obtain a contradiction.

★**52.** Prove that if a function has a bounded derivative in an open interval it is uniformly continuous there.

★**53.** Prove that if $f(x)$ has a bounded derivative on an open interval (a, b), then $f(a+)$ and $f(b-)$ exist and are finite. *Hint:* Cf. Ex. 52, and Ex. 15, § 308.

★**54.** Prove that if the right-hand (left-hand) limit of the derivative of a function (Definition III, § 403) exists and is finite, then the right-hand (left-hand) derivative (Definition II, § 403) exists and is equal to it. *Hint:* For the case $x \to a+$, show that there exists an interval of the form $(a, a + h)$, where $h > 0$, in which $f'(x)$ is bounded (cf. Ex. 9, § 208), and use Exercise 53 to infer that $f(a+) \equiv \lim\limits_{x \to a+} f(x)$ exists. Redefine $f(a) \equiv f(a+)$ and use the Law of the Mean in the form $[f(a + h) - f(a+)]/h = f'(a + \theta h)$.

409. MAXIMA AND MINIMA

We shall assume that the reader is familiar with the standard routine of finding maximum and minimum values of a function $y = f(x)$: (*i*) differentiate; (*ii*) set the derivative equal to zero; (*iii*) solve the equation $f'(x) = 0$ for x; (*iv*) test the values of x thus obtained, by using either the first or second derivative of the function; and (*v*) substitute in $f(x)$ the appropriate values of x to find the maximum and minimum values of $y = f(x)$.

Inasmuch as this routine gives only a partial answer to the story of maxima and minima, we present in this section a more complete summary of the pertinent facts and tests.

Let $f(x)$ be a function defined over a set A, and let ξ be a point of A. If the inequality $f(\xi) \geq f(x)$ $(f(\xi) \leq f(x))$ holds for every x in A, we say that $f(x)$ has a **maximum (minimum)** value on A equal to $f(\xi)$. According to Theorem II, § 213, such maximum and minimum values exist if A is a closed interval and $f(x)$ is continuous on A. If a function has a maximum (minimum) value on its domain of definition, this value is called the **absolute maximum (minimum)** value of the function. If ξ is a point where $f(x)$ is defined, and if within some neighborhood of ξ the inequality $f(\xi) \geq f(x)$ $(f(\xi) \leq f(x))$ holds whenever $f(x)$ is defined, we say that $f(\xi)$ is a **relative maximum (minimum)** value of $f(x)$. By a **critical value** of x for a function $f(x)$ we mean any point c of the domain of definition of $f(x)$ such that either (*i*) $f'(c)$ does not exist (as a finite quantity) or (*ii*) $f'(c) = 0$.

Theorem I. *If a function has a maximum or minimum value on an interval at a point ξ of the interval, then ξ is either an end-point of the interval or a critical value for the function.*

Proof. This theorem extends Theorem I, § 405, to an arbitrary (not necessarily closed) interval and drops continuity and differentiability assumptions. The details of the proof, however, are identical.

Some different kinds of maxima for a function continuous on a closed interval are illustrated in Figure 408.

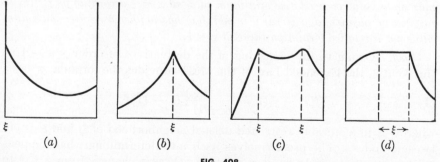

ξ ξ ξ ξ $\leftarrow \xi \rightarrow$

(*a*)   (*b*)   (*c*)   (*d*)

FIG. 408

Theorem II. First Derivative Test. *If $f(x)$ is continuous at a point $x = \xi$ and differentiable in a deleted neighborhood of ξ, and if in this deleted neighborhood $f'(x) > 0$ for $x < \xi$ and $f'(x) < 0$ for $x > \xi$ ($f'(x) < 0$ for $x < \xi$ and $f'(x) > 0$ for $x > \xi$), then $f(x)$ has a relative maximum (minimum) value at $x = \xi$. If, on the other hand, $f'(x)$ is of constant sign throughout the deleted neighborhood, $f(x)$ has neither a relative maximum nor a relative minimum value at $x = \xi$.*

Proof. Let x be an arbitrary point in the deleted neighborhood of ξ. By the Law of the Mean, § 405, there exists a point ξ' between ξ and x such that $f(x) - f(\xi) = f'(\xi')(x - \xi)$. Examination of each individual case leads to an appropriate inequality of the form $f(x) > f(\xi)$ or $f(x) < f(\xi)$. (Check the details.)

NOTE 1. The conditions assumed in Theorem II are sufficient but not necessary, even if $f'(x)$ is continuous and $f'(\xi) = 0$ (cf. Exs. 21-22, § 412).

Theorem II. Second Derivative Test. *If $f(x)$ is differentiable in a neighborhood of a critical value ξ, and if $f''(\xi)$ exists and is negative (positive), then $f(x)$ has a relative maximum (minimum) value at $x = \xi$.*

Proof. Assume $f''(\xi) < 0$. Then, by Exercise 7, § 404, within some neighborhood of ξ, $f'(x) > f'(\xi) = 0$ for $x < \xi$ and $f'(x) < f'(\xi) = 0$ for $x > \xi$. By the First Derivative Test, $f(x)$ has a relative maximum value at $x = \xi$. (Supply the corresponding details for the case $f''(\xi) > 0$.)

NOTE 2. No conclusion regarding maximum or minimum of a function can be drawn from the vanishing of the second derivative at a critical value—the function may have a maximum value or a minimum value or neither at such a point (cf. Ex. 9, § 412).

A useful extension of the Second Derivative Test is the following:

Theorem IV. *Let $f(x)$ be a function which, in some neighborhood of the point $x = \xi$, is defined and has derivatives $f'(x), f''(x), \cdots, f^{(n-1)}(x)$, of order $\leq n - 1$, where $n > 1$. If $f'(\xi) = f''(\xi) = \cdots = f^{(n-1)}(\xi) = 0$, and if $f^{(n)}(\xi)$ exists and is different from zero, then (i) if n is even, $f(x)$ has a relative maximum value or a relative minimum value at $x = \xi$ according as $f^{(n)}(\xi)$ is negative or positive, and (ii) if n is odd, $f(x)$ has neither a relative maximum value nor a relative minimum value at $x = \xi$.*

Proof. Owing to the vanishing of the derivatives of order $< n - 1$ at the point ξ, the Extended Law of the Mean provides the formula

$$(1) \qquad f(x) - f(\xi) = \frac{f^{(n-1)}(\xi')}{(n-1)!} (x - \xi)^{n-1},$$

where x is in a suitably restricted deleted neighborhood of ξ, and ξ' is between ξ and x. The proof resolves itself into determining what happens to the sign of the right-hand member of (1), as x changes from $x < \xi$ to

$x > \xi$, according to the various possibilities for the sign of $f^{(n)}(\xi)$ and the parity of n. We give the details for the case $f^{(n)}(\xi) < 0$, and suggest that the student furnish the corresponding details for the case $f^{(n)}(\xi) > 0$. By Exercise 7, § 404 (applied to the function $f^{(n-1)}(x)$), as x changes from $x < \xi$ to $x > \xi$, $f^{(n-1)}(x)$ changes from $+$ to $-$. Therefore if n is even, the right-hand member of (1) is negative whether $x < \xi$ or $x > \xi$, whence $f(x) < f(\xi)$ for x in the deleted neighborhood of ξ, and $f(\xi)$ is a relative maximum value of $f(x)$. If n is odd, the right-hand member of (1) is positive for $x < \xi$ and negative for $x > \xi$, so that $f(\xi)$ is neither a relative maximum value nor a relative minimum value of $f(x)$ at $x = \xi$.

Example. Examine the function $f(x) \equiv \dfrac{x^{\frac{2}{3}}}{x^2 + 8}$ for critical values of x and relative and absolute maxima and minima. Find its maximum and minimum values (when they exist) for the intervals $[1, 3]$, $(-1, 2)$, and $[1, +\infty)$.

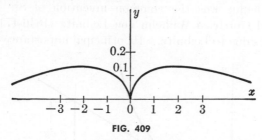

FIG. 409

Solution. The graph of $f(x)$ (Fig. 409) is symmetrical with respect to the y-axis, $\lim\limits_{x \to \infty} f(x) = 0$, and from the definition of one-sided derivatives, the derivative from the right at $x = 0$ is $+\infty$ and the derivative from the left at $x = 0$ is $-\infty$. For $x \neq 0$,

$$f'(x) = \frac{4(4 - x^2)}{3\sqrt[3]{x}\,(x^2 + 8)^2}.$$

The critical values of x are $x = 0, 2$, and -2. At $x = 0$ the function has both a relative and an absolute minimum value of 0. At $x = \pm 2$ the function has a relative and an absolute maximum value of $\frac{1}{12}\sqrt[3]{4} = 0.1326$ (approximately, to four decimal places). On the interval $[1, 3]$ the function has a maximum of $f(2)$ and a minimum of $f(1) = \frac{1}{9} = 0.1111$ ($f(3) = 0.1224$). On the interval $(-1, 2)$ $f(x)$ has a minimum of $f(0) = 0$, but no maximum. On the interval $[1, +\infty)$ $f(x)$ has a maximum of $f(2)$, but no minimum.

At this point, the student may wish to do a few of the Exercises of § 412. Some that are suitable for performance now are Exercises 1-22.

410. DIFFERENTIALS

The student of Calculus becomes familiar with the differential notation, and learns to appreciate its convenience in the treatment of composite, inverse, and implicit functions and functions defined parametrically, and in the technique of integration by substitution.   Differentials also lend themselves simply and naturally to such procedures as the solving of differential equations.   Such techniques and their legitimacy will not be discussed here.   In the present section we restrict ourselves to basic definitions and theoretical facts.

If $y = f(x)$ is a differentiable function of x, we introduce two symbols, dx and dy, devised for the purpose of permitting the derivative symbol to be regarded and manipulated as a fraction.

To this end we let dx denote an arbitrary real number, and define $dy = d(f(x))$ to be a function of the *two* independent variables x and dx, prescribed by the equation

$$(1) \qquad\qquad dy \equiv f'(x)\, dx.$$

The differentials dx and dy are interpreted geometrically in Figure 410.

Although Calculus was the common invention of Sir Isaac Newton (1642-1727) and Gottfried Wilhelm von Leibnitz (1646-1716), the differential notation is due to Leibnitz.   Its principal importance lies ultimately

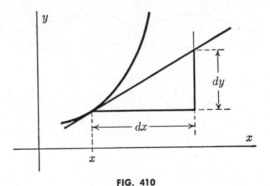

FIG. 410

in the fact that formula (1), initially true under the hypothesis that y is a function of the independent variable x, remains true under any possible reinterpretation of the dependence or independence of the variables x and y.   This fact is given explicit formulation in the two theorems that follow. Before proceeding to these theorems we point out a further justification of the differential notation which is of so elementary a character that it is frequently overlooked, but which follows directly from the definition (1): If two variables are related by the identity relation, $y \equiv x$, their differentials are also related by the identity relation, $dy \equiv dx$ (Ex. 23, § 412).

Theorem I.   *If $x = \phi(y)$ is a differentiable function of the independent variable y in a certain interval, if $\phi(y) \neq 0$ in this interval, and if dy and dx denote the differentials of the independent variable y and the dependent variable x, respectively, related by definition by the equation $dx \equiv \phi'(y)\, dy$, then if*

$y = f(x)$ denotes the inverse function of $x = \phi(y)$, these differentials are also related by equation (1): $dy = f'(x)\,dx$.

Proof. By the Corollary to Theorem IV, § 406, the derivatives dx/dy and dy/dx are reciprocals, so that $\phi'(y) = 1/f'(x)$.   Therefore

$$dx = (1/f'(x))\,dy,$$

and $dy = f'(x)\,dx$.

Theorem II. *If $y = f(x)$ is a differentiable function of the variable x, and if x is a differentiable function of the variable t, then if x and y are both regarded as dependent variables, depending on the independent variable t, their differentials are related by equation (1): $dy = f'(x)\,dx$.*

Proof. Let $x = \phi(t)$ and $y = \psi(t) \equiv f(\phi(t))$ denote the dependence of x and y on the independent variable t.   Then by definition, $dx \equiv \phi'(t)\,dt$ and $dy \equiv \psi'(t)\,dt$.   By the Chain Rule (Theorem I, § 402),

$$dy/dt = (dy/dx)(dx/dt),$$

or $\psi'(t) = f'(x)\phi'(t) = f'(\phi(t))\phi'(t)$, so that

$$dy = \psi'(t)\,dt = f'(\phi(t))(\phi'(t)\,dt) = f'(x)\,dx.$$

This completes the proof and shows that Theorem II is, in essence, simply a reformulation of the Chain Rule.

411. APPROXIMATIONS BY DIFFERENTIALS

In order to compare the differentials dx and dy, on the one hand, and the increments Δx and Δy, on the other, we observe that whereas the differentials can be associated with the *tangent* to the curve $y = f(x)$ (Fig. 410), the increments are associated with the *curve* itself.   It is often convenient to regard the real number dx as an increment in the variable $x : dx = \Delta x$. In this case the quantities just discussed find their geometric interpretation in Figure 411.   Throughout this section we shall identify dx and Δx.   It

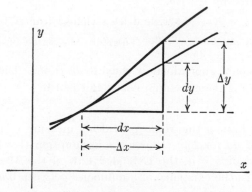

FIG. 411

should be noted, however, that under this assumption dy and Δy are *not* in general the same.

Although in theory the increment Δy is a simpler concept than the differential dy, in practice the differential is usually easier to compute than the increment, and dy is often a useful approximation to Δy. The statement that for a numerically small increment $dx = \Delta x$, the quantity dy is a good approximation to the quantity Δy, has a precise formulation, and means much more than the statement that dy and Δy are approximately equal (which is trivially true since they are both approximately equal to zero). The precise relation (under the assumption that the given function is differentiable at the point in question) is given by equation (4), § 402, rewritten in the form

$$(1) \qquad\qquad \Delta y = dy + \epsilon \Delta x,$$

where, *for a fixed* x, $\epsilon \equiv \epsilon(\Delta x)$ is an infinitesimal function of Δx ($\epsilon \to 0$ as $\Delta x \to 0$).

Using equation (1) we can formulate the statement that (for small $|dx| = |\Delta x|$) dy is a good approximation to Δy by means of the equation

$$(2) \qquad\qquad \lim_{\Delta x \to 0} \frac{\Delta y - dy}{\Delta x} = 0,$$

or, in case dy is not identically zero, by the equation

$$(3) \qquad\qquad \lim_{\Delta x \to 0} \frac{\Delta y}{dy} = 1. \quad \text{(Ex. 24, § 412).}$$

Example 1. If $y = f(x) \equiv x^3$, then $\Delta y = f(x + \Delta x) - f(x) = 3x^2 \Delta x + 3x \Delta x^2 + \Delta x^3$, and $dy = 3x^2 dx$. Therefore, in equation (1), the function $\epsilon(\Delta x)$ is $3x \Delta x + \Delta x^2$, equation (2) takes the form $\lim_{\Delta x \to 0} (3x \Delta x + \Delta x^2) = 0$, and equation (3) becomes $\lim_{\Delta x \to 0} \dfrac{3x^2 + 3x \Delta x + \Delta x^2}{3x^2} = 1$.

Example 2. Prove that for numerically small h the quantity $\sqrt{1 + h}$ is closely approximated by $1 + \frac{1}{2}h$.

Solution. Let $y = f(x) \equiv \sqrt{x}$, and let x change from 1 to $1 + h$. Then $dx = \Delta x = h$, and $dy = \dfrac{dx}{2\sqrt{x}} = \dfrac{h}{2}$. Therefore the value of y changes from $\sqrt{1} = 1$ by an amount approximately equal to $dy = \frac{1}{2}h$. The new value of y (which is $\sqrt{1 + h}$) is therefore approximately equal to $1 + \frac{1}{2}h$. (Cf. Ex. 41, § 408.)

The Extended Law of the Mean provides a measure of the accuracy of approximation of dy for Δy. Under the assumption that $f''(x)$ exists in the neighborhood of $x = a$, the Extended Law of the Mean ((12), § 407, for $n = 2$) ensures the existence of a number θ between 0 and 1 such that

$$(4) \qquad\qquad f(a + h) = f(a) + f'(a)h + \tfrac{1}{2}f''(a + \theta h)h^2,$$

for numerically small h. Expressed in terms of differentials, with $\Delta x = h$, $\Delta y = f(a + h) - f(a)$ and $dy = f'(a)h$, (4) becomes

$$(5) \qquad \Delta y - dy = \tfrac{1}{2}f''(a + \theta\Delta x)\Delta x^2.$$

If B is a bound for the absolute value of $f''(x)$ (that is, $|f''(x)| \leq B$) for x in a certain neighborhood of $x = a$, and if Δx is so restricted that $a + \Delta x$ (and therefore $a + \theta\Delta x$) is in this neighborhood, then (5) gives the inequality

$$(6) \qquad |\Delta y - dy| \leq \tfrac{1}{2}B\Delta x^2.$$

Example 3. Find an estimate for the accuracy of the approximation established in Example 2, if $|h| \leq 0.1$.

Solution. If $f(x) = \sqrt{x}$, then $f'(x) = \dfrac{1}{2\sqrt{x}}$, $f''(x) = -\dfrac{1}{4x\sqrt{x}}$, and formula (5) becomes

$$(7) \qquad \Delta y - dy = (\sqrt{1 + h} - 1) - (\tfrac{1}{2}h) = -\frac{h^2}{8(1 + \theta h)^{\frac{3}{2}}}.$$

If h is positive (whether $h \leq 0.1$ or $h > 0.1$), $1 + \theta h > 1$ and therefore the third member of (7) is between $-h^2/8$ and 0. We thus have the inequalities

$$(8) \qquad 1 + \tfrac{1}{2}h - \tfrac{1}{8}h^2 < \sqrt{1 + h} < 1 + \tfrac{1}{2}h, \quad h > 0.$$

(Illustration: $1.058 < \sqrt{1.12} < 1.06$.)

If $-0.1 \leq h < 0$, $1 + \theta h > 0.9$, and the third member of (7) is between $-h^2/6$ and 0. Therefore

$$(9) \qquad 1 + \tfrac{1}{2}h - \tfrac{1}{6}h^2 < \sqrt{1 + h} < 1 + \tfrac{1}{2}h, \quad -0.1 \leq h < 0.$$

(Illustration: $0.9694 < \sqrt{0.94} < 0.97$.)

Note. Formula (7) permits sharper results than those just obtained. For example, if h is between -0.1 and 0, the third member of (7) is between $-h^2/6$ and $-h^2/8$, so that $0.9694 < \sqrt{0.94} < 0.9696$. For computations where a high degree of accuracy is desired, however, the methods of this section are inadequate, and the reader is referred to Chapter 8.

412. EXERCISES

In Exercises 1-4, find the relative and absolute maximum and minimum values of the function, and the intervals within which the function is increasing, or decreasing. Draw a figure.

1. $x^3 - 6x^2 + 9x + 5$.

2. $\dfrac{2x}{1 + x^2}$.

3. $x^{\frac{2}{3}}(1 - x)$.

4. $\sqrt{x(x - 1)^2}$.

In Exercises 5-8, find the maximum and minimum values of the given function (whenever they exist) for the designated interval. Draw a figure.

5. $x + 2x^2 - 4x^3$, $[-\tfrac{1}{3}, 1]$.

6. $\dfrac{x^2 + 100}{x^2 - 25}$, $[-1, 3]$.

7. $\cos x + \cos 2x$, $(-\infty, +\infty)$.   **8.** xe^x, $(-\infty, 0)$.

9. Show that the three functions x^4, $-x^4$, and x^3 all have the property of possessing a continuous second derivative which vanishes at $x = 0$, whereas at this point the functions have an absolute minimum, an absolute maximum, and neither a maximum nor a minimum, respectively. Thus justify Note 2, § 409.

10. Show that the function $x^m(x - 1)^n$, where m and n are positive integers, has a relative minimum regardless of the values of m and n, and that it has an absolute minimum if and only if m and n have the same parity ($m + n$ is even). Draw figures.

★11. Show that the function $|x|^p \cdot |x - 1|^q$, where p and q are positive, has a relative maximum value of $p^p q^q / (p + q)^{p+q}$.

★12. Show that the function $\dfrac{ax + b}{cx + d}$ has neither a relative maximum nor a relative minimum unless it is a constant.

★13. If $a_1, a_2, \cdots, a_n$ are given constants, show that the expression $\displaystyle\sum_{i=1}^{n} (a_i - x)^2$ is minimized if and only if x is their arithmetic mean, $x = \dfrac{1}{n} \displaystyle\sum_{i=1}^{n} a_i$.

★14. Show that the function $x^3 + 3px + q$ has either a relative maximum and a relative minimum or neither. Draw figures corresponding to the various cases.

15. A publisher is planning on putting out a new magazine, and an efficiency expert has estimated that if the price per copy is x cents, the profit is given by a formula of the type

$$Profit = K\left[\frac{x - a}{x^2 + 25} - b\right],$$

where K, a, and b are positive constants. Determine what price should be set for maximum profit, in each of the following cases:

(a) x is a multiple of 5, $a = 10$, $b = .02$;
(b) x is a multiple of 5, $a = 11$, $b = .02$;
(c) x is an integer, $a = 10$, $b = .02$;
(d) x is an integer, $a = 11$, $b = .03$.

16. A truck has a top speed of 60 miles per hour and, when traveling at the rate of x miles per hour, consumes gasoline at the rate of $\dfrac{1}{200}\left(\dfrac{400}{x} + x\right)$ gallons per mile. This truck is to be taken on a 200 mile trip by a driver who is to be paid at the rate of b dollars per hour plus a commission of c dollars. Since the time required for this trip, at x miles per hour, is $200/x$, the total cost, if gasoline costs a dollars per gallon, is

$$\left(\frac{400}{x} + x\right)a + \frac{200}{x}b + c.$$

Find the most economical possible speed under each of the following sets of conditions:

(a) $b = 0$;
(b) $a = .25$, $b = 1.25$, $c = 5$;
(c) $a = .20$, $b = 4$ (a crew).

17. A problem in maxima and minima can frequently be simplified by such devices as eliminating constant terms and factors, squaring, and taking reciprocals. Suppose, for example, we wish to find the values of x on the interval $1 \leqq x \leqq 2$ that maximize and minimize the function $17x/50\sqrt{x^4 + 2x^2 + 2}$. The value of x that maximizes (minimizes) this function is the same as that which maximizes (minimizes) the function $x/\sqrt{x^4 + 2x^2 + 2}$ or $x^2/(x^4 + 2x^2 + 2)$, and is the same as that which minimizes (maximizes) the reciprocal $(x^4 + 2x^2 + 2)/x^2$ or, equivalently, $x^2 + 2x^{-2}$. Let us now substitute $t = x^2$, and seek the value of t ($1 \leqq t \leqq 4$) that minimizes (maximizes) the function $g(t) \equiv t + 2t^{-1}$. Since $g'(t) = 1 - 2t^{-2}$, $g(t)$ is minimized on the interval by $t = \sqrt{2}$, and is maximized by $t = 4$. Therefore the original function is maximized on $1 \leqq x \leqq 2$ by $x = \sqrt[4]{2}$ and minimized by $x = 2$. Discuss this technique in general for a function $y = f(x)$ defined on a set A, a strictly monotonic function $v = \phi(y)$ over the range of $f(x)$, and a suitably restricted substitution function $t = t(x)$. For the function $\phi(y)$, treat in particular $y + k$, py, y^n, $\sqrt[n]{y}$, and $1/y$, where k, p, and n are constants. (Be careful to explain under what circumstances squaring is legitimate.)

★18. Prove that the function

$$a|x| + b|x - 1|$$

has a relative minimum value for the interval $(-\infty, +\infty)$ if and only if $a + b \geq 0$, and that if $a + b \geq 0$ its minimum value is the smaller of the two numbers a and b.

★19. Find the value of x that minimizes the function $t\sqrt{x^2 + a^2} + s|b - x|$ on the interval $(-\infty, +\infty)$, where a, b, s, and t are positive constants. Thus solve the following problem: The shore of a lake extends for a considerable distance along the x-axis of a co-ordinate system. The lake lies in the first two quadrants and has an island on the y-axis at the point A: $(0, a)$. A man on the island wishes to go to the point B: $(b, 0)$ on the positive half of the x-axis by rowing straight to the point P: $(x, 0)$ at a rate of s miles an hour, and walking from P to B at a rate of t miles an hour. What course should he steer?

★20. Find the minimum value of the function $|x^2 - ax| + rx^2$ on the interval $[0, +\infty)$, where a is a positive number and r is a real number.

★21. Show that the function $f(x)$ defined to be $x^4 \left(2 + \sin \dfrac{1}{x} \right)$ when $x \neq 0$ and

0 when $x = 0$ has an absolute strict minimum at $x = 0$ ($f(x) > f(0)$ if $x \neq 0$) and a continuous derivative everywhere, but that this derivative does not change sign from $-$ to $+$ as x changes from $x < 0$ to $x > 0$. Thus show that the conditions of the First Derivative Test (§ 409) are only sufficient and not necessary for a maximum (minimum). (Cf. Ex. 22 for a converse of the First Derivative Test.) Sketch a graph of the function given above. (It oscillates infinitely many times between the two curves $y = x^4$ and $y = 3x^4$.)

★22. Prove the following converse of the First Derivative Test: *Let $f(x)$ be differentiable in a neighborhood of a point $x = \xi$ at which $f(x)$ has a relative maximum (minimum) value, and assume that in this neighborhood $f'(x)$ vanishes at only a finite number of points. Then there exists a neighborhood of $x = \xi$*

within which $f'(x) > 0$ for $x < \xi$ and $f'(x) < 0$ for $x > \xi$ ($f'(x) < 0$ for $x < \xi$ and $f'(x) > 0$ for $x > \xi$). (Cf. Ex. 21.)

23. Prove that if two variables are related by the identity relation, $y \equiv x$, their differentials are also related by the identity relation $dy \equiv dx$.

24. If y is a function of x which is differentiable for a particular value of x, prove the limit statements (2) and (3), § 411: As $\Delta x \to 0$, $\dfrac{\Delta y - dy}{\Delta x} \to 0$, and if furthermore $dy \neq 0$, $\dfrac{\Delta y}{dy} \to 1$.

In Exercises 25-28, express the given relation $x = \phi(y)$ in the form $y = f(x)$, write down both equations $dx = \phi'(y)\, dy$ and $dy = f'(x)\, dx$, and thus verify Theorem I, § 410. Draw figures.

25. $x = y^2$, $y > 0$.
26. $x = y^2 - 4y + 5$, $y < 2$.
27. $x = \ln(y^2 + 1)$, $y > 0$.
28. $x = \cos y$, $0 < y < \pi$.

In Exercises 29-32, use the given relations $x = \phi(t)$ and $y = \psi(t)$ to express y as a function of x, $y = f(x)$, write down the three equations $dx = \phi'(t)\, dt$, $dy = \psi'(t)\, dt$, and $dy = f'(x)\, dx$, and thus verify Theorem II, § 410. Draw figures.

29. $x = t$, $y = 5t^2 - 7t - 6$.
30. $x = t^2$, $y = t^3 - t$, $t < 0$.
31. $x = \ln t$, $y = e^t$, $t > 0$.
32. $x = \cos t$, $y = \sin t$, $0 < t < \frac{1}{2}\pi$.

In Exercises 33-35, find Δy, dy, and $\epsilon(\Delta x)$, and verify the limit statements (2) and (3), § 411.

33. $y = x^4 - 5x^2 + 7$.

34. $y = \dfrac{1}{x}$.

35. $y = \sqrt{x}$. *Hint:* Rationalize a numerator (cf. Ex. 5, § 404).

36. Prove that if $y = f(x)$ has a continuous second derivative y'', then

$$y'' = \lim_{\Delta x \to 0} 2 \cdot \frac{\Delta y - dy}{\Delta x^2}.$$

Use this relation to obtain directly (without first finding the first derivative) the second derivative of each of the functions of Exercises 33-35. (Cf. Ex. 11, § 421.)

In Exercises 37-48, use differentials to obtain an approximation to the given number, or the given function for values of the variable near the specified value.

37. $\sqrt{110}$ (use $10.5^2 = 110.25$).
38. $\ln(1 + h)$, h near 0.
39. $\ln(0.94)$ (cf. Ex. 38).
40. $\sin x$, x near 0.
41. $\tan x$, x near 0.

42. $\cos x$, x near $\frac{\pi}{3}$.

43. Arctan x, x near 0.

44. $\sqrt[n]{1 + h}$, h near 0, n an integer > 1.

45. $\ln \cos x$, x near 0.

46. $\dfrac{\ln (1 + h)}{1 + h}$, h near 0.

47. $e^{\sin x}$, x near 0.

48. $f(x) \equiv x^2 \sin \dfrac{1}{x}$ $(f(0) \equiv 0)$, x near 0.

In Exercises 49-60, verify the given inequalities, which give estimates of the errors in the approximations of Exercises 37-48.

★49. $10.48808 < \sqrt{110} < 10.48810$.

★50. $h - \frac{1}{2}h^2 < \ln (1 + h) < h$, $h > 0$,
$$h - \frac{2}{3}h^2 < \ln (1 + h) < h, \ -0.1 \leqq h < 0.$$

★51. $-0.0622 < \ln 0.94 < -0.06$.

★52. $x - \dfrac{x^3}{6} < \sin x < x$, $x > 0$.   *Hint:* Show that
$$\Delta y - dy = -\tfrac{1}{6} \cos (\theta x)\, x^3, \ 0 < \theta < 1.$$

★53. $x + \frac{1}{3}x^3 < \tan x < x + \frac{1}{2}x^3$, $0 < x < 0.1$.   *Hint:* Show that
$$\Delta y - dy = \tfrac{1}{3}(1 + 3t^2)(1 + t^2)x^3, \text{ where } t = \tan (\theta x), \ 0 < \theta < 1.$$

★54. $\frac{1}{2} - \frac{1}{2}\sqrt{3}\,(x - \frac{1}{3}\pi) - \frac{1}{2}(x - \frac{1}{3}\pi)^2 \leqq \cos x \leqq \frac{1}{2} - \frac{1}{2}\sqrt{3}\,(x - \frac{1}{3}\pi)$,
$$0 \leqq x \leqq \tfrac{1}{2}\pi.$$

★55. $x - \frac{1}{3}x^3 < $ Arctan $x < x$, $0 < x < \frac{1}{2}\pi$.

★56. $1 + \dfrac{h}{n} - \dfrac{(n - 1)h^2}{2n^2} < \sqrt[n]{1 + h} < 1 + \dfrac{h}{n}$, $h > 0$;
$$1 + \dfrac{h}{n} - \dfrac{(n - 1)h^2}{n^2} < \sqrt[n]{1 + h} < 1 + \dfrac{h}{n}, \ -\tfrac{1}{4} < h < 0.$$

★57. $-x^2 < \ln \cos x < -\frac{1}{2}x^2$, $0 < x < \frac{1}{4}\pi$.

★58. $h - \dfrac{9}{4}h^2 < \dfrac{\ln (1 + h)}{1 + h} < h - h^2$, $0 < |h| < 0.1$.

★59. $1 + x + 0.4x^2 < e^{\sin x} < 1 + x + 0.61x^2$, $0 < |x| < 0.1$.

★60. $x^2 \sin \dfrac{1}{x} \leqq x^2$.

413. L'HOSPITAL'S RULE.   INTRODUCTION

In the following three sections we consider the most important types of indeterminate forms, with some proofs given in the text, and others deferred to the following Exercises. The principles established in these sections are called upon in many of the problems in curve tracing that follow. Evaluation of indeterminate expressions by means of infinite series is discussed in § 812.

414. THE INDETERMINATE FORM 0/0

The statement that 0/0 is an indeterminate form means that the fact that two functions have the limit 0, as the independent variable approaches some limit, does not in itself imply anything about the limit of their quotient. The four examples x/x, x^2/x, x/x^2, and $\left(x \sin \dfrac{1}{x}\right)/x$, show that as $x \to 0+$, the quotient of functions, each tending toward zero, may have a limit 1, or 0, or $+\infty$, or it may have no limit at all, finite or infinite. That the involvement of infinity or the apparent division by zero does not in itself constitute an indeterminacy was seen in Exercises 31, 32, 50, § 208. Furthermore, the fact that 0/0 is an indeterminate form, in the sense explained above, certainly does not mean that a quotient of functions, each tending toward zero, cannot have a limit. Indeed, the simple examples above show this, as does any evaluation of a derivative as the limit of the quotient of two increments.

Frequently limits of quotients of functions, each tending toward zero, can be determined by the device known as l'Hospital's Rule. This is stated first in general form. The behavior of the independent variable is then specified in the separate cases. The letter a represents a real number.

Theorem. L'Hospital's Rule. *If $f(x)$ and $g(x)$ are differentiable functions and $g'(x) \neq 0$, for values of x concerned, if $\lim f(x) = \lim g(x) = 0$, and if*

$$\lim \frac{f'(x)}{g'(x)} = L \text{ (finite, } +\infty, -\infty, \text{ or } \infty),$$

then

$$\lim \frac{f(x)}{g(x)} = L.$$

Case 1. $x \to a+$.   (Proof below.)
Case 2. $x \to a-$.   (Ex. 31, § 417.)
Case 3. $x \to a$.   (Ex. 32, § 417.)
Case 4. $x \to +\infty$.   (Proof below.)
Case 5. $x \to -\infty$.   (Ex. 33, § 417.)
Case 6. $x \to \infty$.   (Ex. 34, § 417.)

Proof of Case 1.   Let $f(a)$ and $g(a)$ be defined (or redefined if necessary) to be zero. Then they are both continuous on some closed interval $[a, a + \epsilon]$, where $\epsilon > 0$. The number ϵ can be chosen so small that $g'(x)$ does not vanish in the open interval $(a, a + \epsilon)$ and the conditions of the Generalized Law of the Mean (Theorem IV, § 405) are fulfilled for any x such that $a < x \leqq a + \epsilon$. Thus, for any such x there exists a number ξ

such that $a < \xi < x$ and

$$\frac{f(x)}{g(x)} = \frac{f'(\xi)}{g'(\xi)}.$$

As $x \to a+$, $\xi \to a+$ and the limit of the right-hand member of this equation exists (finite or infinite) by hypothesis. Therefore the limit of the left-hand member of the equation also exists (finite or infinite) and is equal to it.

Proof of Case 4. Use reciprocals:

$$L \equiv \lim_{x \to +\infty} \frac{f'(x)}{g'(x)} = \lim_{t \to 0+} \frac{f'(1/t)}{g'(1/t)} = \lim_{t \to 0+} \frac{-f'(1/t)t^{-2}}{-g'(1/t)t^{-2}}$$

(multiplying and dividing by $-t^{-2}$)

$$= \lim_{t \to 0+} \frac{\frac{d}{dt} f(1/t)}{\frac{d}{dt} g(1/t)} = \lim_{t \to 0+} \frac{f(1/t)}{g(1/t)} = \lim_{x \to +\infty} \frac{f(x)}{g(x)}.$$

The next-to-the-last equality is true by Case 1. The sequence of equalities implies that the limit under consideration exists and is equal to L.

Example 1. $\lim\limits_{x \to 0} \dfrac{\sin x}{x} = \lim\limits_{x \to 0} \dfrac{\cos x}{1} = 1$.   (Cf. Ex. 16, § 604.)

Example 2.

$$\lim_{x \to 0} \frac{\sin x - x}{x^3} = \lim_{x \to 0} \frac{\cos x - 1}{3x^2} = \lim_{x \to 0} \frac{-\sin x}{6x} = \lim_{x \to 0} \frac{-\cos x}{6} = -\frac{1}{6}.$$

In this case l'Hospital's Rule is iterated. The existence of each limit implies that of the preceding and their equality.

Example 3. $\lim\limits_{x \to +\infty} \dfrac{e^{-x}}{\dfrac{1}{x}} = \lim\limits_{x \to +\infty} \dfrac{-e^{-x}}{-\dfrac{1}{x^2}} = \lim\limits_{x \to +\infty} \dfrac{e^{-x}}{\dfrac{2}{x^3}}$!

Things are getting worse! See Example 1, § 415.

It is important before applying l'Hospital's Rule to check on the indeterminacy of the expression being treated. The following example illustrates this.

Example 4. A routine and thoughtless application of l'Hospital's Rule may yield an incorrect result as follows:

$$\lim_{x \to 1} \frac{2x^2 - x - 1}{x^2 - x} = \lim_{x \to 1} \frac{4x - 1}{2x - 1} = \lim_{x \to 1} \frac{4}{2} = 2.$$

The first equality is correct, and the answer is obtained by direct substitution of 1 for x in the continuous function $(4x - 1)/(2x - 1)$, to give the correct value of 3.

415. THE INDETERMINATE FORM ∞/∞

The symbol ∞/∞ indicates that a limit is being sought for the quotient of two functions, each of which is becoming infinite (the absolute value approaches $+\infty$) as the independent variable approaches some limit. L'Hospital's Rule is again applicable, but the proof is more difficult.

Theorem. L'Hospital's Rule. *If $f(x)$ and $g(x)$ are differentiable functions and $g'(x) \neq 0$, for values of x concerned, if $\lim f(x) = \lim g(x) = \infty$, and if*

$$\lim \frac{f'(x)}{g'(x)} = L \text{ (finite, } +\infty, -\infty, \text{ or } \infty\text{)},$$

then

$$\lim \frac{f(x)}{g(x)} = L.$$

Case 1. $x \to a+$.   (Ex. 35, § 417.)

Case 2. $x \to a-$.   (Ex. 36, § 417.)

Case 3. $x \to a$.   (Ex. 37, § 417.)

Case 4. $x \to +\infty$.   (Proof below.)

Case 5. $x \to -\infty$.   (Ex. 38, § 417.)

Case 6. $x \to \infty$.   (Ex. 39. § 417.)

★ *Proof of Case 4.* Observe that whenever x is sufficiently large to prevent the vanishing of $f(x)$ and $g(x)$, and N_1 is sufficiently large to prevent the vanishing of $g'(\xi)$ for $\xi > N_1$, the generalized mean value theorem guarantees the relation

(1) $$\frac{f(x) - f(N_1)}{g(x) - g(N_1)} = \frac{f(x)}{g(x)} \cdot \frac{1 - f(N_1)/f(x)}{1 - g(N_1)/g(x)} = \frac{f'(\xi)}{g'(\xi)},$$

and therefore,

(2) $$\frac{f(x)}{g(x)} = \frac{f'(\xi)}{g'(\xi)} \frac{1 - g(N_1)/g(x)}{1 - f(N_1)/f(x)},$$

for $x > N_1$ and a suitable ξ between x and N_1. First choose N_1 so large that if $\xi > N_1$, then $f'(\xi)/g'(\xi)$ is within a specified degree of approximation of L. (If L is infinite, the term *approximate* should be interpreted liberally, in accordance with the definitions of infinite limits, § 206). Second, using the hypotheses that $\lim\limits_{x \to +\infty} |f(x)| = \lim\limits_{x \to +\infty} |g(x)| = +\infty$, let N_2 be so large that if $x > N_2$, then the fraction $[1 - g(N_1)/g(x)]/[1 - f(N_1)/f(x)]$ is within a specified degree of approximation of the number 1. In combination, by equation (2), these two approximations guarantee that $f(x)/g(x)$ approximates L. This completes the outline of the proof, but for more complete rigor, we present the "epsilon" details for the case where L is finite. (Cf. Ex. 40, § 417.)

Let L be an arbitrary real number and ϵ an arbitrary positive number. We shall show first that there exists a positive number δ such that $|y - L| < \frac{1}{2}\epsilon$ and $|z - 1| < \delta$, imply $|yz - L| < \epsilon$. To do this we use the triangle inequality to write

$$|yz - L| \leqq |yz - y| + |y - L| = |y| \cdot |z - 1| + |y - L|.$$

If $|y - L| < \frac{1}{2}\epsilon$, $|y| < |L| + \frac{1}{2}\epsilon$, so that if $\delta \equiv \frac{1}{2}\epsilon(|L| + \frac{1}{2}\epsilon)^{-1}$ the assumed inequalities imply

$$|yz - L| < (|L| + \tfrac{1}{2}\epsilon)\frac{\epsilon}{2(|L| + \frac{1}{2}\epsilon)} + \frac{\epsilon}{2} = \epsilon,$$

which is the desired result. The rest is simple. First choose N_1 such that

$$\xi > N_1 \text{ implies } \left|\frac{f'(\xi)}{g'(\xi)} - L\right| < \tfrac{1}{2}\epsilon,$$

and second choose $N_2 > N_1$ such that

$$x > N_2 \text{ implies } \left|\frac{1 - g(N_1)/g(x)}{1 - f(N_1)/f(x)} - 1\right| < \delta.$$

Then, by (2),

$$x > N_2 \text{ implies } \left|\frac{f(x)}{g(x)} - L\right| < \epsilon.$$

Example 1. Show that $\lim\limits_{x \to +\infty} \dfrac{x^a}{e^x} = 0$ for any real a.

Solution. If $a \leqq 0$ the expression is not indeterminate. Assume $a > 0$. Then $\lim\limits_{x \to +\infty} \dfrac{x^a}{e^x} = \lim\limits_{x \to +\infty} \dfrac{ax^{a-1}}{e^x}$, and if this process is continued, an exponent for x is ultimately found that is zero or negative. This example shows that e^x increases, as $x \to +\infty$, faster than any power of x, and therefore faster than any polynomial.

Example 2. Show that $\lim\limits_{x \to +\infty} \dfrac{\ln x}{x^a} = 0$ for any $a > 0$.

Solution. $\lim\limits_{x \to +\infty} \dfrac{\ln x}{x^a} = \lim\limits_{x \to +\infty} \dfrac{\frac{1}{x}}{ax^{a-1}} = \lim\limits_{x \to +\infty} \dfrac{1}{ax^a} = 0.$ (Cf. Ex. 7, § 602.)
In other words, $\ln x$ increases, as $x \to +\infty$, more slowly than any positive power of x.

Example 3. Show that $\lim\limits_{n \to +\infty} \dfrac{e^n}{n!} = 0$.

Solution. This is an indeterminate form to which l'Hospital's Rule does not apply, since $n!$ (unless the Gamma function is used to define $n!$ for all positive real numbers) cannot be differentiated. We can establish the limit as follows: Let n be greater than 3. Then

$$\frac{e^n}{n!} = \left(\frac{e}{1} \cdot \frac{e}{2} \cdot \frac{e}{3}\right)\left(\frac{e}{4} \cdots \frac{e}{n}\right) < \frac{e^3}{6} \cdot \left(\frac{e}{4}\right)^{n-3}.$$

As $n \to +\infty$, the last factor approaches zero.

Example 4. Criticize: $\lim\limits_{x \to +\infty} \dfrac{\sin x}{x} = \lim\limits_{x \to +\infty} \dfrac{\cos x}{1}$, and therefore does not exist!

Solution. L'Hospital's Rule does not apply, since the given expression is not indeterminate. Since $|\sin x/x| \leqq 1/x$, the limit is 0.

416. OTHER INDETERMINATE FORMS

In the sense discussed in § 414, the forms

$$0 \cdot \infty, \quad \infty - \infty, \quad 0^0, \quad \infty^0, \quad \text{and} \quad 1^\infty$$

are indeterminate (Ex. 42, § 417.) The first type can often be evaluated by writing the product $f(x) \, g(x)$ as a quotient and then using l'Hospital's Rule (Example 1). The second type sometimes lends itself to rearrangement, use of identities, or judicious multiplication by unity (Examples 2-3). The remaining three forms are handled by first taking a logarithm: if $y = f(x)^{g(x)}$, then $\ln y = g(x) \ln (f(x))$, and an indeterminacy of the first type above results. Then, by continuity of the exponential function (cf. § 602), $\lim y = \lim (e^{\ln y}) = e^{\lim (\ln y)}$. (Examples 4-6). Finally, other devices, including separation of determinate from indeterminate expressions and substitution of a reciprocal variable, are possible (Examples 7-9).

Example 1. Find $\lim\limits_{x \to 0+} x^a \ln x$.

Solution. If $a \leqq 0$, the expression is not indeterminate (cf. Ex. 7, § 602), and the limit is $-\infty$. If $a > 0$, the limit can be written

$$\lim_{x \to 0+} \frac{\ln x}{x^{-a}} = \lim_{x \to 0+} \frac{1/x}{-ax^{-a-1}} = \lim_{x \to 0+} \frac{x^a}{-a} = 0.$$

In other words, whenever the expression $x^a \ln x$ is indeterminate, the algebraic factor "dominates" the logarithmic factor (cf. Example 2, § 415).

Example 2. $\lim\limits_{x \to \frac{\pi}{2}} (\sec x - \tan x) = \lim\limits_{x \to \frac{\pi}{2}} \dfrac{1 - \sin x}{\cos x} = \lim\limits_{x \to \frac{\pi}{2}} \dfrac{-\cos x}{-\sin x} = 0.$

Alternatively,

$$\lim_{x \to \frac{\pi}{2}} (\sec x - \tan x) = \lim_{x \to \frac{\pi}{2}} \frac{\sec^2 x - \tan^2 x}{\sec x + \tan x} = \lim_{x \to \frac{\pi}{2}} \frac{1}{\sec x + \tan x} = 0.$$

Example 3. $\lim\limits_{x \to \infty} [\sqrt{x^2 - a^2} - |x|] = \lim\limits_{x \to \infty} \dfrac{\sqrt{x^2 - a^2} - |x|}{1} \cdot \dfrac{\sqrt{x^2 - a^2} + |x|}{\sqrt{x^2 - a^2} + |x|}$

$$= \lim_{x \to \infty} \frac{-a^2}{\sqrt{x^2 - a^2} + |x|} = 0.$$

Example 4. Find $\lim\limits_{x \to 0+} x^x$.

Solution. Let $y = x^x$. Then $\ln y = x \ln x$ and, by Example 1, $\ln y \to 0$. Therefore, by continuity of the function e^x, $y = e^{\ln y} \to e^0 = 1$.

Example 5. Find $\lim\limits_{x \to +\infty} (1 + ax)^{\frac{1}{x}}, a > 0.$

Solution. If $y = (1 + ax)^{\frac{1}{x}}$, $\ln y = \dfrac{\ln(1 + ax)}{x} \to 0$.

Therefore $y = e^{\ln y} \to e^0 = 1$.

Example 6. Show that $\lim\limits_{x \to 0} (1 + ax)^{\frac{1}{x}} = e^a$.

Solution. If $a \neq 0$ and if $y = (1 + ax)^{\frac{1}{x}}$,

$$\lim_{x \to 0} \ln y = \lim_{x \to 0} \frac{\ln(1 + ax)}{x} = \lim_{x \to 0} \frac{a}{1 + ax} = a,$$

and $y = e^{\ln y} \to e^a$. (Cf. Ex. 10, § 602.)

Example 7. Find $\lim\limits_{x \to 0+} x\, e^{\frac{1}{x}}$.

Solution. If this is written $\lim\limits_{x \to 0+} \dfrac{e^{\frac{1}{x}}}{\frac{1}{x}}$, differentiation leads to the answer.

However, the limit can be written $\lim\limits_{t \to +\infty} \dfrac{e^t}{t} = +\infty$.

Example 8. $\lim\limits_{x \to 0} (\csc^2 x - x \csc^3 x) = \lim\limits_{x \to 0} \dfrac{\sin x - x}{x^3} \cdot \dfrac{x^3}{\sin^3 x}$

$$= \left(-\frac{1}{6} \right) \cdot \left(\lim_{x \to 0} \frac{x}{\sin x} \right)^3 = -\frac{1}{6},$$

by Example 2, § 414, and the continuity of the function x^3 (the limit of the cube is the cube of the limit).

Example 9. $\lim\limits_{x \to 1} \dfrac{12 \sin \dfrac{\pi}{2x} \ln x}{(x^3 + 5)(x - 1)}$

$$= \lim_{x \to 1} \frac{12 \sin \dfrac{\pi}{2x}}{x^3 + 5} \cdot \lim_{x \to 1} \frac{\ln x}{x - 1} = \frac{12 \cdot 1}{6} \cdot \lim_{x \to 1} \frac{\frac{1}{x}}{1} = 2.$$

417. EXERCISES

In Exercises 1-30, evaluate the limit.

1. $\lim\limits_{x \to 2} \dfrac{3x^2 + x - 14}{x^2 - x - 2}$.

2. $\lim\limits_{x \to -3} \dfrac{x^3 + x + 30}{4x^3 + 11x^2 + 9}$.

3. $\lim\limits_{x \to 1} \dfrac{\ln x}{x^2 + x - 2}$.

4. $\lim\limits_{x \to 1} \dfrac{\cos \frac{1}{2}\pi x}{x - 1}$.

5. $\lim\limits_{x \to 0} \dfrac{\cos x - 1 + \frac{1}{2}x^2}{x^4}$.

6. $\lim\limits_{x \to 0} \dfrac{\ln(1 + x) - x}{\cos x - 1}$.

7. $\lim\limits_{x \to \pi} \dfrac{\sin^2 x}{\tan^2 4x}$.

8. $\lim\limits_{x \to \infty} \dfrac{\sin(1/x)}{\text{Arc} \tan(1/x)}$.

9. $\lim\limits_{x\to 0} \dfrac{a^x - 1}{b^x - 1}$.

10. $\lim\limits_{x\to 0} \dfrac{\tan x - x}{\text{Arc sin } x - x}$.

11. $\lim\limits_{x\to\infty} \dfrac{8x^5 - 5x^2 + 1}{3x^5 + x}$.

12. $\lim\limits_{x\to\frac{1}{2}\pi} \dfrac{\tan x - 6}{\sec x + 5}$.

13. $\lim\limits_{x\to\frac{1}{2}\pi-} \dfrac{\ln \sin 2x}{\ln \cos x}$.

14. $\lim\limits_{x\to\pi} \dfrac{\ln \sin x}{\ln \sin 2x}$.

15. $\lim\limits_{x\to+\infty} \dfrac{\cosh x}{e^x}$ (cf. § 607).

16. $\lim\limits_{x\to\frac{1}{2}-} \dfrac{\ln (1 - 2x)}{\tan \pi x}$.

17. $\lim\limits_{x\to+\infty} \dfrac{(\ln x)^n}{x}$, $n > 0$.

18. $\lim\limits_{x\to+\infty} \dfrac{a^x}{x^b}$, $a > 1$, $b > 0$.

19. $\lim\limits_{x\to 0+} x(\ln x)^n$, $n > 0$.

20. $\lim\limits_{x\to a} (x - a) \tan \dfrac{\pi x}{2a}$.

21. $\lim\limits_{x\to\frac{1}{2}\pi} \left[x \tan x - \dfrac{\pi}{2} \sec x \right]$.

22. $\lim\limits_{x\to 1+} \left[\dfrac{x}{x - 1} - \dfrac{1}{\ln x} \right]$.

23. $\lim\limits_{x\to+\infty} (1 + x^2)^{\frac{1}{x}}$.

24. $\lim\limits_{x\to 0} (1 + 2 \sin x)^{\cot x}$.

25. $\lim\limits_{x\to 0+} x^{\frac{1}{\ln x}}$.

26. $\lim\limits_{x\to 0} (x + e^{2x})^{\frac{1}{x}}$.

27. $\lim\limits_{x\to 0+} x^{x^x} (x^{x^x} \equiv x^{(x^x)})$.

28. $\lim\limits_{x\to 0+} [\ln (1 + x]^x$.

29. $\lim\limits_{x\to 0} (\cos 2x)^{\frac{1}{x^2}}$.

30. $\lim\limits_{x\to 0+} \left[\dfrac{\ln x}{(1 + x)^2} - \ln \dfrac{x}{1 + x} \right]$.

31. Prove Case 2 of l'Hospital's Rule, § 414.

32. Prove Case 3 of l'Hospital's Rule, § 414. *Hint:* Make sensible use of Cases 1 and 2.

33. Prove Case 5 of l'Hospital's Rule, § 414.

34. Prove Case 6 of l'Hospital's Rule, § 414.

35. Prove Case 1 of l'Hospital's Rule, § 415. *Hint:* Apply Case 4 (cf. proof of Case 4, § 414).

★36. Prove Case 2 of l'Hospital's Rule, § 415.

★37. Prove Case 3 of l'Hospital's Rule, § 415.

★38. Prove Case 5 of l'Hospital's Rule, § 415.

★39. Prove Case 6 of l'Hospital's Rule, § 415.

★40. For Case 4 of l'Hospital's Rule, § 415, supply the "epsilon" details for the case $L = +\infty$.

41. Prove that the forms $(+0)^{+\infty}$, $(+\infty)^{+\infty}$, and $a^{+\infty}$ (where $a > 0$ and $a \neq 1$) are determinate. What can you say about $(+0)^{-\infty}$? $(+\infty)^{-\infty}$? $(+0)^{\infty}$? $(+\infty)^{\infty}$?

42. Show by examples that all of the forms of § 416 are indeterminate, as stated.

43. Criticize the following alleged "proof" of l'Hospital's Rule for the form $0/0$ as $x \to a+$: By the Law of the Mean, for any $x > a$, there exist ξ_1 and ξ_2 between a and x such that $f(x) - f(a+) = f'(\xi_1)$ and $g(x) - g(a+) = g'(\xi_2)$.

Therefore

$$\frac{f(x)}{g(x)} = \frac{f(x) - f(a+)}{g(x) - g(a+)} = \frac{f'(\xi_1)}{g'(\xi_2)} \to \frac{f'(a+)}{g'(a+)} = \lim_{x \to a+} \frac{f'(x)}{g'(x)}.$$

418. CURVE TRACING

It is not our purpose in this section to give an extensive treatment of curve tracing. Rather, we wish to give the reader an opportunity to review in practice such topics from differential calculus as increasing and decreasing functions, maximum and minimum points, symmetry, concavity, and points of inflection. Certain basic principles we do wish to recall explicitly, however.

(*i*) *Composition of ordinates.* The graph of a function represented as the sum of terms can often be obtained most simply by graphing the separate terms, and adding the ordinates visually, as indicated in Figure 412.

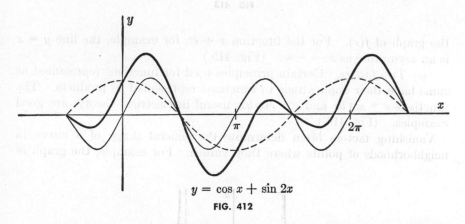

$$y = \cos x + \sin 2x$$

FIG. 412

(*ii*) *Dominant terms.* If different terms dominate an expression for different values of the independent variable, the general shape of the curve can often be inferred. For example, for positive values of x, the function $x + \dfrac{1}{x}$ is dominated by the second term if x is small and by the first term if x is large (Fig. 413).

(*iii*) *Vertical and horizontal asymptotes.* A function represented as a quotient $f(x)/g(x)$ of continuous functions has a vertical asymptote at a point a where $g(a) = 0$ and $f(a) \neq 0$. If $\lim f(x)/g(x)$, as x becomes infinite ($+\infty$, $-\infty$, or ∞), exists and is a finite number b, then $y = b$ is a horizontal asymptote. (Fig. 414.)

(*iv*) *Other asymptotes.* If $f(x) - mx - b$ approaches zero as x becomes infinite ($+\infty$, $-\infty$, or ∞), then the line $y = mx + b$ is an asymptote for

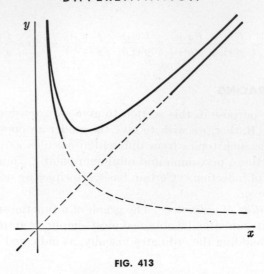

FIG. 413

the graph of $f(x)$. For the function $x + e^x$, for example, the line $y = x$ is an asymptote as $x \to -\infty$. (Fig. 415.)

(v) *Two factors*. Certain principles used for functions represented as sums have their applications to functions represented as products. The functions $e^{-ax} \sin bx$ and $e^{-ax} \cos bx$, useful in electrical theory, are good examples. (Fig. 416.)

Vanishing factors often determine the general shape of a curve in neighborhoods of points where they vanish. For example, the graph of

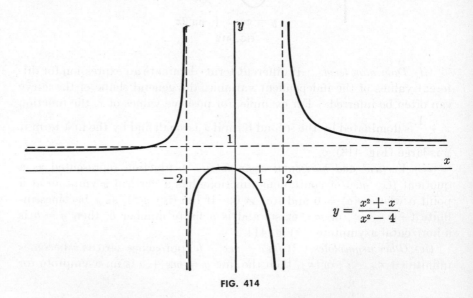

$$y = \frac{x^2 + x}{x^2 - 4}.$$

FIG. 414

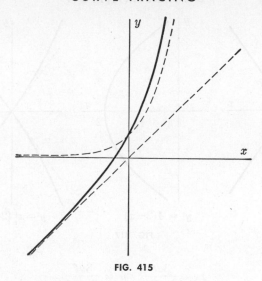

FIG. 415

$y^2 = x^2(2 - x)$ is approximated by that of $y^2 = 2x^2$ for x near 0 and by that of $y^2 = 4(2 - x)$ for x near 2.   (Fig. 417.)

A further aid in graphing an equation like that of Figure 417, of the form $y^2 = f(x)$, is graphing the function $f(x)$ itself to determine the values of x for which $f(x)$ is positive, zero, or negative, and hence for which y is double-valued, zero, or imaginary.   (Fig. 418.)

(vi) *Parametric equations.*   If $x = f(t)$ and $y = g(t)$, we recall two formulas:

$$(1) \qquad\qquad y' = \frac{dy}{dx} = \frac{g'(t)}{f'(t)};$$

$$(2) \qquad\qquad y'' = \frac{d^2y}{dx^2} = \frac{\dfrac{dy'}{dt}}{f'(t)}.$$

The folium of Descartes,

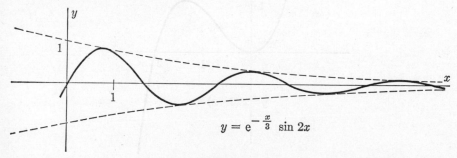

$$y = e^{-\frac{x}{3}} \sin 2x$$

FIG. 416

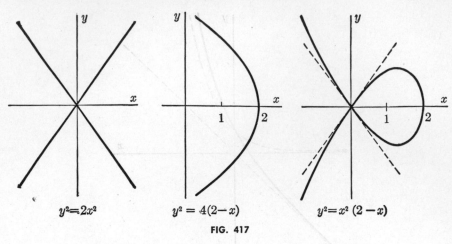

$$y^2 = 2x^2 \qquad y^2 = 4(2-x) \qquad y^2 = x^2(2-x)$$

FIG. 417

(3)
$$x = \frac{3at}{t^3 + 1}, \quad y = \frac{3at^2}{t^3 + 1},$$

is illustrated in Figure 419.   Since

(4)
$$\frac{dy}{dx} = \frac{t(t^3 - 2)}{2t^3 - 1},$$

horizontal tangents correspond to the values of t for which the numerator of (4) vanishes: $t = 0$ (the point $(0, 0)$) and $t = \sqrt[3]{2}$ (the point $(a\sqrt[3]{2}, a\sqrt[3]{4})$). Vertical tangents correspond to the values of t for which (4) becomes infinite: $t = \infty$ (the point $(0, 0)$) and $t = \sqrt[3]{\frac{1}{2}}$ (the point $(a\sqrt[3]{4}, a\sqrt[3]{2})$).

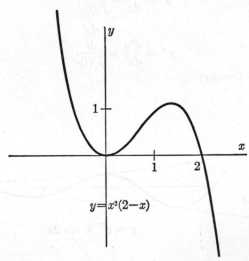

$$y = x^2(2-x)$$

FIG. 418

Since $x + y = 3at/(t^2 - t + 1)$, the line $x + y + a = 0$ is an asymptote (let $t \to -1$).

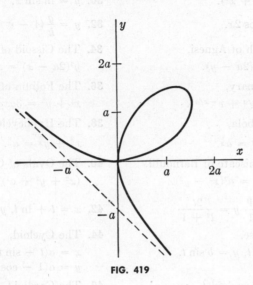

FIG. 419

419. EXERCISES

In Exercises 1-50, graph the equation, showing essential shape and asymptotic behavior.

1. $y = x^2(x^2 - 9)$.

2. $y = \dfrac{2}{x^2 + 1}$.

3. $y = \dfrac{x^2 - 4}{x^2 - 9}$.

4. $y = \dfrac{x^2 - 9}{x^2 - 4}$.

5. $y = x + \dfrac{4}{x}$.

6. $y = x^2 + \dfrac{2}{x}$.

7. $y = x + \dfrac{4}{x^2}$.

8. $y^2 = x^2(x^2 - 9)$.

9. $y^2 = \dfrac{x^2 - 4}{x^2 - 9}$.

10. $y^2 = \dfrac{x^2 - 9}{x^2 - 4}$.

11. $y^2 = (x - 1)(x - 2)^2(x - 3)^3$.

12. $y^2 = (x - 1)^3(x - 2)(x - 3)^2$.

13. $x^2 + xy + y^2 = 4$.

14. $x^2 + 4xy + y^2 = 4$.

15. $y = e^{-x^2}$.

16. $y = e^{1/x}$.

17. $y = xe^x$.

18. $y = x^2 e^{-x}$.

19. $y = xe^{-x^2}$.

20. $y = e^x - x$.

21. $y = \ln |x|$.

22. $y = x \ln x$.

23. $y = \dfrac{\ln x}{x}$.

24. $y = \dfrac{x}{\ln x}$.

25. $y = \dfrac{1}{x \ln x}$.

26. $y = x^2 \ln x$.

27. $y = x + \sin x$.

28. $y = \ln x \cdot e^{-x}$.

29. $y = \ln (1 + x^2)$.

30. $y = \ln \sin x$.

31. $y = e^{-x} \cos 2x$.

32. $y = \dfrac{g}{k} (1 - e^{-kx})$.

33. The Witch of Agnesi,
$x^2 y = 4a^2(2a - y)$.

34. The Cissoid of Diocles,
$y^2(2a - x) = x^3$.

35. The Catenary,
$y = \frac{1}{2}a(e^{x/a} + e^{-x/a})$.

36. The Folium of Descartes,
$x^3 + y^3 = 3axy$.

37. The Parabola,
$\pm x^{\frac{1}{2}} \pm y^{\frac{1}{2}} = a^{\frac{1}{2}}$.

38. The Hypocycloid,
$x^{\frac{2}{3}} + y^{\frac{2}{3}} = a^{\frac{2}{3}}$.

39. The Lemniscate of Bernoulli,
$(x^2 + y^2)^2 = a^2(x^2 - y^2)$.

40. The Ovals of Cassini,
$(x^2 + y^2 + a^2)^2 - 4a^2x^2 = c^4$.

41. $x = \dfrac{t^2 - 1}{t^2 + 1}$, $y = \dfrac{2t}{t^2 + 1}$.

42. $x = t + \ln t$, $y = t + e^t$.

43. The Ellipse,
$x = a \cos t$, $y = b \sin t$.

44. The Cycloid,
$x = a(t - \sin t)$,
$y = a(1 - \cos t)$.

45. The Hypocycloid,
$x = a \cos^3 t$, $y = a \sin^3 t$.

46. The Cardioid,
$x = a(2 \cos t - \cot 2t)$,
$y = a(2 \sin t - \sin 2t)$.

47. The Serpentine,
$x = a \cot t$, $y = b \sin t \cos t$.

48. The Witch of Agnesi,
$x = a \cot t$, $y = a \sin^2 t$.

49. The Hypocycloid of Three Cusps,
$x = 2a \cos t + a \cos 2t$
$y = 2a \sin t - a \sin 2t$.

50. The Hyperbolic Spiral,
$x = \dfrac{a}{t} \cos t$, $y = \dfrac{a}{t} \sin t$.

51. Graph $f(x) \equiv \dfrac{1}{1 + e^{-1/x}}$, and show that $f(0+) = 1$ and $f(0-) = f'(0+)$
$= f'(0-) = 0$.

52. Graph $f(x) \equiv e^{-1/x^2}$, $x \neq 0$, $f(0) \equiv 0$. Prove that $\lim\limits_{x \to 0} x^{-n}f(x) = 0$ for
every positive integer n, and hence show that $f(x)$ has everywhere continuous
derivatives of all orders, all of which vanish at $x = 0$. (Cf. Example 2, § 805,
for a use of this function as a counterexample.)

★53. Show by a graph that a function $f(x)$ exists having the following properties: (*i*) $f(x)$ is strictly increasing, (*ii*) $f'(x)$ exists for every real x, (*iii*) $f(x)$
is bounded above, (*iv*) the statement $\lim\limits_{x \to +\infty} f'(x) = 0$ is false.

★54. Show that the function $f(x) \equiv x/(1 + e^{1/x})$, $x \neq 0$, $f(0) \equiv 0$, is everywhere continuous, and has unequal right-hand and left-hand derivatives at
$x = 0$.

★55. Graph $(y - x^2)^2 = x^5$, with particular attention to a neighborhood of
the origin.

★420. WITHOUT LOSS OF GENERALITY

One of the standard techniques of an analytic proof is to reduce a general proposition to a special case "without loss of generality." This means that it is possible to construct a proof of the general theorem on the assumption that the special form of that theorem is true. Following the establishment of this inference, proof of the special case implies proof of the general proposition. This device was used in two proofs given in § 204: in the proof that the limit of the product of two sequences is the product of their limits (Theorem VIII) we saw that it could be assumed without loss of generality that one of the limits is zero; in the proof that the limit of the quotient of two sequences is the quotient of their limits (Theorem IX) we assumed without loss of generality that the numerators were identically equal to unity. Another instance of the same principle is the proof of the Law of the Mean (§ 405) by reducing it to the special case called Rolle's Theorem.

In the following Exercises are a few problems in showing that the special implies the general.

★421. EXERCISES

In Exercises 1-10, prove the stated proposition on the basis of the assumption given in the braces { }.

★1. If m and n are relatively prime positive integers, there exist positive integers x and y such that $mx - ny = 1$. {If m and n are relatively prime positive integers, there exist positive integers x and y such that $|mx - ny| = 1$.}

★2. If m and n are nonzero integers and if d is their greatest common divisor, then there exist integers x and y such that $mx + ny = d$. {If m and n are relatively prime positive integers, there exist integers x and y such that $mx + ny = 1$.}

★3. If I_1, I_2, $\cdots I_n$ are open intervals and if I is the set of all x such that x is a member of every I_k, $k = 1, 2, \cdots, n$, then I is either empty or an open interval. {$n = 2$.}

★4. The Schwarz inequality (Ex. 43, § 107). {All of the numbers $a_1, \cdots, a_n, b_1, \cdots, b_n$ are positive.}

★5. $\dfrac{\sin px}{x} < p$, for $p > 0$ and $x > 0$. {$p = 1$.}

★6. $\lim\limits_{x\to 0+} x^p \ln x = 0$, $p > 0$. {$p = 1$.}

★7. Any bounded sequence $\{a_n\}$ that does not converge to a contains a subsequence $\{a_{n_k}\}$ converging to some $b \neq a$. {$|a_n - a| \geq \epsilon > 0$ for all n.}

★8. The trigonometric functions are continuous where they are defined. {$\sin x$ and $\cos x$ are continuous at $x = 0$.}

★9. If $f'(x) \leq g'(x)$ for $a \leq x \leq b$, then $f(x) - f(a) \leq g(x) - g(a)$. {$f(x) = 0$ for $a \leq x \leq b$.}

★10. Theorem III, § 213. {$a = 0, b = 1$.}

★**11.** Show that in proving that if $f(x)$ and $f'(x)$ are defined in a neighborhood of $x = a$ and if $f''(a)$ exists, then

$$(2) \qquad f''(a) = \lim_{h \to 0} \frac{f(a + h) + f(a - h) - 2f(a)}{h^2},$$

it may be assumed without loss of generality, that $a = 0$, $f(0) = 0$, $f'(0) = 0$, and $f''(0) = 0$. Hence prove (2). *Hints:* To show that one may assume $f(0) = 0$, define a new function $g(x) \equiv f(x) - f(0)$. To show that one may assume $f'(0) = 0$, define a new function $g(x) \equiv f(x) - f'(0) \cdot x$. (Cf. Ex. 36, § 412.)

5

Integration

~~~~~~~~~~~~~~~~~~~~~~~~~~~~~~~~~~~~~~

501. THE DEFINITE INTEGRAL

It will be assumed that the reader is already familiar with some of the properties and many of the applications of the definite integral. It is our purpose in this section to give a precise definition and a few of the simpler properties of the integral, with analytical proofs that do not depend on the persuasion of a geometrical picture.

We shall be dealing in the main with a fixed closed interval $[a, b]$. On such an interval a finite set of points $a = a_0 < a_1 < a_2 < \cdots < a_n = b$ is called a **net,** and denoted $\mathfrak{N}$. (Cf. Fig. 501.) The closed intervals $[a_{i-1}, a_i]$, $i = 1, 2, \cdots, n$, are called the **subintervals** of $[a, b]$ for the net $\mathfrak{N}$, and their lengths are denoted $\Delta x_i \equiv a_i - a_{i-1}$, $i = 1, 2, \cdots, n$. The maximum length of the subintervals is called the **norm** of the net $\mathfrak{N}$ and denoted $|\mathfrak{N}|$: $|\mathfrak{N}| \equiv \max \Delta x_i$, $i = 1, 2, \cdots, n$.

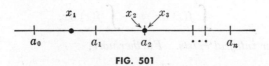

FIG. 501

Let $f(x)$ be defined over the closed interval $[a, b]$, and (for a net $\mathfrak{N}$) let x_i be an arbitrary point of the ith subinterval $(a_{i-1} \leqq x_i \leqq a_i)$, $i = 1, 2, \cdots, n$ (Fig. 501). Consider the sum

$$(1) \qquad \sum_{i=1}^{n} f(x_i) \Delta x_i = f(x_1) \Delta x_1 + \cdots + f(x_n) \Delta x_n.$$

The definite integral of the function $f(x)$ is defined as the limit of sums of the form (1). We shall first explain what is meant by such a limit.

Definition I. *The limit statement*

$$(2) \qquad \lim_{|\mathfrak{N}| \to 0} \sum_{i=1}^{n} f(x_i) \Delta x_i = I,$$

where I is a (finite) number, means that corresponding to $\epsilon > 0$ there exists $\delta > 0$ such that for any net $\mathfrak{N}$ of norm less than δ and any choice of points x_i such that $a_{i-1} \leqq x_i \leqq a_i$, $i = 1, 2, \cdots , n$, the inequality

$$(3) \qquad \left| \sum_{i=1}^{n} f(x_i) \, \Delta x_i - I \right| < \epsilon$$

holds.

NOTE 1. Closely though Definition I may resemble the definition of the limit of a single-valued function of a real variable as the independent variable approaches 0, the type of limit just introduced should be recognized as a new concept. Although, for a given net $\mathfrak{N}$ and points $x_1, x_2, \cdots , x_n$, the sum (1) is uniquely determined, the limit (2) is formed with respect to the norm alone as the independent variable. For a given positive number $p < b - a$ there are infinitely many nets $\mathfrak{N}$ of norm $|\mathfrak{N}|$ equal to p, and for each such net there are infinitely many choices of the points $x_1, x_2, \cdots , x_n$. In other words, as a function of the independent variable $|\mathfrak{N}|$, the sum (1) is 'an infinitely many valued function,† and it is the limit of such a function that is prescribed in Definition I. It should not be forgotten, however, that each sum (1) appearing in the inequality (3) is simply a number obtained by adding together a finite number of terms.

Definition II. *A function $f(x)$, defined on $[a, b]$, is **integrable**‡ there if and only if the limit (2) exists (and is finite). In case the limit exists it is called the **definite integral**‡ of the function, and denoted*

$$(4) \qquad \int_a^b f(x) \, dx \equiv \lim_{\cdot |\mathfrak{N}| \to 0} \sum_{i=1}^{n} f(x_i) \, \Delta x_i.$$

Definition III. *If $b < a$,*

$$(5) \qquad \int_a^b f(x) \, dx \equiv - \int_b^a f(x) \, dx,$$

in case the latter integral exists. Furthermore,

$$(6) \qquad \int_a^a f(x) \, dx \equiv 0.$$

Certain questions naturally come to mind. Does the limit (2) always

---

† The expression "infinitely many valued" should be interpreted here to mean "possibly infinitely many valued" since for any constant function $f(x)$, the sums (1) can have only one value (cf. Theorem VII). It can be shown that for any function $f(x)$ that is not constant on $[a, b]$, and for any positive number δ less than half the length of the interval $[a, b]$, the sum (1), as a function of $|\mathfrak{N}|$, is strictly infinitely many valued for the particular value $|\mathfrak{N}| = \delta$.

‡ The terms *Riemann integrable* and *Riemann integral* are also used, especially if it is important to distinguish the integral defined in this section from some other type, such as the Riemann-Stieltjes integral (§ 517) or the Lebesgue integral (not discussed in this book). When a definite integral is to be distinguished from an improper integral (§§ 511-515), it is customary to call it a *proper integral*.

exist? If it does not always exist, under what circumstances does it exist? When it does exist is it unique?

Let us remark first that the limit (2) *never* exists for unbounded functions. In other words, *every integrable function is bounded.* To see this, let $\mathfrak{N}$ be an arbitrary net and let $f(x)$ be unbounded in the kth subinterval $[a_{k-1}, a_k]$. Then whatever may be the choice of points x_i for $i \neq k$, the point x_k can be picked so that the sum (1) is numerically larger than any preassigned quantity.

On the other hand, not all bounded functions are integrable. For example, the function of Example 6, § 201, which is 1 on the rational numbers from 0 to 1 and 0 on the irrational numbers from 0 to 1, is not integrable on $[0, 1]$. For, no matter how small the norm of a net $\mathfrak{N}$ may be, every subinterval contains both rational and irrational points $((v)$, § 112, and Ex. 2, § 113) and the sums (1) can be made to have either the extreme value 1 (if every point x_i is chosen to be rational) or the extreme value 0 (if every point x_i is chosen to be irrational). The limit (2), then, cannot exist for this function (let $\epsilon \equiv \frac{1}{2}$).

One answer to the question of integrability lies in the concept of *continuity.* The function just considered, which is not integrable, is *nowhere* continuous. At the opposite extreme is a function which is *everywhere* continuous (on a closed interval). We shall see that such a function is *always* integrable (Theorem VIII). Between these two extremes are bounded functions which are somewhere but not everywhere continuous. It will be seen that such functions are certainly integrable if they have only *finitely* many discontinuities (Theorem IX), that they *may* be integrable even with *infinitely* many discontinuities (Example 2, § 502), and that a *criterion* for integrability lies in the intriguing concept of *continuity almost everywhere* (Ex. 54, § 503).

We proceed now to the establishment of some of the simpler properties of the definite integral.

Theorem I. *If* $\lim\limits_{|\mathfrak{N}|\to 0} \sum\limits_{i=1}^{n} f(x_i) \, \Delta x_i$ *exists, the limit is unique.*

Proof. Assume that

$$\lim_{|\mathfrak{N}|\to 0} \sum_{i=1}^{n} f(x_i) \, \Delta x_i = I \quad \text{and} \quad \lim_{|\mathfrak{N}|\to 0} \sum_{i=1}^{n} f(x_i) \, \Delta x_i = J,$$

where $I > J$, and let $\epsilon \equiv \frac{1}{2}(I - J)$. Then there exists a positive number δ so small that for any net $\mathfrak{N}$ of norm less than δ, and for any choice of points $x_1, x_2, \cdots, x_n$, the following inequalities hold simultaneously:

$$I - \epsilon < \sum_{i=1}^{n} f(x_i) \, \Delta x_i < J + \epsilon.$$

But this implies $I - \epsilon < J + \epsilon$, or $\epsilon > \frac{1}{2}(I - J)$. (Contradiction.)

Theorem II. *If $f(x)$ and $g(x)$ are integrable on $[a,b]$, and if $f(x) \leqq g(x)$ there, then*

$$\int_a^b f(x) \, dx \leqq \int_a^b g(x) \, dx.$$

Proof. Let $I \equiv \int_a^b f(x) \, dx$ and $J \equiv \int_a^b g(x) \, dx$, assume $I > J$, and let $\epsilon \equiv \frac{1}{2}(I - J)$. Then there exists a positive number δ so small that for any net $\mathfrak{N}$ of norm less than δ and any choice of points $x_1, x_2, \cdots, x_n$, the following inequalities hold simultaneously:

$$\sum_{i=1}^n g(x_i) \, \Delta x_i < J + \epsilon = I - \epsilon < \sum_{i=1}^n f(x_i) \, \Delta x_i.$$

But this implies an inequality inconsistent with the assumed inequality $f(x) \leqq g(x)$.

Theorem III. *If $f(x)$ is integrable on $[a, b]$ and if k is a constant, then $k \, f(x)$ is integrable on $[a, b]$ and*

$$(7) \qquad \int_a^b k \, f(x) \, dx = k \int_a^b f(x) \, dx.$$

Proof. If $k = 0$, the proof is trivial. If $k \neq 0$, and if $\epsilon > 0$ is given, let $\delta > 0$ be such that $|\mathfrak{N}| < \delta$ implies $\left| \sum_{i=1}^n f(x_i) \, \Delta x_i - I \right| < \epsilon/|k|$, and therefore

$$\left| \sum_{i=1}^n k \, f(x_i) \, \Delta x_i - k \, I \right| < |k| \epsilon/|k| = \epsilon.$$

Theorem IV. *If $f(x)$ and $g(x)$ are integrable on $[a, b]$, then so are their sum and difference, and*

$$(8) \qquad \int_a^b [f(x) \pm g(x)] \, dx = \int_a^b f(x) \, dx \pm \int_a^b g(x) \, dx.$$

Proof. Let $I \equiv \int_a^b f(x) \, dx$ and $J \equiv \int_a^b g(x) \, dx$, and if $\epsilon > 0$ is given, let $\delta > 0$ be such that $|\mathfrak{N}| < \delta$ implies simultaneously the inequalities

$$\left| \sum_{i=1}^n f(x_i) \, \Delta x_i - I \right| < \tfrac{1}{2}\epsilon, \quad \left| \sum_{i=1}^n g(x_i) \, \Delta x_i - J \right| < \tfrac{1}{2}\epsilon,$$

and hence, by the triangle inequality,

$$\left| \sum_{i=1}^n [f(x_i) \pm g(x_i)] \, \Delta x_i - (I \pm J) \right|$$

$$\leqq \left| \sum_{i=1}^n f(x_i) \, \Delta x_i - I \right| + \left| \sum_{i=1}^n g(x_i) \, \Delta x_i - J \right| < \epsilon.$$

Theorem V. *If $a < b < c$, and if $f(x)$ is integrable on the intervals $[a, b]$ and $[b, c]$, then it is integrable on the interval $[a, c]$ and*

$$(9) \qquad \int_a^c f(x) \, dx = \int_a^b f(x) \, dx + \int_b^c f(x) \, dx.$$

Proof. Let $|f(x)| < K$ for $a \leqq x \leqq c$, let

$$I \equiv \int_a^b f(x) \, dx \text{ and } J \equiv \int_b^c f(x) \, dx,$$

and let $\epsilon > 0$ be given. Let δ be a positive number less than $\epsilon/4K$ and so small that for any net on $[a, b]$ or $[b, c]$ with norm less than δ any sum of the form (1) differs from I or J, respectively, by less than $\frac{1}{4}\epsilon$. We shall show that for $[a, c]$, $|\mathfrak{N}| < \delta$ implies $\left| \sum_{i=1}^n f(x_i) \, \Delta x_i - (I + J) \right| < \epsilon$. Accordingly, for such a net $\mathfrak{N}$ let $a_{k-1} < b \leqq a_k$ (the kth subinterval is the first containing the point b), and write the sum (1) in the form

$$S \equiv \sum_{i=1}^{k-1} f(x_i) \, \Delta x_i + f(x_k) \, \Delta x_k + \sum_{i=k+1}^n f(x_i) \, \Delta x_i.$$

The following sum,

$$S' \equiv \left[\sum_{i=1}^{k-1} f(x_i) \, \Delta x_i + f(b)(b - a_{k-1}) \right] + \left[f(b)(a_k - b) + \sum_{i=k+1}^n f(x_i) \, \Delta x_i \right],$$

can be considered as made up of two parts, which approximate I and J, each by less than $\frac{1}{4}\epsilon$. Thus $|S' - (I + J)| < \frac{1}{2}\epsilon$. On the other hand, $|S - S'| = |f(x_k) - f(b)| \, \Delta x_k < 2K(\epsilon/4K) = \frac{1}{2}\epsilon$. Therefore,

$$|S - (I + J)| \leqq |S - S'| + |S' - (I + J)| < \frac{1}{2}\epsilon + \frac{1}{2}\epsilon = \epsilon.$$

NOTE 2. By virtue of Definition III, the relation (9) is universally true whenever the three integrals exist, whatever may be the order relation between the numbers a, b, and c. For example, if $c < a < b$, then

$$\int_c^b f(x) \, dx = \int_c^a f(x) \, dx + \int_a^b f(x) \, dx.$$

Hence

$$\int_a^c f(x) \, dx = - \int_c^a f(x) \, dx = \int_a^b f(x) \, dx - \int_c^b f(x) \, dx = \int_a^b f(x) \, dx + \int_b^c f(x) \, dx.$$

By mathematical induction, the relation (9) can be extended to an arbitrary number of terms:

$$(10) \qquad \int_{a_0}^{a_n} f(x) \, dx = \sum_{i=1}^n \int_{a_{i-1}}^{a_i} f(x) \, dx,$$

where $a_0, a_1, \cdots, a_n$ are any $n + 1$ real numbers, and where every integral of (10) is assumed to exist. (The student should satisfy himself regarding (9), by considering other order relations between a, b, and c, including possible equalities of some of these letters, and he should give the details of the proof of (10). (Cf. Ex. 1, § 503.)

Theorem VI. *If the values of a function defined on a closed interval are changed at a finite number of points of the interval, neither the integrability nor the value of the integral is affected.*

Proof. Thanks to mathematical induction, the proof can (and will) be reduced to showing the following: If $f(x)$ is integrable on $[a, b]$, with integral I, and if $g(x)$ is defined on $[a, b]$ and equal to $f(x)$ at every point of $[a, b]$ except for one point c, then $g(x)$ is integrable on $[a, b]$ with integral I.

For any net $\mathfrak{N}$, the terms of the sum $\sum_{i=1}^{n} g(x_i)\,\Delta x_i$ must be identical with the terms of the sum $\sum_{i=1}^{n} f(x_i)\,\Delta x_i$ with the exception of at most two terms (in case $x_{i-1} = x_i = c$ for some i). Therefore

$$\left| \sum_{i=1}^{n} g(x_i)\,\Delta x_i - \sum_{i=1}^{n} f(x_i)\,\Delta x_i \right| \leq 2(|f(c)| + |g(c)|) \cdot |\mathfrak{N}|.$$

Thus, for a given $\epsilon > 0$, let δ be a positive number less than

$$\epsilon/4(|f(c)| + |g(c)|)$$

and so small that $|\mathfrak{N}| < \delta$ implies $\left| \sum_{i=1}^{n} f(x_i)\,\Delta x_i - I \right| < \tfrac{1}{2}\epsilon$. Then $|\mathfrak{N}| < \delta$ implies

$$\left| \sum_{i=1}^{n} g(x_i)\,\Delta x_i - I \right| \leq \left| \sum_{i=1}^{n} g(x_i)\,\Delta x_i - f(x_i)\,\Delta x_i \right|$$

$$+ \left| \sum_{i=1}^{n} f(x_i)\,\Delta x_i - I \right| < \tfrac{1}{2}\epsilon + \tfrac{1}{2}\epsilon = \epsilon.$$

NOTE 3. Theorem VI makes it possible to define integrability and integral for a function which is defined on a closed interval except for a finite number of points. This is done by assigning values to the function at the exceptional points in any manner whatsoever. Theorem VI assures us that the result of applying Definition II is independent of the values assigned. Since the assignment of values does not affect the value of the integral, where it exists, we shall assume that the definition is extended to include such functions even though they remain undefined at the exceptional points.

Theorem VII. *If $f(x)$ is constant, $f(x) \equiv k$, on the interval $[a, b]$, then $f(x)$ is integrable there and*

$$\int_{a}^{b} f(x)\,dx = k(b - a).$$

Proof. For any net $\mathfrak{N}$, $\sum_{i=1}^{n} f(x_i)\,\Delta x_i = k \sum_{i=1}^{n} x_i = k(b - a)$.

For the sake of convenience and accessibility we state now the three best-known sufficient conditions for integrability (the first being a special case of the second). The proofs are given in § 502 and Exercise 33, § 503.

Theorem VIII.   *A function continuous on a closed interval is integrable there.*

Theorem IX.   *A function defined and bounded on a closed interval and continuous there except for a finite number of points is integrable there.*

Theorem X.   *A function defined and monotonic on a closed interval is integrable there.*

Example.   Prove that $\int_0^b x \, dx = \frac{1}{2}b^2$ if $b > 0$, and, more generally, that

$$\int_a^b x \, dx = \frac{1}{2}(b^2 - a^2),$$

where a and b are any real numbers.

Solution.   Let us first observe that since the function $f(x) \equiv x$ is everywhere continuous the integrals exist.   The problem is one of *evaluation.*   To evaluate $\int_0^b x \, dx$, where $b > 0$, we form a particular simple net by means of the points

$$a_0 \equiv 0, \; a_1 \equiv b/n, \; \cdots, \; a_i \equiv ib/n, \; \cdots, \; a_n \equiv nb/n = b,$$

and choose $x_i \equiv a_i, i = 1, 2, \cdots, n$.   The sum $\sum_{i=1}^{n} f(x_i) \, \Delta x_i$ becomes

$$\left[\frac{b}{n} + \frac{2b}{n} + \cdots + \frac{nb}{n} \right] \cdot \frac{b}{n} = \frac{b^2}{n^2} [1 + 2 + \cdots + n] = \frac{b^2}{n^2} \cdot \frac{n(n+1)}{2},$$

the last equality having been obtained in Exercise 12, § 107.   Therefore $\int_0^b x \, dx = \lim_{n \to +\infty} \frac{1}{2}b^2 \frac{n+1}{n} = \frac{1}{2}b^2$, as stated.   It is left to the student to show, first, that $\int_0^b x \, dx = \frac{1}{2}b^2$ if $b \leq 0$ (cf. Exs. 7-8, § 503) and then, by using formula (9) of Theorem V and formula (5) of Definition III, that $\int_a^b x \, dx = \frac{1}{2}(b^2 - a^2)$.

Other evaluations of this type are given in Exercises 15-21, § 503.

In conclusion we present a useful basic theorem (give the proof in Ex. 5, § 503).

Theorem XI.   First Mean Value Theorem for Integrals.   *If $f(x)$ is continuous on $[a, b]$ there exists a point ξ such that $a < \xi < b$ and*

$$(11) \qquad \int_a^b f(x) \, dx = f(\xi) \cdot (b - a).$$

For other mean value theorems for integrals, see Exercise 6, § 503, Exercise 14, § 506, and Exercises 27-29, § 518.   Also see Exercise 9, § 506.

At this point, the student may wish to do a few of the Exercises of § 503. Some that are suitable for performance now are Exercises 1-30.

★502. MORE INTEGRATION THEOREMS

Definition. A **step-function** is a function, defined on a closed interval $[a, b]$, that is constant in the interior of each subinterval of some net on $[a, b]$. (Fig. 502.)

Notation

Step-function: $\sigma(x)$ or $\tau(x)$.

Net: $\mathfrak{M} : a = \alpha_0 < \alpha_1 < \cdots < \alpha_m = b$.

Constant values: σ_i or τ_i, $i = 1, \cdots, m$.

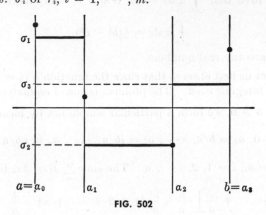

FIG. 502

Theorem I. *Any step-function is integrable and, with the preceding notation,* $\displaystyle\int_a^b \sigma(x) \, dx = \sum_{i=1}^m \sigma_i(\alpha_i - \alpha_{i-1})$.

Proof. We need prove this only for the case $m = 1$, since Theorem V, § 501, and mathematical induction will extend this special case to the general result. Accordingly, let $\sigma(x)$ be identically equal to a constant k for $a < x < b$, and redefine $\sigma(x)$, if necessary, at the end-points of the interval so that $\sigma(x) \equiv k$ for $a \leq x \leq b$. Since the new function is integrable with integral $k(b - a)$ (Theorem VII, § 501), the original step-function is also integrable with the same integral (Theorem VI, § 501), and the proof is complete.

The purpose of introducing step-functions in our discussion of the definite integral is to make use of the fact established in the following theorem that a function is integrable if and only if it can be appropriately "squeezed" between two step-functions. (Cf. Fig. 503.)

Theorem II. *A function* $f(x)$, *defined on a closed interval* $[a, b]$, *is integrable there if and only if, corresponding to an arbitrary positive number* ϵ, *there exist step-functions* $\sigma(x)$ *and* $\tau(x)$ *such that*

$$(1) \qquad\qquad\qquad \sigma(x) \leq f(x) \leq \tau(x),$$

for $a \leq x \leq b$, *and*

(2)
$$\int_a^b [\tau(x) - \sigma(x)]\, dx < \epsilon.$$

Proof. We first establish the "if" part by assuming, for $\epsilon > 0$, the existence of step-functions $\sigma(x)$ and $\tau(x)$ satisfying (1) and (2). Let us observe initially that for *any* step-functions satisfying (1),

$$\int_a^b \sigma(x)\, dx \leq \int_a^b \tau(x)\, dx$$

(Theorem II, § 501), so that the *least upper bound* I of the integrals $\int_a^b \sigma(x)\, dx$, for *all* $\sigma(x) \leq f(x)$, and the *greatest lower bound* J of the integrals $\int_a^b \tau(x)\, dx$, for *all* $\tau(x) \geq f(x)$, both exist and are finite, and $I \leq J$ (supply the details). Because of (2) and the arbitrariness of $\epsilon > 0$, integrals of the form $\int_a^b \sigma(x)\, dx$ and $\int_a^b \tau(x)\, dx$ can be found arbitrarily close to each other, so that I cannot be *less* than J, and therefore $I = J$. Now let $\epsilon > 0$ be given, and choose step-functions $\sigma(x)$ and $\tau(x)$ satisfying (1) and (2) and such that

$$\int_a^b \sigma(x)\, dx > I - \tfrac{1}{2}\epsilon \text{ and } \int_a^b \tau(x)\, dx < J + \tfrac{1}{2}\epsilon.$$

Then choose $\delta > 0$ so that $|\mathfrak{N}| < \delta$ implies

$$\sum_{i=1}^n \sigma(x_i)\, \Delta x_i > \int_a^b \sigma(x)\, dx - \tfrac{1}{2}\epsilon,$$

$$\sum_{i=1}^n \tau(x_i)\, \Delta x_i < \int_a^b \tau(x)\, dx + \tfrac{1}{2}\epsilon.$$

For any such net $\mathfrak{N}$,

$$I - \epsilon < \sum_{i=1}^n \sigma(x_i)\, \Delta x_i \leq \sum_{i=1}^n f(x_i)\, \Delta x_i \leq \sum_{i=1}^n \tau(x_i)\, \Delta x_i < I + \epsilon.$$

Therefore (Definition II, § 501), $f(x)$ is integrable on $[a, b]$, and

$$\int_a^b f(x)\, dx = I = J.$$

We now prove the "only if" part by assuming that $f(x)$ is integrable on $[a, b]$, with integral $I \equiv \int_a^b f(x)\, dx$, and letting $\epsilon > 0$ be given. Choose a net $\mathfrak{N}$, to be held fixed, of such a small norm that

$$I - \tfrac{1}{3}\epsilon < \sum_{i=1}^n f(x_i)\, \Delta x_i < I + \tfrac{1}{3}\epsilon,$$

for all x_i in $[a_{i-1}, a_i]$, $i = 1, 2, \cdots, n$. For each $i = 1, 2, \cdots, n$, let σ_i be the greatest lower bound of $f(x)$ for $a_{i-1} \leq x \leq a_i$ ($f(x)$ is bounded since it is integrable) and let τ_i be the least upper bound of $f(x)$ for $a_{i-1} \leq x \leq a_i$.

Then (give the details in Ex. 32, § 503)

$$I - \tfrac{1}{3}\epsilon \leqq \sum_{i=1}^{n} \sigma_i \, \Delta x_i \leqq \sum_{i=1}^{n} f(x_i) \, \Delta x_i \leqq \sum_{i=1}^{n} \tau_i \, \Delta x_i \leqq I + \tfrac{1}{3}\epsilon,$$

and if the step-functions $\sigma(x)$ and $\tau(x)$ are defined to have the values σ_i and τ_i, respectively, for $a_{i-1} < x < a_i$, $i = 1, 2, \cdots, n$, and the values $f(a_i)$ for $x = a_i$, $i = 0, 1, \cdots, n$, then $\sigma(x) \leqq f(x) \leqq \tau(x)$ and

$$\int_a^b [\tau(x) - \sigma(x)] \, dx = \sum_{i=1}^{n} (\tau_i - \sigma_i) \, \Delta x_i \leqq \tfrac{2}{3}\epsilon < \epsilon.$$

NOTE. The definite integral $\int_a^b f(x) \, dx$ is defined as the limit of sums of

the form $\sum_{i=1}^{n} f(x_i) \, \Delta x_i$. If, for a given net $\mathfrak{N}$ and points x_i from the subinterval $[a_{i-1}, a_i]$, $i = 1, 2, \cdots, n$, a step-function $\sigma(x)$ is defined to have the values $f(x_i)$ for $a_{i-1} < x < a_i$, $i = 1, 2, \cdots, n$, and arbitrary values at the points a_i, $i = 0, 1, \cdots, n$ (cf. Fig. 503), then $\sum_{i=1}^{n} f(x_i) \, \Delta x_i = \int_a^b \sigma(x) \, dx$, and the definite integral of $f(x)$ can be thought of as the limit of the definite integrals of such "approximating" step-functions:

$$\int_a^b f(x) \, dx = \lim_{|\mathfrak{N}| \to 0} \int_a^b \sigma(x) \, dx.$$

With the aid of the theorem just established it is easy to prove that *any function continuous on a closed interval is integrable there:*

Proof of Theorem VIII, § 501. Let $f(x)$ be continuous on the closed interval $[a, b]$. Then $f(x)$ is uniformly continuous there (Theorem II, § 307), and therefore, if ϵ is any positive number there exists a positive number δ such that $|x' - x''| < \delta$ implies $|f(x') - f(x'')| < \epsilon/(b - a)$. Let $\mathfrak{N}$ be any net of norm less than δ, and let σ_i and τ_i, for $i = 1, 2, \cdots, n$, be defined as the minimum and maximum values, respectively, of $f(x)$ on the subinterval $[a_{i-1}, a_i]$. If $x_i{}'$ and $x_i{}''$ are points of $[a_{i-1}, a_i]$ such that

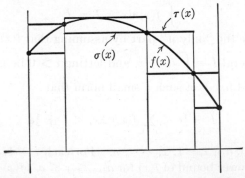

FIG. 503

$f(x_i') = \sigma_i$ and $f(x_i'') = \tau_i$, $i = 1, 2, \cdots, n$, and if the step-functions $\sigma(x)$ and $\tau(x)$ are defined to have the values σ_i and τ_i, respectively, for $a_{i-1} < x < a_i$, $i = 1, 2, \cdots, n$, and the values $f(a_i)$ for $x = a_i$, $i = 0, 1, \cdots, n$ (see Fig. 503), then $\sigma(x) \leq f(x) \leq \tau(x)$ and

$$\int_a^b [\tau(x) - \sigma(x)]\, dx = \sum_{i=1}^n (\tau_i - \sigma_i)\, \Delta x_i$$

$$= \sum_{i=1}^n |f(x_i') - f(x_i'')|\, \Delta x_i < \frac{\epsilon}{b-a} \sum_{i=1}^n \Delta x_i = \epsilon.$$

We generalize the theorem just proved, to permit a finite number of discontinuities:

Proof of Theorem IX, § 501. Thanks to Theorem V, § 501, and mathematical induction we need prove this only for the case of a function $f(x)$ that is defined and bounded on a closed interval and continuous in the interior. Because of the theorem just established, this special case is a simple consequence of the following theorem.

Theorem III. *If $f(x)$ is bounded on $[a, b]$ and integrable on every $[c, d]$, where $a < c < d < b$, then $f(x)$ is integrable on $[a, b]$.*

Proof. If $|f(x)| < K$ for $a \leq x \leq b$, and if $\epsilon > 0$, let $0 < \eta < \epsilon/8K$. Construct step-functions $\sigma(x)$ and $\tau(x)$ such that $\sigma(x) = -K$ and $\tau(x) = K$

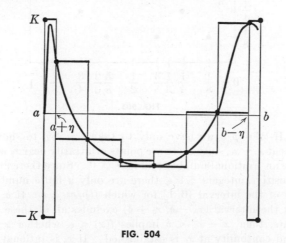

FIG. 504

on the intervals $[a, a + \eta)$ and $(b - \eta, b]$ (see Fig. 504), and such that for the closed interval $[a + \eta, b - \eta]$, $\sigma(x) \leq f(x) \leq \tau(x)$ and

$$\int_{a+\eta}^{b-\eta} [\tau(x) - \sigma(x)]\, dx < \tfrac{1}{2}\epsilon$$

(see Theorem II). Then for the interval $[a, b]$, $\sigma(x) \leq f(x) \leq \tau(x)$ and

$$\int_a^b [\tau(x) - \sigma(x)]\, dx < 2K\eta + \tfrac{1}{2}\epsilon + 2K\eta < \epsilon.$$

Example 1. The function $\sin \dfrac{1}{x}$ (whether or however it is defined at $x = 0$) is integrable on the interval $[0, 1]$.

Example 2. Let $f(x)$ be a function defined on $[0, 1]$ as follows: If x is irrational let $f(x) \equiv 0$; if x is a positive rational number equal to p/q, where p and q are relatively prime positive integers (cf. Ex. 23, § 107), let $f(x) \equiv 1/q$; let $f(0) \equiv 1$. (See Fig. 505.) Prove that $f(x)$ is continuous at every irrational point of $[0, 1]$ and discontinuous with a removable discontinuity at every rational point of $[0, 1]$. Prove that in spite of having infinitely many discontinuities $f(x)$ is integrable on $[0, 1]$. Show, in fact, that $\displaystyle\int_0^1 f(x)\, dx = 0$.

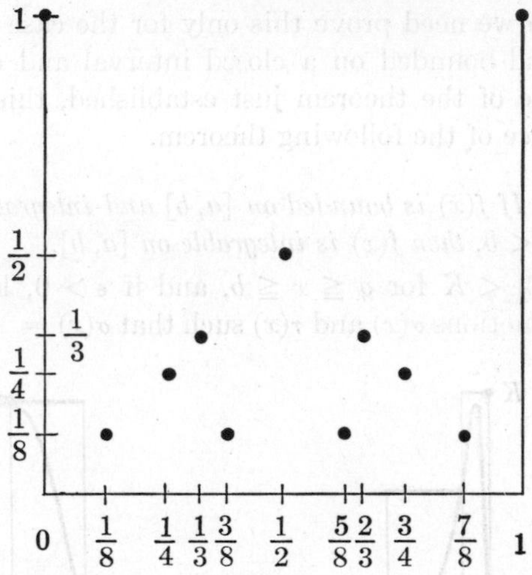

FIG. 505

Solution. If $x_0 = p/q$ we have only to take $\epsilon = 1/q$ to show that $f(x)$ is discontinuous at $x = x_0$, since there are points arbitrarily near x_0 where $f(x) = 0$. Now let x_0 be an irrational number and let $\epsilon > 0$. Since there are only a finite number of positive integers $\leqq 1/\epsilon$, there are only a finite number of rational numbers p/q of the interval $[0, 1]$ for which $f(p/q) \geqq \epsilon$. If $\delta > 0$ is chosen so small that the interval $(x_0 - \delta, x_0 + \delta)$ excludes all of these finitely many rational points, then $|x - x_0| < \delta$ implies $f(x) < \epsilon$, whether x is rational or irrational, and continuity at x_0 is established. If x_0 is rational and if $f(x_0)$ is redefined to be 0, continuity at x_0 is established by the same argument. Finally, if $\epsilon > 0$, since $f(x) \geqq 0$ all that remains to be shown is the existence of a step-function $\tau(x) \geqq f(x)$ such that $\displaystyle\int_0^1 \tau(x)\, dx < \epsilon$. Let $x_1, x_2, \cdots, x_n$ be the rational points of $[0, 1]$ such that $f(x_i) \geqq \frac{1}{2}\epsilon$, $i = 1, 2, \cdots, n$, and let I_i be a neighborhood of x_i of length $< \epsilon/2n$, $i = 1, 2, \cdots, n$. Define $\tau(x)$ to be 1 on all of the intervals $I_1, I_2, \cdots, I_n$ and $\frac{1}{2}\epsilon$ on the remaining points of $[0, 1]$. Then $\displaystyle\int_0^1 \tau(x)\, dx$ can be split into two parts, each $< \frac{1}{2}\epsilon$.

503. EXERCISES

1. Extend Theorems IV and V, § 501, to an arbitrary finite number of terms, and Theorem V to an arbitrary order relation between a, b, and c.   (Cf. Note 2, § 501.)

2. Assuming that $f(x)$ is integrable on $[a, b]$ and that $|f(x)| \leq K$ there, prove that

$$\left| \int_a^b f(x) \, dx \right| \leq K(b - a).$$

It can be proved (cf. Ex. 38) that if $f(x)$ is integrable on $[a, b]$, then so is $|f(x)|$.   Assuming that both $f(x)$ and $|f(x)|$ are integrable on $[a, b]$, prove that

$$\left| \int_a^b f(x) \, dx \right| \leq \int_a^b |f(x)| \, dx.$$

Hint: Use Theorem II, § 501, and the inequalities

$$-K \leq f(x) \leq K \quad \text{or} \quad -|f(x)| \leq f(x) \leq |f(x)|.$$

3. Prove that if $f(x)$ is continuous on $[a, b]$ and $f(x) \geq 0$ but not identically zero there, then $\int_a^b f(x) \, dx > 0$.   *Hint:* Use Ex. 18, § 212.

4. Prove that if $f(x)$ and $g(x)$ are continuous on $[a, b]$ and $f(x) \leq g(x)$ but $f(x)$ and $g(x)$ are not identical there, then $\int_a^b f(x) \, dx < \int_a^b g(x) \, dx$.   (Cf. Ex. 3.)

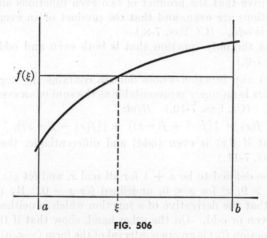

FIG. 506

5. Prove and give a geometric interpretation to the First Mean Value Theorem for Integrals (Theorem XI, § 501).   Also consider the case $a > b$.   (See Fig. 506.)   *Hint:* If m and M are the minimum and maximum values, respectively, of $f(x)$ on $[a, b]$ and if $f(x)$ is not a constant, use Ex. 4 to show that $m < \left[\int_a^b f(x) \, dx \right] \Big/ (b - a) < M$.   Conclude by applying Theorem IV, § 213.

6. Prove the following generalized form of the First Mean Value Theorem for Integrals (Theorem XI, § 501): *If $f(x)$ and $g(x)$ are continuous on $[a, b]$ and if $g(x)$ never changes sign there, then there exists a point ξ such that $a < \xi < b$ and*

(2) $$\int_a^b f(x)\, g(x)\, dx = f(\xi) \int_a^b g(x)\, dx.$$

Also consider the case $a > b$. (Cf. Ex. 5.)

7. A function $f(x)$ is said to be **even** if and only if the equality $f(-x) = f(x)$ holds for all x in the domain of definition of the function. (Examples: constants, x^{2n}, $\cos x$, $|x|$.) Prove that if $f(x)$ is even on $[-a, a]$, and integrable on $[0, a]$, where $a > 0$, then $f(x)$ is integrable on $[-a, a]$ and $\int_{-a}^a f(x)\, dx = 2 \int_0^a f(x)\, dx$. Prove that if $f(x)$ is even on $(-\infty, +\infty)$ and a and b are any real numbers, then $\int_{-b}^{-a} f(x)\, dx = \int_a^b f(x)\, dx$, whenever the integrals exist.

8. A function $f(x)$ is said to be **odd** if and only if the equality $f(-x) = -f(x)$ holds for all x in the domain of definition of the function. (Examples: $10x$, x^{2n+1}, $\sin x$, the signum function of Example 1, § 206.) Prove that if $f(x)$ is odd on $[-a, a]$, and integrable on $[0, a]$, where $a > 0$, then $f(x)$ is integrable on $[-a, a]$ and $\int_{-a}^a f(x)\, dx = 0$. Prove that if $f(x)$ is odd on $(-\infty, +\infty)$ and a and b are any real numbers, then $\int_{-a}^{-b} f(x)\, dx = \int_a^b f(x)\, dx$, whenever the integrals exist.

9. Prove that any sum of even functions is even and any sum of odd functions is odd. Prove that the product of two even functions and the product of two odd functions are even, and that the product of an even function and an odd function is odd. (Cf. Exs. 7-8.)

10. Prove that the only function that is both even and odd is identically zero. (Cf. Exs. 7-9.)

11. Prove that any function whose domain contains the negative of every one of its members is uniquely representable as the sum of an even function and an odd function. (Cf. Exs. 7-10.) *Hint:*
$$f(x) = \tfrac{1}{2}[f(x) + f(-x)] + \tfrac{1}{2}[f(x) - f(-x)].$$

12. Prove that if $f(x)$ is even (odd) and differentiable, then $f'(x)$ is odd (even). (Cf. Exs. 7-11.)

★13. Let $f(x)$ be defined to be $x + 1$ for all real x, and let $g(x)$ be defined to be $x^2 + 1$ for $x > 0$, x^2 for $x < 0$, undefined for $x = 0$. By means of these examples show that the derivative of a function which is neither even nor odd may be either even or odd. On the other hand, show that if the domain of a differentiable function $f(x)$ is an open interval of the form $(-a, a)$ or $(-\infty, +\infty)$ and if $f'(x)$ is odd, then $f(x)$ is even; similarly, that if $f'(x)$ is even, then $f(x)$ plus a suitable constant is odd. (Cf. Exs. 7-12.) *Hint:* $f(x)$ and $f(-x)$ have the same derivative, and must therefore differ by a constant.

14. If $f(x)$ is the bracket function of Example 5, § 201, $f(x) \equiv [x]$, evaluate $\int_0^1 f(x)\, dx$ and $\int_0^3 f(x)\, dx$. More generally, if n is a positive integer, evaluate $\int_0^n f(x)\, dx$.

15. Prove that $\int_a^b x^2\, dx = \frac{1}{3}(b^3 - a^3)$.   (Cf. the Example, § 501, and Ex. 13, § 107.)

16. Prove that $\int_a^b x^3\, dx = \frac{1}{4}(b^4 - a^4)$.   (Cf. the Example, § 501, and Ex. 14, § 107.)

17. Prove that $\int_a^b x^4\, dx = \frac{1}{5}(b^5 - a^5)$.   (Cf. the Example, § 501, and Ex. 15, § 107.)

★18. Prove that if m is a positive integer, then

$$\int_a^b x^m\, dx = \frac{1}{m+1}\,(b^{m+1} - a^{m+1}).$$

(Cf. the Example, § 501, and Ex. 42, § 107.)

★19. Prove that $\int_a^b \sin x\, dx = \cos a - \cos b$.   *Hint:* As in the Example, § 501, let $b > 0$ and $a = 0$, and write

$$\int_0^b \sin x\, dx = \lim_{n \to +\infty} \left(\sin \frac{b}{n} + \cdots + \sin \frac{nb}{n} \right) \cdot \frac{b}{n}.$$

Multiply each term by $2 \sin \dfrac{b}{2n}$, and use the identity

$$2 \sin A \sin B = \cos (A - B) - \cos (A + B)$$

to obtain

$$\int_0^b \sin x\, dx = \lim_{n \to +\infty} \left[\left(\cos \frac{b}{2n} - \cos \frac{3b}{2n} \right) + \left(\cos \frac{3b}{2n} - \cos \frac{5b}{2n} \right) + \cdots \right.$$
$$\left. + \left(\cos \frac{(2n - 1)b}{2n} - \cos \frac{(2n + 1)b}{2n} \right) \right] \cdot \frac{b}{2n \sin \dfrac{b}{2n}}.$$

★20. Prove that $\int_a^b \cos x\, dx = \sin b - \sin a$.   (Cf. Ex. 19.)

★21. Prove that $\int_a^b e^x\, dx = e^b - e^a$.

★22. Prove the **Trapezoidal Rule** for approximating a definite integral: *If $f(x)$ is integrable on $[a, b]$, if $[a, b]$ is subdivided into n equal subintervals of length Δx, and if the values of $f(x)$ at the $n + 1$ points of subdivision, $x_0, x_1, x_2, \cdots, x_n$, are $y_0, y_1, y_2, \cdots, y_n$, respectively, then*

$$\int_a^b f(x)\, dx = \lim_{n \to +\infty} \left(\tfrac{1}{2}y_0 + y_1 + y_2 + \cdots + y_{n-1} + \tfrac{1}{2}y_n \right) \Delta x.$$

Also prove the following estimate for the error in the trapezoidal formula, assuming existence of $f''(x)$ on $[a, b]$:

$$\int_a^b f(x)\, dx - \left[\tfrac{1}{2}y_0 + y_1 + \cdots + \tfrac{1}{2}y_n \right] \Delta x = -\frac{b - a}{12} f''(\xi)\, \Delta x^2,$$

where $a < \xi < b$.

Hints: For the first part, write the expression in brackets in the form $(y_1 + \cdots + y_n) + (\tfrac{1}{2}y_0 - \tfrac{1}{2}y_n)$. For the second part, reduce the problem to that of approximating $\int_a^b f(x)\,dx$ by a *single* trapezoid, and assume without loss of generality that the interval $[a, b]$ is $[-h, h]$. The problem reduces to that of evaluating K, defined by the equation

$$\int_a^b f(x)\,dx = \frac{b-a}{2}\,[f(b) + f(a)] + K(b-a)^3,$$

or

$$\int_{-h}^h f(t)\,dt = h[f(h) + f(-h)] + 8K\,h^3.$$

Define the function

$$\phi(x) \equiv \int_{-x}^x f(t)\,dt - x[f(x) + f(-x)] - 8K\,x^3.$$

Show that $\phi(h) = \phi(0) = 0$, and hence there must exist, by Rolle's Theorem (§ 407), a number x_1 between 0 and h such that $\phi'(x_1) = 0$. (Cf. Ex. 2, § 506.)

★**23.** Prove **Simpson's Rule** for approximating a definite integral: *Under the assumptions and notation of Exercise 22, where n is even,*

$$\int_a^b f(x)\,dx = \lim_{n\to+\infty}\ \tfrac{1}{3}(y_0 + 4y_1 + 2y_2 + 4y_3 + 2y_4 + \cdots + 4y_{n-1} + y_n)\,\Delta x.$$

Also prove the following estimate for the error in Simpson's Rule, assuming existence of $f''''(x)$ on $[a, b]$:

$$\int_a^b f(x)\,dx - \frac{1}{3}\,[y_0 + 4y_1 + \cdots + y_n]\,\Delta x = -\frac{b-a}{180}\,f''''(\xi)\,\Delta x^4,$$

where $a < \xi < b$. (Cf. Example 5, § 813.)

Hint: Proceed as in Ex. 22, making use of the auxiliary function

$$\phi(x) \equiv \int_{-x}^x f(t)\,dt - \frac{x}{3}\,[f(-x) + 4f(0) + f(x)] - 32K\,x^5.$$

Evaluate $\phi'''(x_1)$. (Cf. Ex. 2, § 506.)

★**24.** Evaluate $\displaystyle\lim_{n\to+\infty}\left(\frac{1}{n+1} + \frac{1}{n+2} + \cdots + \frac{1}{2n}\right)$. *Hint:* The sum, when rewritten $\left(\dfrac{1}{1+\dfrac{1}{n}} + \dfrac{1}{1+\dfrac{2}{n}} + \cdots + \dfrac{1}{1+\dfrac{n}{n}}\right)\cdot\dfrac{1}{n}$, can be interpreted as one of the approximating sums for $\displaystyle\int_0^1 \frac{dx}{1+x}$. (For the specific evaluation of this as $\ln 2$, see § 504.)

★**25.** Evaluate $\displaystyle\lim_{n\to+\infty} n\cdot\left(\frac{1}{n^2+1^2} + \frac{1}{n^2+2^2} + \cdots + \frac{1}{2n^2}\right)$. (Cf. Ex. 24.)

★**26.** Evaluate $\displaystyle\lim_{n\to+\infty}\left(\frac{1}{\sqrt{4n^2-1^2}} + \frac{1}{\sqrt{4n^2-2^2}} + \cdots + \frac{1}{\sqrt{3n^2}}\right)$. (Cf. Ex. 24.)

★**27.** Evaluate

$$\lim_{n\to+\infty} n\cdot\left[\frac{1}{(2n+3)^2 - 1^2} + \frac{1}{(2n+6)^2 - 2^2} + \cdots + \frac{1}{(5n)^2 - n^2}\right].$$

(Cf. Ex. 24.)

★**28.** It can be proved (cf. Ex. 31) that a function integrable on a closed interval is integrable on any closed subinterval. Assuming that $f(x)$ is integrable on $[a, b]$ and also on $[c; d]$ for all c and d such that $a \leq c < d \leq b$, prove that

$$\int_a^b f(x)\, dx = \lim_{\eta \to 0+} \int_{a+\eta}^b f(x)\, dx = \lim_{\eta \to 0+} \int_a^{b-\eta} f(x)\, dx. \quad Hint: \text{ If } |f(x)| \leq K \text{ for}$$

$$a \leq x \leq b, \left| \int_{a+\eta}^b f(x)\, dx - \int_a^b f(x)\, dx \right| = \left| \int_a^{a+\eta} f(x)\, dx \right| \leq K\eta.$$

★29. It can be proved (cf. Ex. 35) that if $f(x)$ and $g(x)$ are integrable on $[a, b]$, then so is $f(x)\, g(x)$, and hence so are $[f(x)]^2$ and $[g(x)]^2$. Assuming that these functions are all integrable on $[a, b]$, establish the **Schwarz** (or **Cauchy**) inequality (cf. Ex. 43, § 107, Ex. 26, § 711, Ex. 14, § 717):

$$(3) \qquad \left[\int_a^b f(x)\, g(x)\, dx \right]^2 \leq \int_a^b [f(x)]^2\, dx \cdot \int_a^b [g(x)]^2\, dx.$$

Hint: First show that $[f(x) + tg(x)]^2$ is integrable for all real t. With the notation $A \equiv \int_a^b [f(x)]^2\, dx$, $B = \int_a^b f(x)\, g(x)\, dx$, and $C \equiv \int_a^b [g(x)]^2\, dx$, show that $A + 2Bt + Ct^2 \geq 0$ for all real t. If $C = 0$, then $B = 0$, and if $C \neq 0$ the discriminant of $A + 2Bt + Ct^2$ must be nonpositive.

★30. Use the Schwarz inequality to establish the **Minkowski inequality** (cf. Ex. 44, § 107, Ex. 14, § 717), assuming that the integrals exist (cf. Ex. 29):

$$(4) \qquad \left\{ \int_a^b [f(x) + g(x)]^2\, dx \right\}^{\frac{1}{2}} \leq \left\{ \int_a^b [f(x)]^2\, dx \right\}^{\frac{1}{2}} + \left\{ \int_a^b [g(x)]^2\, dx \right\}^{\frac{1}{2}}.$$

Hint: Use the hint of Ex. 44, § 107.

★31. Prove that a function integrable on a closed interval is integrable on any closed subinterval.

★32. Supply the details requested in the second part of the proof of Theorem II, § 502. *Hint:* If $\sum \tau_i \Delta x_i > I + \frac{1}{3}\epsilon$, define $\eta \equiv \frac{1}{n} [\sum \tau_i \Delta x_i - (I + \frac{1}{3}\epsilon)] > 0$. For each $i = 1, \cdots, n$, choose x_i such that $f(x_i) > \tau_i - (\eta/\Delta x_i)$, and obtain a contradiction.

★33. Prove Theorem X, § 501. *Hint:* Assume for definiteness that $f(x)$ is monotonically increasing on $[a, b]$, and for a given net $\mathfrak{N}$ define the step-functions $\sigma(x) \equiv f(a_{i-1})$ for $a_{i-1} \leq x < a_i$ $(\sigma(b) \equiv f(b))$ and $\tau(x) \equiv f(a_i)$ for $a_{i-1} < x \leq a_i$ $(\tau(a) \equiv f(a))$, $i = 1, 2, \cdots, n$. Then $\sigma(x) \leq f(x) \leq \tau(x)$ and $\int_a^b [\tau(x) - \sigma(x)]\, dx = \sum_{i=1}^n [f(a_i) - f(a_{i-1})] \Delta x_i \leq |\mathfrak{N}| \cdot \sum_{i=1}^n [f(a_i) - f(a_{i-1})] = |\mathfrak{N}| \cdot (f(b) - f(a))$.

★34. Prove that $f(x)$ is integrable on $[a, b]$ if and only if corresponding to $\epsilon > 0$ there exists $\delta > 0$ such that for every net of norm less than δ and every choice of points x_i and x_i' such that $a_{i-1} \leq x_i \leq a_i$ and $a_{i-1} \leq x_i' \leq a_i$, $i = 1, 2, \cdots, n$,

$$\sum_{i=1}^n |f(x_i) - f(x_i')| \Delta x_i < \epsilon.$$

Hint: If $f(x)$ is integrable there exist step-functions $\sigma(x)$ and $\tau(x)$ such that $\sigma(x) \leq f(x) \leq \tau(x)$ and $\int_a^b [\tau(x) - \sigma(x)]\, dx < \epsilon/3$. Let $\delta > 0$ be so small that $|\mathfrak{N}| < \delta$ implies $\sum \tau(x_i) \Delta x_i < \int_a^b \tau(x)\, dx + \frac{1}{3}\epsilon$ and $\sum \sigma(x_i) \Delta x_i > \int_a^b \sigma(x)\, dx - \frac{1}{3}\epsilon$.

To simplify the notation, after x_i and x_i' are chosen as specified let ξ_i and η_i denote these points x_i and x_i' in such a way that $f(\xi_i) \leqq f(\eta_i)$, $i = 1, \cdots, n$. Then

$$\sum |f(x_i) - f(x_i')|\,\Delta x_i = \sum [f(\eta_i) - f(\xi_i)]\,\Delta x_i$$
$$\leqq \sum \tau(\eta_i)\,\Delta x_i - \sum \sigma(\xi_i)\,\Delta x_i < \int_a^b [\tau(x) - \sigma(x)]\,dx + \tfrac{2}{3}\epsilon < \epsilon.$$

On the other hand, if the condition stated exists, let $\mathfrak{N}$ be any fixed net for which $\sum |f(x_i) - f(x_i')|\,\Delta x_i < \tfrac{1}{2}\epsilon$. Define σ_i and τ_i as in the second part of the proof of Theorem II, § 502, and show that $\sum (\tau_i - \sigma_i)\,\Delta x_i \leqq \tfrac{1}{2}\epsilon < \epsilon$.

★35. Prove that the product of two integrable functions is integrable, and extend the result to the product of any finite number of integrable functions. *Hint:*

$$\sum |f(x_i)\,g(x_i) - f(x_i')\,g(x_i')|\cdot\Delta x_i$$
$$= \sum |g(x_i)\,[f(x_i) - f(x_i')] + f(x_i')\,[g(x_i) - g(x_i')]|\cdot\Delta x_i$$
$$\leqq K\cdot[\sum |f(x_i) - f(x_i')|\,\Delta x_i + \sum |g(x_i) - g(x_i')|\,\Delta x_i].$$

(Cf. Ex. 34.)

★36. Prove that the reciprocal of an integrable function is integrable if the given function is bounded from zero. That is, if $f(x)$ is integrable on $[a, b]$ and if $|f(x)| \geqq \eta > 0$ on $[a, b]$, then $1/f(x)$ is integrable on $[a, b]$. *Hint:* Use Ex. 34 and

$$\sum_{i=1}^n \left|\frac{1}{f(x_i)} - \frac{1}{f(x_i')}\right|\Delta x_i = \sum_{i=1}^n \frac{|f(x_i') - f(x_i)|}{|f(x_i)\,f(x_i')|}\,\Delta x_i \leqq \frac{1}{\eta^2}\sum_{i=1}^n |f(x_i) - f(x_i')|\,\Delta x_i.$$

What happens if we merely assume $|f(x)| > 0$?

★37. Prove that the quotient of two integrable functions is integrable if the second (denominator) function is bounded from zero (cf. Ex. 36).

★38. Prove that if $f(x)$ is integrable on $[a, b]$, then so is $|f(x)|$. Construct an example to show that the converse implication is false. *Hints:*

$$\sum |\,|f(x_i)| - |f(x_i')|\,|\,\Delta x_i \leqq \sum |f(x_i) - f(x_i')|\,\Delta x_i$$

(cf. Ex. 34). Consider a function like that of Example 6, § 201, with values ± 1.

★39. If $f(x)$ and $g(x)$ are defined on a set A, the functions $M(x) \equiv \max [f(x), g(x)]$ and $m(x) \equiv \min [f(x), g(x)]$ are defined, for each x in A, to be the larger and smaller, respectively, of the two numbers $f(x)$ and $g(x)$ (equal to them if they are equal). (See Fig. 507.) Prove that if $f(x)$ and $g(x)$ are integrable on $[a, b]$, then so are $M(x)$ and $m(x)$. *Hint:* $M(x) = \tfrac{1}{2}[f(x) + g(x)] + \tfrac{1}{2}|f(x) - g(x)|$, $m(x) = \tfrac{1}{2}[f(x) + g(x)] - \tfrac{1}{2}|f(x) - g(x)|$. (Cf. Ex. 38.)

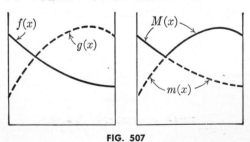

FIG. 507

★**40.** If $f(x)$ is defined on a set A, the nonnegative functions $f^+(x)$ and $f^-(x)$ are defined: $f^+(x) \equiv \max [f(x), 0]$, $f^-(x) \equiv \max [-f(x), 0]$. (See Fig. 508.) Prove that if $f(x)$ is integrable on $[a, b]$ then so are $f^+(x)$ and $f^-(x)$. Prove that the integrability of any two of the following four functions implies that of all: $f(x)$, $f^+(x)$, $f^-(x)$, $|f(x)|$. *Hint:* $f(x) = f^+(x) - f^-(x)$, $|f(x)| = f^+(x) + f^-(x)$. (Cf. Ex. 39.)

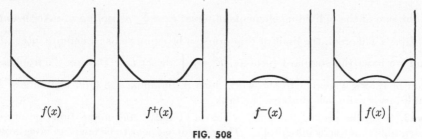

FIG. 508

★**41.** Prove **Bliss's Theorem**:† *If $f(x)$ and $g(x)$ are integrable on $[a, b]$, then* the limit $\lim\limits_{|\mathfrak{N}| \to 0} \sum\limits_{i=1}^{n} f(x_i)\, g(x_i')\, \Delta x_i$, where $a_{i-1} \leqq x_i \leqq a_i$ and $a_{i-1} \leqq x_i' \leqq a_i$, $i = 1, 2, \cdots, n$, the limit being interpreted in the sense of Definition I, § 501, exists and is equal to $\int_a^b f(x)g(x)\, dx$. *Hint:* Use the identity

$$\sum f(x_i)\, g(x_i')\, \Delta x_i = \sum f(x_i)\, g(x_i)\, \Delta x_i + \sum f(x_i)\, [g(x_i') - g(x_i)]\, \Delta x_i,$$

the inequality

$$|f(x_i)\, [g(x_i') - g(x_i)]\, \Delta x_i| \leqq K \cdot \sum |g(x_i') - g(x_i)|\, \Delta x_i,$$

and Ex. 34.

★**42.** Bliss's Theorem (Ex. 41) is used in such applied problems as work performed by a variable force and total fluid force on a submerged plate. In the latter case, for example, assume that a vertical plane area is submerged in a liquid of constant density ρ, and that the width at depth x is $w(x)$ (cf. Fig. 509). Then (with appropriate continuity assumptions) the element of area, between

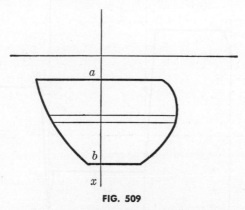

FIG. 509

† Cf. G. A. Bliss, "A Substitute for Duhamel's Theorem," *Annals of Mathematics,* Vol. 16 (1914-15), pp. 45-49.

x_i and $x_i + \Delta x_i$ is neither $w(x_i)\, \Delta x_i$ nor $w(x_i + \Delta x_i)\, \Delta x_i$, but $w(\eta_i)\, \Delta x_i$ for some appropriate intermediate $\mathfrak{N}_i$ (cf. the Mean Value Theorem for Integrals, and Ex. 5). Furthermore, the total force on this element of area is greater than the area times the pressure at the top of the strip, and less than the area times the pressure at the bottom of the strip. It is therefore equal to product of the area and an intermediate pressure, $\rho \xi_i$. Therefore the total force on the plate is the sum of the individual elements of force: $F = \sum\limits_{i=1}^{n} \rho \xi_i w(\eta_i)\, \Delta x_i$. According to Bliss's Theorem, the limit of this sum can be expressed as a definite integral, and we have the standard formula, $F = \rho \int_a^b x w(x)\, dx$. Discuss the application of Bliss's Theorem to the work done in pumping the fluid contents of a tank to a certain height above the tank.

★43. It can be proved (cf. Ex. 55) that a bounded continuous function of an integrable function is integrable. The reverse happens to be false: an integrable function of a bounded continuous function may not be integrable. (A counterexample can be constructed with the aid of the "Cantor set," well known in Lebesgue Theory.) By means of the following two functions show that an integrable function of an integrable function may not be integrable: Let $g(x)$ be the function of Example 2, § 502, and let $f(x)$ be the signum function (Example 1, § 206). Then $f(g(x))$ is the function of Example 6, § 201, discussed in a paragraph following Definition III, § 501.

★44. The numbers I and J defined in the first part of the proof of Theorem II, § 502, are called the **lower** and **upper integral**, respectively, of $f(x)$ on $[a, b]$, and are written $\int_{\underline{a}}^{b} f(x)\, dx \equiv I,\ \overline{\int_a^b} f(x)\, dx \equiv J$. Prove that for a bounded function $f(x)$ the lower and upper integrals always exist, that $\int_{\underline{a}}^{b} f(x)\, dx \leqq \overline{\int_a^b} f(x)\, dx$, and that $f(x)$ is integrable if and only if its lower and upper integrals are equal and, in the case of integrability, its integral is equal to their common value.

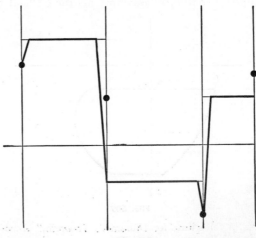

FIG. 510

★45. Prove that if $\sigma(x)$ is any step-function on the interval $[a, b]$, and if $\epsilon > 0$, then there exist continuous functions $\phi(x)$ and $\psi(x)$ on $[a, b]$ such that $\phi(x) \leq \sigma(x) \leq \psi(x)$ and $\int_a^b [\psi(x) - \phi(x)] \, dx < \epsilon$. Hence prove that if $f(x)$ is any bounded function on $[a, b]$, $\underline{\int_a^b} f(x) \, dx = \sup \int_a^b \phi(x) \, dx$, taken for all continuous functions $\phi(x)$ such that $\phi(x) \leq f(x)$, and $\overline{\int_a^b} f(x) \, dx = \inf \int_a^b \psi(x) \, dx$, taken for all continuous functions $\psi(x)$ such that $\psi(x) \geq f(x)$. Prove that Theorem II, § 502, remains true if the word *step-functions* is replaced by the words *continuous functions*. (Cf. Ex. 44.) *Hint:* See Fig. 510, for $\phi(x)$.

★★46. Define a step-function of **positive compact type** to be either the function identically zero or a nonnegative step-function whose nonzero values are assumed as constants on disjoint closed intervals (of positive length). (See Fig. 511.) Prove that if $f(x)$ is a bounded nonnegative function on $[a, b]$, then $\underline{\int_a^b} f(x) \, dx = \sup \int_a^b \sigma(x) \, dx$ taken for all step-functions $\sigma(x)$ of positive compact type such that $(0 \leq) \, \sigma(x) \leq f(x)$.

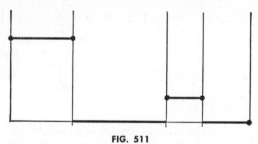

FIG. 511

★★47. Assume $K \geq f(x) \geq g(x) \geq 0$ on $[a, b]$, and let $\sigma(x)$ be a step-function such that $f(x) \geq \sigma(x) \geq 0$ and $\int_a^b \sigma(x) \, dx > \underline{\int_a^b} f(x) \, dx - \epsilon$, where $\epsilon > 0$. Establish the existence of a step-function $\tau(x)$ of positive compact type (Ex. 46) such that $g(x) \geq \tau(x) \, (\geq 0)$, $\sigma(x) \geq \tau(x)$, and $\int_a^b \tau(x) \, dx > \underline{\int_a^b} g(x) \, dx - \epsilon$.

Hint: Abbreviating $\int_a^b F(x) \, dx$ and $\underline{\int_a^b} F(x) \, dx$ by $\int F \, dx$ and $\underline{\int} F \, dx$, respectively, define $\eta \equiv \int \sigma \, dx - \underline{\int} f \, dx + \epsilon > 0$, and let $\rho(x)$ be a step-function such that $0 \leq \rho(x) \leq g(x)$ and $\int \rho \, dx > \underline{\int} g \, dx - \eta$. If $\phi(x) \equiv \min(\sigma(x), \rho(x))$ and $\psi(x) \equiv \max(\sigma(x), \rho(x))$, then $\phi(x)$ and $\psi(x)$ are step-functions, $\int \psi \, dx \leq \underline{\int} f \, dx$, and $\sigma(x) + \rho(x) = \phi(x) + \psi(x)$. Then $\int \phi \, dx + \int \psi \, dx = \int \sigma \, dx + \int \rho \, dx > \underline{\int} f \, dx + \underline{\int} g \, dx - \epsilon$, and $\int \phi \, dx > \underline{\int} g \, dx - \epsilon$. Finally, use Ex. 46.

★★48. Assume $K \geq f_1(x) \geq f_2(x) \geq \cdots \geq f_n(x) \geq f_{n+1}(x) \geq \cdots$ and

$$\lim_{n \to +\infty} f_n(x) = 0$$

for every x on $[a, b]$. Prove that $\int_a^b f_n(x)\, dx \to 0$. *Hint:* With the notation

of Ex. 47, assume $\int f_n\, dx \nrightarrow 0$. Then, since $\int f_n\, dx \downarrow$, $\lim\limits_{n \to +\infty} \int f_n\, dx$ exists

and is equal to a positive number 3ϵ. By Ex. 47, there exists a sequence $\{\sigma_n(x)\}$ of step-functions of positive compact type such that $(0 \leq) \sigma_n(x) \leq f_n(x)$, $\sigma_n(x) \geq \sigma_{n+1}(x)$, and $\int \sigma_n\, dx > 2\epsilon$, for $n = 1, 2, \cdots$. If A_n is defined to be the set of points such that $\sigma_n(x) \geq \epsilon/(b-a)$, then $\{A_n\}$ is a compact nonempty set, for $n = 1, 2, \cdots$, and A_n is a decreasing sequence (Ex. 26, § 312). If x_0 is a point common to every set of this sequence (Ex. 26, § 312), $f_n(x_0) \geq \sigma_n(x_0) \geq \epsilon/b - a)$, and $f_n(x_0) \nrightarrow 0$. (Contradiction.)

★★49. Prove the **Lebesgue Theorem on Bounded Convergence** for Riemann Integrals:[†] *If $\{f_n(x)\}$ is a sequence of Riemann-integrable functions converging on $[a, b]$ to a Riemann-integrable function $f(x)$, and if $|f_n(x)| \leq K$ for $a \leq x \leq b$ and $n = 1, 2, \cdots$, then $\lim\limits_{n \to +\infty} \int_a^b f_n(x)\, dx = \int_a^b f(x)\, dx = \int_a^b \lim\limits_{n \to +\infty} f_n(x)\, dx$.* *Hint:* Define $g_n(x) \equiv |f_n(x) - f(x)|$, $h_n(x) \equiv \sup(g_n(x), g_{n+1}(x), \cdots)$. Then (Exs. 16-18, § 305), $h_n(x) \downarrow$, $h_n(x) \to 0$, and the result of Ex. 48 shows that

$\int h_n\, dx \to 0$. Therefore, since $0 \leq g_n(x) \leq h_n(x)$, $\int g_n\, dx \to 0$, whence $\int f_n\, dx$

$\to \int f\, dx$. (Cf. Ex. 46, § 515.)

★★50. Let $r_1, r_2, r_3, \cdots$ be the rational numbers on the interval $[0, 1]$, and define the function $f_n(x)$ to be 1 if $x = r_1, r_2, \cdots$, or r_n, and 0 otherwise, $0 \leq x \leq 1$. Show that $\lim\limits_{n \to +\infty} f_n(x) = f(x)$ exists and that the convergence is bounded and monotonic (Ex. 49), but that $f(x)$ is not Riemann-integrable. (Even if all of the functions $f_n(x)$ are continuous on $[0, 1]$ and the convergence is bounded and monotonic, the limit function need not be Riemann-integrable.)

★★51. Let $f(x)$ be defined on a closed interval $[\alpha, \beta]$ and assume that there exists a positive number η such that the oscillation $\omega(x)$ (cf. Ex. 31, § 312) of $f(x)$ at each point x of $[\alpha, \beta]$ is less than η. Prove that there exists a net $\mathfrak{N}$ for $[\alpha, \beta]$ such that on each closed subinterval of $\mathfrak{N}$ the difference between the least upper bound of $f(x)$ and the greatest lower bound of $f(x)$ is less than η (that is, the oscillation of $f(x) < \eta$). *Hint:* Each point of $[\alpha, \beta]$ has a neighborhood I in which the oscillation of $f(x)$ is less than η. Use the Heine-Borel theorem (Ex. 28, § 312) to reduce this covering of $[\alpha, \beta]$ to a finite covering. Finally, obtain the desired net from this finite covering.

　† This theorem was stated by Arzelà in 1885, before the invention of the Lebesgue Integral, and given a simplified proof (whose essential ideas we have outlined here) by Hausdorff in 1927. If the integrals concerned are Lebesgue integrals, the integrability of the limit function $f(x)$ is a consequence of the other hypotheses and need not be specifically assumed. (Cf. Ex. 50.) However, the theorem as stated above has useful applications in cases where the limit function is known to be Riemann-integrable.

⚹ ★★52. A set S of real numbers is said to be of (**Lebesgue**) **measure zero** if and only if corresponding to $\epsilon > 0$ there exists a (finite or infinite) sequence of open intervals I_1, I_2, $\cdots$ of lengths L_1, L_2, $\cdots$, which cover S (cf. Ex. 28, § 312) and such that for every n,

$$L_1 + L_2 + \cdots + L_n < \epsilon.$$

Prove that any finite set of points is of measure zero. Prove that any denumerable set (cf. Ex. 12, § 113) is of measure zero. (The rational numbers form a set of measure zero.) Prove that any subset of a set of measure zero is of measure zero. *Hint:* For a denumerable set x_1, x_2, $\cdots$, x_n, $\cdots$, if $\epsilon > 0$, let I_n be a neighborhood of x_n of length $L_n \leqq \epsilon/2^n$, $n = 1, 2, \cdots$.

★★53. Let S_1, S_2, $\cdots$ be a (finite or infinite) sequence of sets of measure zero and let S be the set of points x such that x is a number of at least one set S_n of the sequence (S is the "union" of the sets of the sequence). Prove that S is of measure zero. *Hint:* If $\epsilon > 0$, define for each m the sequence $I_1^{(m)}$, $I_2^{(m)}$, $\cdots$ of open intervals covering S_m, of lengths $L_1^{(m)}$, $L_2^{(m)}$, $\cdots$ such that for every n, $L_1^{(m)} + L_2^{(m)} + \cdots + L_n^{(m)} < \epsilon/2^m$. The entire collection of intervals $I_n^{(m)}$ can be arranged as a sequence (cf. Ex. 13, § 113).

★★54. A property is said to hold **almost everywhere** if and only if the set of points where it fails is of measure zero. Prove that a function $f(x)$, defined on a closed interval, is integrable there if and only if it is bounded and almost everywhere continuous. *Hints:* (i) If $f(x)$ is integrable on $[a, b]$ and if $\epsilon > 0$ and $\eta > 0$, there exist step-functions $\sigma(x)$ and $\tau(x)$, over the same net $\mathfrak{M}$, such that $\sigma(x) \leqq f(x) \leqq \tau(x)$ and $\int_a^b [\tau(x) - \sigma(x)] \, dx < \epsilon\eta$. Then the sum of the lengths of the subintervals of $\mathfrak{M}$ for which $\tau_i - \sigma_i \geqq \epsilon$ is less than η. By appropriately enclosing the points of $\mathfrak{M}$ in small neighborhoods, show that the set $D\epsilon$ of points x where $\omega(x) \geqq \epsilon$ (cf. Ex. 32, § 312) is contained in a finite set of open intervals the sum of whose lengths $< \eta$, and is therefore a set of measure zero. Conclude by referring to Ex. 33, § 312, and Ex. 53 above. (ii) With the notation of Ex. 33, § 312, assume that D is of measure zero. Then (Ex. 52) D_ϵ, for any $\epsilon > 0$, is of measure zero. If $|f(x)| < K$ and if $\epsilon > 0$, let I_1, I_2, $\cdots$ be a sequence of open intervals covering D_η, where $\eta \equiv \epsilon/2(b - a)$, of such small lengths L_1, L_2, $\cdots$ that for every n, $L_1 + L_2 + \cdots + L_n < \epsilon/4K$. By the Heine-Borel Theorem (Ex. 28, § 312) there exists a finite sequence I_1, I_2, $\cdots$, I_n covering D_η. On each of the closed subintervals $[\alpha, \beta]$ of $[a, b]$ remaining after removal of I_1, I_2, $\cdots$, I_n, use Ex. 51 to construct step-functions $\sigma(x)$ and $\tau(x)$ such that $\sigma(x) \leqq f(x) \leqq \tau(x)$ and such that the sum of the integrals $\int [\tau(x) - \sigma(x)] \, dx$ over these intervals $< \eta(b - a) = \frac{1}{2}\epsilon$. Extend $\sigma(x)$ and $\tau(x)$ to the entire interval $[a, b]$ by defining them equal to $-K$ and K, respectively on the intervals I_1, I_2, $\cdots$, I_n. Then $\int_a^b [\tau(x) - \sigma(x)] \, dx < \epsilon$.

★★55. Prove that a bounded continuous function of an integrable function is integrable. In particular, if $f(x)$ is integrable on $[a, b]$ and $p > 0$, prove that $|f(x)|^p$ is integrable on $[a, b]$. *Hint:* The composite function is continuous almost everywhere (cf. Ex. 54).

★★56. Prove that if $f(x)$ is integrable and positive on a closed interval $[a, b]$, then $\int_a^b f(x)\ dx > 0$. *Hint:* By Ex. 54 $f(x)$ is continuous at some point of $[a, b]$.

★★57. Prove that in Exercise 56 the word *positive* may be replaced by the expression *positive almost everywhere*. In fact, prove that if $f(x)$ is a nonnegative integrable function and if $\int_a^b f(x)\ dx = 0$, then $f(x) = 0$ almost everywhere.

504. THE FUNDAMENTAL THEOREM OF INTEGRAL CALCULUS

Evaluation of a definite integral by actually taking the limit of a sum, as in the Example of § 501 and Exercises 15-21, § 503, is usually extremely arduous. Historically, many of the basic concepts of the definite integral as the limit of a sum were appreciated by the ancient Greeks long before the invention of the Differential Calculus by Newton and Leibnitz. Before the invention of derivatives, an area or a volume could be computed only by such a limiting process as is involved in the definition of the definite integral. The introduction of the notion of a derivative provided a spectacular impetus to the development of mathematics, not only by its immediate application as a rate of change, but also by permitting the evaluation of a definite integral by the process of reversing differention, known as *antidifferention* or *integration*. It is the purpose of this section to study certain basic relations between the two fundamental concepts of Calculus, the derivative and the definite integral.

Theorem I. *Let $f(x)$ be defined and continuous on a closed interval $[a, b]$ or $[b, a]$, and define the function $F(x)$ on this interval:*

$$(1) \qquad\qquad F(x) \equiv \int_a^x f(t)\ dt.\dagger$$

Then $F(x)$ is differentiable there with derivative $f(x)$:

$$(2) \qquad\qquad F'(x) = f(x).$$

(Cf. Exs. 22-23, § 506.)

Proof. Let x_0 and $x_0 + \Delta x$, where $\Delta x \neq 0$, belong to the given interval. Then, by Theorem V and Note 2, § 501,

---

† Since the letter x designates the upper limit of integration, it might be confusing to use this same symbol simultaneously in a second role as the variable of integration, and write $\int_a^x f(x)\ dx$.   Note that the integral $\int_a^b f(x)\ dx$ is *not* a function of x. Rather, the letter x in this case serves only as a *dummy variable* (cf. Ex. 36, § 107), and any other letter could be substituted, thus: $\int_a^b f(x)\ dx = \int_a^b f(t)\ dt = \int_a^b f(u)\ du$. Therefore, instead of $\int_a^x f(x)\ dx$ we write $\int_a^x f(t)\ dt$, $\int_a^x f(u)\ du$, etc.

$$F(x_0 + \Delta x) - F(x_0) = \int_a^{x_0+\Delta x} f(t)\,dt - \int_a^{x_0} f(t)\,dt = \int_{x_0}^{x_0+\Delta x} f(t)\,dt.$$

By the First Mean Value Theorem for Integrals (Theorem XI, § 501),

$$\frac{F(x_0 + \Delta x) - F(x_0)}{\Delta x} = \frac{1}{\Delta x} \int_{x_0}^{x_0+\Delta x} f(t)\,dt = f(\xi)$$

for some number ξ between x_0 and $x_0 + \Delta x$. Therefore if $\Delta x \to 0$, $\xi \to x_0$ and

$$F'(x_0) = \lim_{\Delta x \to 0} \frac{F(x_0 + \Delta x) - F(x_0)}{\Delta x} = f(x_0),$$

as stated in the theorem.

If a **primitive** or **antiderivative** or **indefinite integral** of a given function is defined to be any function whose derivative is the given function, Theorem I asserts that *any continuous function has a primitive.* The next theorem gives a method for evaluating the definite integral of any continuous function in terms of a given primitive.

Theorem II. Fundamental Theorem of Integral Calculus. *If $f(x)$ is continuous on the closed interval $[a, b]$ or $[b, a]$ and if $F(x)$ is any primitive of $f(x)$ on this interval, then*

$$(3) \qquad \int_a^b f(x)\,dx = F(b) - F(a).$$

(Cf. Exs. 19-20, § 506.)

Proof. By Theorem I and the hypotheses of Theorem II, the two functions $\int_a^x f(t)\,dt$ and $F(x)$ have the same derivative on the given interval. Therefore, by Theorem II, § 406, they differ by a constant:

$$(4) \qquad \int_a^x f(t)\,dt - F(x) = C.$$

Substitution of $x = a$ gives the value of this constant: $C = -F(a)$. Upon substitution for C in (4) we have $\int_a^x f(t)\,dt = F(x) - F(a)$ which, for the particular value $x = b$, is the desired result.

By virtue of the Fundamental Theorem of Integral Calculus, the integral symbol $\int$, suggested by the letter S (the definite integral is the limit of a *sum*), is appropriate for the *indefinite* integral as well as the *definite* integral. If $F(x)$ is an arbitrary indefinite integral of a function $f(x)$, we write the equation

$$(5) \qquad \int f(x)\,dx = F(x) + C,$$

where C is an arbitrary **constant of integration,** and call the symbol $\int f(x)\,dx$ **the indefinite integral** of $f(x)$. The Fundamental Theorem can thus be considered as an expression of the relation between the two kinds of integrals, definite and indefinite.

505. INTEGRATION BY SUBSTITUTION

The question before us is essentially one of appropriateness of notation: In the expression $\int f(x)\,dx$, does the "dx," which looks like a differential, really behave like one? Happily, the answer is in the affirmative:

Theorem. *If $f(v)$ is a continuous function of v and if $v(x)$ is a differentiable function of x, then*

$$(1) \qquad \int f(v(x))\,v'(x)\,dx = \int f(v(x))\,d(v(x)) = \int f(v)\,dv.$$

If $v(a) = c$ and $v(b) = d$, then

$$(2) \qquad \int_a^b f(v(x))\,v'(x)\,dx = \int_c^d f(v)\,dv.$$

Proof. Equation (1) is a statement that a function $F(v)$ whose derivative with respect to v is $f(v)$ has a derivative with respect to x equal to $f(v)\dfrac{dv}{dx}$, and this statement is a reformulation for the rule for differentiating a function of a function. Equation (2) follows from (1) by the Fundamental Theorem of Integral Calculus: $F(v(b)) - F(v(a)) = F(d) - F(c)$.

506. EXERCISES

1. Let the constant a and the variable x belong to an interval I throughout which the function $f(x)$ is continuous. Prove that

$$(1) \qquad \frac{d}{dx}\int_a^x f(t)\,dt = f(x), \qquad \frac{d}{dx}\int_x^a f(t)\,dt = -f(x).$$

Hint: Use Theorem V and Note 2, § 501.

2. Let $u(x)$ and $v(x)$ be differentiable functions whose values lie in an interval I throughout which $f(t)$ is continuous. Prove that

$$(2) \qquad \frac{d}{dx}\int_{u(x)}^{v(x)} f(t)\,dt = f(v(x))\,v'(x) - f(u(x))\,u'(x).$$

Hint: Write $\displaystyle\int_{u(x)}^{v(x)} f(t)\,dt = \int_a^{v(x)} f(t)\,dt - \int_a^{u(x)} f(t)\,dt$, and define $F(v) \equiv \displaystyle\int_a^v f(t)\,dt$, with $v = v(x)$.

In Exercises 3-8, find the derivative with respect to x. The letters a and b represent constants. (Cf. Exs. 1-2.)

3. $\displaystyle\int_a^b \sin x^2\, dx.$

4. $\displaystyle\int_a^x \sin t^2\, dt.$

5. $\displaystyle\int_x^b \sin t^2\, dt.$

6. $\displaystyle\int_a^{x^3} \sin t^2\, dt.$

7. $\displaystyle\int_{x^3}^{x^4} \sin t^2\, dt.$

8. $\displaystyle\int_{\sin^2 x}^{\sin x^2} \sin t^2\, dt.$

9. Assume necessary conditions of continuity on $f(x)$ and $f'(x)$ in an interval $[a, b]$ and use the Fundamental Theorem of Integral Calculus to show that the Mean Value Theorems for Integrals and Derivatives are merely alternative expressions of the same fact. *Hint:* Note that $f(x)$ is a primitive for $f'(x)$.

10. Show that the integration by parts formula,

(3)
$$\int u\, dv = uv - \int v\, du,$$

is equivalent to the formula for the differential of the product of two functions: $d(uv) = u\, dv + v\, du$. On occasion integrations by parts can be more readily evaluated by judicious differentiation of products than by use of (3). (Cf. Exs. 11-12.)

11. Obtain the integrals

(4)
$$\int e^{ax} \sin bx\, dx = \frac{e^{ax}}{a^2 + b^2} (a \sin bx - b \cos bx) + C,$$

(5)
$$\int e^{ax} \cos bx\, dx = \frac{e^{ax}}{a^2 + b^2} (b \sin bx + a \cos bx) + C,$$

as follows: (*i*) Differentiate the products $e^{ax} \sin bx$ and $e^{ax} \cos bx$; (*ii*) multiply both members of each of the resulting equations by constants so that addition or subtraction eliminates either the terms involving $\cos bx$ or the terms involving $\sin bx$. (Cf. Ex. 10.)

12. Find a primitive of $x^4 e^x$ by the methods suggested in Exercises 10-11. Devise additional examples to illustrate both methods of integrating by parts.

13. Establish the following integration by parts formula, where $u(x)$, $v(x)$, $u'(x)$, and $v'(x)$ are continuous on $[a, b]$:

(6)
$$\int_a^b u(x)\, v'(x)\, dx = u(b)\, v(b) - u(a)\, v(a) - \int_a^b v(x)\, u'(x)\, dx.$$

14. Prove the **Second Mean Value Theorem for Integrals:** *If $f(x)$, $\phi(x)$, and $\phi'(x)$ are continuous on the closed interval $[a, b]$, and if $\phi(x)$ is monotonic there* (equivalently, by Exercise 45, § 408, $\phi'(x)$ does not change sign there), *then there exists a number ξ such that $a < \xi < b$ and*

(7)
$$\int_a^b f(x)\, \phi(x)\, dx = \phi(a) \int_a^\xi f(x)\, dx + \phi(b) \int_\xi^b f(x)\, dx.$$

(For a generalization that eliminates assumptions on $\phi'(x)$ see Ex. 28, § 518; also cf. Ex. 29, § 518.) *Hint:* Use integration by parts, letting $F(x) \equiv \int_a^x f(t)\, dt$:

$$\int_a^b f(x)\, \phi(x)\, dx = \phi(x)\, F(x) \Big]_a^b - \int_a^b F(x)\, \phi'(x)\, dx,$$

and apply the generalized form of the First Mean Value Theorem (Ex. 6, § 503) to this last integral.

15. Show that the function $f(x)$ defined on $[0, 1]$ to be 1 if x is rational and 0 if x is irrational (Example 6, § 201) has neither integral nor primitive there. *Hint:* Cf. Ex. 47, § 408.

16. Show that although $\int_a^x f(t)\, dt$ is always a primitive of a given continuous function $f(x)$, not every primitive of $f(x)$ is of the form $\int_a^x f(t)\, dt$. *Hint:* Consider $f(x) \equiv \cos x$.

17. Show that the function $f(x) \equiv 0$ for $0 \leq x \leq 1$ and $f(x) \equiv 1$ for $1 < x \leq 2$ is integrable on the interval $[0, 2]$, although it has no primitive there. (Cf. Ex. 47, § 408.)

18. Show that the function $F(x) \equiv x^2 \sin \dfrac{1}{x^2}$ $(F(0) \equiv 0)$ has an unbounded derivative $f(x)$ on $[0, 1]$, so that a function may have a primitive without being integrable.

19. Prove the following general form for the Fundamental Theorem of Integral Calculus: *If $f(x)$ is integrable on the interval $[a, b]$, and if it has a primitive $F(x)$ there, then $\int_a^b f(x)\, dx = F(b) - F(a)$.* *Hint:* Let $a_0 < a_1 < \cdots < a_n$ be an arbitrary net $\mathfrak{N}$ on $[a, b]$, and write

$$F(b) - F(a) = \sum_{i=1}^{n} \{F(a_i) - F(a_{i-1})\}\, \Delta x_i = \sum_{i=1}^{n} f(x_i)\, \Delta x_i$$

(with the aid of the Law of the Mean, § 405).

★20. Generalize Exercise 19 as follows: *If $F(x)$ is continuous at every point of $[a, b]$, if $F'(x)$ exists at all but a finite number of points of $[a, b]$, and if $f(x) \equiv F'(x)$ is integrable on $[a, b]$, then $\int_a^b f(x)\, dx = F(b) - F(a)$.* (Cf. Ex. 5, § 508.) *Hint:* Use the method suggested in Ex. 19 but require the points of $\mathfrak{N}$ to include the points where $F'(x)$ fails to exist.

★21. Prove the following general form for integration by parts: If $u(x)$ and $v(x)$ are continuous on $[a, b]$, if $u'(x)$ and $v'(x)$ exist for all but a finite number of points of $[a, b]$, and if two (and therefore all three) of the functions $(uv)'$, uv', and vu' are integrable on $[a, b]$, then

$$\int_a^b u(x)\, v'(x)\, dx = u(b)\, v(b) - u(a)\, v(a) - \int_a^b v(x)\, u'(x)\, dx.$$

(Cf. Exs. 13, 20; also Ex. 7, § 508.)

★22. Prove that if $f(x)$ is integrable on $[a, b]$, then $F(x) \equiv \int_a^x f(t)\, dt$ is continuous on $[a, b]$. *Hint:* $|F(x) - F(x_0)| \leq \left| \int_{x_0}^x |f(t)|\, dt \right|$.

★23. Prove that if $f(x)$ is integrable on $[a, b]$, then $F(x) \equiv \int_a^x f(t)\, dt$ is differentiable at every point x at which $f(x)$ is continuous, and at such points of continuity of $f(x)$, $F'(x) = f(x)$. *Hint:*

$$\left| \frac{F(x) - F(x_0)}{x - x_0} - f(x_0) \right| \leq \left| \frac{1}{x - x_0} \int_{x_0}^x |f(t) - f(x_0)|\, dt \right|.$$

★507. SECTIONAL CONTINUITY AND SMOOTHNESS

In many applications certain discontinuous functions play an important role. In such applications it is necessary, however, that the discontinuities be within reason, both as to their nature and as to their number. An extremely useful class of such functions, frequently employed in the study of Fourier Series, is given in the following definition.

Definition I. *A function $f(x)$ is* **sectionally continuous** *on the closed interval $[a, b]$ if and only if it is continuous there except for at most a finite number of removable or jump discontinuities. That is, the one-sided limits $f(a+)$ and $f(b-)$ exist and are finite and $f(x+)$ and $f(x-)$ exist and are finite for all x between a and b, and $f(x+) = f(x-) = f(x)$ for all x between a and b with at most a finite number of exceptions. For sectional continuity the function $f(x)$ may or may not be defined at a or b or at any of the exceptional points of discontinuity.* (See Fig. 512.)

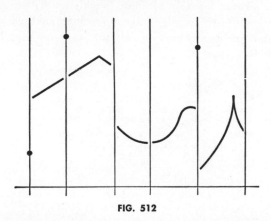

FIG. 512

An example of a sectionally continuous function is the signum function (§ 206) on the interval $[-1, 1]$. Another example is the derivative of $|x|$ (on the same interval), which is identical with the signum function, except that it is not defined at $x = 0$. Neither $1/x$ nor $\sin(1/x)$ is sectionally continuous on $[0, 1]$, or $[-1, 1]$, since there is no finite limit for either, as $x \to 0+$.

One of the most important properties of a sectionally continuous function is its integrability. This statement is made more precise and complete in the following theorem, whose proof is requested in Exercise 4, § 508, with hints.

Theorem. *If $f(x)$ is sectionally continuous on the closed interval $[a, b]$, and is continuous there except possibly at the points*

$$a = a_0 < a_1 < \cdots < a_n = b,$$

then the integrals $\int_a^b f(x)\,dx$ *and* $\int_{a_{i-1}}^{a_i} f(x)\,dx$, $i = 1, 2, \cdots, n$, *exist and*

(1)
$$\int_a^b f(x)\,dx = \sum_{i=1}^n \int_{a_{i-1}}^{a_i} f(x)\,dx.$$

The values of the integrals in formula (1) *are not affected by any values that might be assigned or reassigned to* $f(x)$ *at the exceptional points.*

Closely related to sectional continuity is the more restrictive property of sectional smoothness:

Definition II. *A function* $f(x)$ *is* **sectionally smooth** *on the closed interval* $[a, b]$ *if and only if both* $f(x)$ *and* $f'(x)$ *are sectionally continuous there.* (Cf. Ex. 8, § 508.)

Examples. On the interval $[-1, 1]$ the following functions are sectionally smooth: (a) the signum function (§ 206); (b) $|x|$; (c) $f(x) \equiv x - 1$ if $x > 0$, $f(x) \equiv x + 1$ if $x < 0$. On $[-1, 1]$ the following functions are sectionally continuous but not sectionally smooth: (d) $\sqrt{1 - x^2}$; (e) $\sqrt[3]{x^2}$; (f) $x^2 \sin (1/x)$ (Example 3, § 403).

★508. EXERCISES

★1. Show that the function $[x]$ (Example 5, § 201) is sectionally smooth on any finite closed interval. Draw the graph of its derivative.

★2. Show that $|\sin x|$ is sectionally smooth on any finite interval. Draw the graphs of the function and its derivative.

★3. Prove that a function that is sectionally continuous on a closed interval is bounded there. Must it have a maximum value and a minimum value there? Must it take on all values between any two of its values?

★4. Prove the Theorem of § 507. *Hint:* For the interval $[a_{i-1}, a_i]$, if $f(x)$ is defined or redefined: $f(a_{i-1}) \equiv f(a_{i-1}+)$ and $f(a_i) \equiv f(a_i-)$, then $f(x)$ becomes continuous there. Apply Theorem V, § 501, and induction.

★5. Let $F(x)$ be sectionally smooth on $[a, b]$, with exceptional points a_i, $i = 1, 2, \cdots, n - 1$, and possibly $a_0 = a$ and $a_n = b$, and denote by J_i the jump of $F(x)$ at a_i: $J_i \equiv F(a_i+) - F(a_i-)$, $i = 1, 2, \cdots, n - 1$. Prove that

(1)
$$\int_a^b F'(x)\,dx = F(b-) - F(a+) - \sum_{i=1}^{n-1} J_i.$$

(Cf. Ex. 20, § 506.)

★6. Prove that if $f(x)$ and $g(x)$ are sectionally continuous (smooth) then so are $f(x) + g(x)$ and $f(x)\,g(x)$. Extend by induction to n terms and n factors.

★7. Generalize Exercise 5 to the following integration by parts formula: If $F(x)$ is sectionally smooth on $[a, b]$ and if $G(x)$ has a continuous derivative there, then (with the notation of Ex. 5)

(2) $\displaystyle \int_a^b F'(x)\,G(x)\,dx = F(b-)\,G(b) - F(a+)\,G(a)$

$$- \int_a^b F(x)\,G'(x)\,dx - \sum_{i=1}^{n-1} J_i\,G(a_i).$$

(Cf. Ex. 21, § 506.)

★8. Prove that if $f'(x)$ is sectionally continuous on $[a, b]$, then $f(x)$ is sectionally smooth there. Furthermore, prove that $f(x)$ has a right-hand and a left-hand derivative at each point between a and b, and a right-hand derivative at a and a left-hand derivative at b. (Cf. Exs. 53-54, § 408.)

★9. If $f(x)$ is sectionally continuous on the closed interval $[a, b]$, then $F(x) \equiv \int_a^x f(t)\,dt$ is continuous there and $F'(x)$ exists and is equal to $f(x)$ there with at most a finite number of exceptions (Exs. 22-23, § 506). Prove that any function $\Phi(x)$ that is continuous on $[a, b]$ such that $\Phi'(x)$ exists and is equal to $f(x)$ there with at most a finite number of exceptions must differ from $F(x)$ by at most a constant. If $\Phi(x)$ is not everywhere continuous, what can you say?

★509. REDUCTION FORMULAS

It often happens that the routine evaluation of an integral involves repeated applications of integration by parts, all such integrations by parts being of the same tedious type. For example, in evaluating $I = \int \sin^{10} x\,dx$, we might proceed:

$$I = \int \sin^9 x\,d(-\cos x) = -\sin^9 x \cos x + 9 \int \sin^8 x \cos^2 x\,dx$$

$$= -\sin^9 x \cos x + 9 \int \sin^8 x\,dx - 9I,$$

so that

(1) $\displaystyle I \equiv -\tfrac{1}{10} \sin^9 x \cos x + \tfrac{9}{10} \int \sin^8 x\,dx.$

We have succeeded in reducing the exponent from 10 to 8. We could repeat this labor to reduce the new exponent from 8 to 6; then from 6 to 4; etc.

A more satisfactory method is to establish a *single formula* to handle all integrals of a single type. We present a few derivations of such **reduction formulas** in Examples, and ask for more in the Exercises of the following section. Since differentiation is basically a simpler process than integration, we perform our integrations by parts by means of differentiating certain products.

Example 1. Express $\int \sin^m x \cos^n x\,dx$, where $m + n \neq 0$, in terms of an integral with reduced exponent on $\sin x$ (cf. Exs. 1-2, § 510).

Solution. The derivative of the product $\sin^p x \cos^q x$ is

$$p \sin^{p-1} x \cos^{q+1} x - q \sin^{p+1} x \cos^{q-1} x$$
$$= p \sin^{p-1} x \cos^{q-1} x \,(1 - \sin^2 x) - q \sin^{p+1} x \cos^{q-1} x$$
$$= p \sin^{p-1} x \cos^{q-1} x - (p + q) \sin^{p+1} x \cos^{q-1} x.$$

In other words,

(2) $p \displaystyle\int \sin^{p-1} x \cos^{q-1} x \, dx - (p + q) \int \sin^{p+1} x \cos^{q-1} x \, dx = \sin^p x \cos^q x + C.$

Letting $p \equiv m - 1$ and $q \equiv n + 1$, and absorbing the constant of integration with the $\int$, we have the formula sought:

(3) $\displaystyle\int \sin^m x \cos^n x \, dx = -\frac{\sin^{m-1} x \cos^{n+1} x}{m + n} + \frac{m - 1}{m + n} \int \sin^{m-2} x \cos^n x \, dx.$

Equation (1) is a special case of (3), with $m = 10$, $n = 0$.

Often it is desirable to increase a negative exponent.

Example 2. Establish the reduction formula $(m \neq 1)$ (cf. Exs. 1-2, § 510):

(4) $\displaystyle\int \frac{\cos^n x \, dx}{\sin^m x} = -\frac{\cos^{n+1} x}{(m - 1) \sin^{m-1} x} - \frac{n - m + 2}{m - 1} \int \frac{\cos^n x \, dx}{\sin^{m-2} x}.$

Solution. In (2), let $p \equiv -m + 1$ and $q \equiv n + 1$.

Example 3. Establish the reduction formula $(m \neq 1)$:

(5) $\displaystyle\int \frac{dx}{(a^2 + x^2)^n} = \frac{x}{2(n - 1)a^2(a^2 + x^2)^{n-1}} + \frac{2n - 3}{2(n - 1)a^2} \int \frac{dx}{(a^2 + x^2)^{n-1}}.$

Solution. The derivative of the product $x(a^2 + x^2)^m$ is

$$(a^2 + x^2)^m + 2mx^2(a^2 + x^2)^{m-1}$$
$$= (a^2 + x^2)^m + 2m[(a^2 + x^2) - a^2](a^2 + x^2)^{m-1}$$
$$= (1 + 2m)(a^2 + x^2)^m - 2ma^2(a^2 + x^2)^{m-1}.$$

In other words,

(6) $(1 + 2m) \displaystyle\int (a^2 + x^2)^m \, dx - 2ma^2 \int (a^2 + x^2)^{m-1} \, dx = x(a^2 + x^2)^m + C.$

Now let $m \equiv -n + 1$, from which we obtain (5).

Useful reduction formulas are given in nearly every Table of Integrals.

★510. EXERCISES

In Exercises 1-12, establish the reduction formula.

★1. $\displaystyle\int \sin^m x \cos^n x \, dx = \frac{\sin^{m+1} x \cos^{n-1} x}{m + n}$

$$+ \frac{n - 1}{m + n} \int \sin^m x \cos^{n-2} x \, dx \quad (m + n \neq 0).$$

★2. $\displaystyle\int \frac{\sin^m x \, dx}{\cos^n x} = \frac{\sin^{m+1} x}{(n - 1) \cos^{n-1} x} - \frac{m - n + 2}{n - 1} \int \frac{\sin^m x \, dx}{\cos^{n-2} x} \quad (n \neq 1).$

★3. $\displaystyle\int \tan^n x \, dx = \frac{\tan^{n-1} x}{n - 1} - \int \tan^{n-2} x \, dx \quad (n \neq 1).$

★4. $\displaystyle\int \cot^n x \, dx = -\frac{\cot^{n-1} x}{n-1} - \int \cot^{n-2} x \, dx \quad (n \neq 1).$

★5. $\displaystyle\int \sec^n x \, dx = \frac{\sec^{n-2} x \tan x}{n-1} + \frac{n-2}{n-1} \int \sec^{n-2} x \, dx \quad (n \neq 1).$

★6. $\displaystyle\int \csc^n x \, dx = -\frac{\csc^{n-2} x \cot x}{n-1} + \frac{n-2}{n-1} \int \csc^{n-2} x \, dx \quad (n \neq 1).$

★7. $\displaystyle\int x^n \sin x \, dx = -x^n \cos x + nx^{n-1} \sin x - n(n-1) \int x^{n-2} \sin x \, dx.$

★8. $\displaystyle\int x^n \cos x \, dx = x^n \sin x + nx^{n-1} \cos x - n(n-1) \int x^{n-2} \cos x \, dx.$

★9. $\displaystyle\int x^m (ax + b)^n \, dx = \frac{x^m (ax+b)^{n+1}}{a(m+n+1)}$
$$- \frac{mb}{a(m+n+1)} \int x^{m-1}(ax+b)^n \, dx \quad (m+n+1 \neq 0).$$

★10. $\displaystyle\int x^m (ax + b)^n \, dx = \frac{x^{m+1}(ax+b)^n}{m+n+1}$
$$+ \frac{nb}{n+n+1} \int x^m (ax+b)^{n-1} \, dx \quad (m+n+1 \neq 0).$$

★11. $\displaystyle\int \frac{x^n \, dx}{\sqrt{ax^2 + bx + c}} = \frac{x^{n-1}}{a(n-1)}$
$$- \frac{b}{a} \int \frac{x^{n-1}\,dx}{\sqrt{ax^2 + bx + c}} - \frac{c}{a} \int \frac{x^{n-2}\,dx}{\sqrt{ax^2 + bx + c}} \quad (n \neq 1).$$

★12. $\displaystyle\int x^n \sqrt{2ax - x^2} \, dx = -\frac{x^{n-1}(2ax - x^2)^{\frac{3}{2}}}{n+2}$
$$+ \frac{a(2n+1)}{n+2} \int x^{n-1} \sqrt{2ax - x^2} \, dx \quad (n \neq -2).$$

In Exercises 13-20, perform the integration, using reduction formulas above.

★13. $\displaystyle\int \sin^6 x \, dx.$　　　　　★14. $\displaystyle\int \cos^5 x \, dx.$

★15. $\displaystyle\int \cot^5 \frac{x}{5} \, dx.$　　　　　★16. $\displaystyle\int \sec^7 x \, dx.$

★17. $\displaystyle\int x^4 \sin 2x \, dx.$　　　　　★18. $\displaystyle\int x^{\frac{3}{2}}(x+4)^{\frac{1}{2}} \, dx.$

★19. $\displaystyle\int \frac{x^3 \, dx}{\sqrt{x^2 + x + 1}}.$　　　　★20. $\displaystyle\int x^3 \sqrt{6x - x^2} \, dx.$

★★21. Use mathematical induction to verify the formula:
$$\int_a^b (x-a)^m (b-x)^n \, dx = (b-a)^{m+n+1} \frac{m!\, n!}{(m+n+1)!} \quad (m \text{ and } n \text{ positive integers}).$$

511. IMPROPER INTEGRALS, INTRODUCTION

The definite integral $\int_a^b f(x)\,dx$, as defined in § 501, has meaning only if a and b are finite and $f(x)$ is bounded on the interval $[a, b]$. In the following two sections we shall extend the definition so that under certain circumstances the symbol $\int_a^b f(x)\,dx$ shall be meaningful even when the interval of integration is infinite or the function $f(x)$ is unbounded.

For the sake of conciseness, parentheses will be used in some of the definitions to indicate alternative statements. For a discussion of the use of parentheses for alternatives, see the Preface.

512. IMPROPER INTEGRALS, FINITE INTERVAL

Definition I. *Let $f(x)$ be (Riemann-) integrable on the interval $[a, b - \epsilon]$ $\big([a + \epsilon, b]\big)$ for every number ϵ such that $0 < \epsilon < b - a$, but not integrable on the interval $[a, b]$, and assume that*

$$\lim_{\epsilon \to 0+} \int_a^{b-\epsilon} f(x)\,dx \quad \left(\lim_{\epsilon \to 0+} \int_{a+\epsilon}^b f(x)\,dx\right)$$

*exists. Under these conditions the **improper integral** $\int_a^b f(x)\,dx$ is defined to be this limit:*

(1) $$\int_a^b f(x)\,dx \equiv \lim_{\epsilon \to 0+} \int_a^{b-\epsilon} f(x)\,dx \quad \left(\lim_{\epsilon \to 0+} \int_{a+\epsilon}^b f(x)\,dx\right).$$

*If the limit in (1) is finite the integral $\int_a^b f(x)\,dx$ is **convergent** to this limit and the function $f(x)$ is said to be **improperly integrable** on the half-open interval $[a, b)$ $\big((a, b]\big)$; if the limit in (1) is infinite or does not exist, the integral is **divergent**.*

Note 1. A function improperly integrable on a half-open interval is necessarily unbounded there. In fact, it is unbounded in every neighborhood of the end-point of the interval that is not included. (Cf. Theorem III, § 502, and Ex. 28, § 503.)

Definition II. *Let $[a, b]$ be a given finite interval, let $a < c < b$, and let both integrals $\int_a^c f(x)\,dx$ and $\int_c^b f(x)\,dx$ be convergent improper integrals in the sense of Definition I. Then the **improper integral** $\int_a^b f(x)\,dx$ is **convergent** and defined to be:*

(2) $$\int_a^b f(x)\,dx \equiv \int_a^c f(x)\,dx + \int_c^b f(x)\,dx.$$

If either integral on the right-hand side of (2) *diverges, so does* $\int_a^b f(x)\ dx.$

NOTE 2.   There are four ways in which the integrals (2) may be improper, corresponding to the points in the neighborhoods of which $f(x)$ is unbounded: (*i*) $c-$ and $c+$, (*ii*) $a+$ and $c+$, (*iii*) $c-$ and $b-$, and (*iv*) $a+$ and $b-$.   In this last case (*iv*), the definition (2) is meaningful only if the value of $\int_a^b f(x)\ dx$ is independent of the interior point c.   This independence is indeed a fact (cf. Ex. 11, § 515).   As illustration of this independence of the point c, see Example 4, below.

NOTE 3.   In case the function $f(x)$ is (Riemann-) integrable on the interval $[a, b]$ it is often convenient to refer to the integral $\int_a^b f(x)\ dx$ as a **proper** integral, in distinction to the improper integrals defined above, and to call the integral $\int_a^b f(x)\ dx$ **convergent,** even though it is not improper.   (Cf. Example 3, below, and Ex. 28, § 503.)

Example 1.   Evaluate $\int_4^5 \dfrac{dx}{\sqrt{x-4}}.$

Solution.   The integrand becomes infinite as $x \to 4+$.   The given improper integral has the value

$$\lim_{\epsilon \to 0+} \int_{4+\epsilon}^5 \frac{dx}{\sqrt{x-4}} = \lim_{\epsilon \to 0+} \left[2\sqrt{x-4}\,\right]_{4+\epsilon}^5 = \lim_{\epsilon \to 0+} \left[2 - 2\sqrt{\epsilon}\,\right] = 2.$$

Example 2.   Evaluate $\int_{-1}^1 \dfrac{dx}{x^2}.$

Solution.   A thoughtless, brash, and incorrect "evaluation" would yield the ridiculous negative result:

$$\int_{-1}^1 \frac{dx}{x^2} = \left[-\frac{1}{x} \right]_{-1}^1 = [-1] - [1] = -2.$$

Since the integrand becomes infinite as $x \to 0$, a correct evaluation is

$$\int_{-1}^1 \frac{dx}{x^2} = \lim_{\epsilon \to 0+} \int_{-1}^{-\epsilon} \frac{dx}{x^2} + \lim_{\epsilon \to 0+} \int_\epsilon^1 \frac{dx}{x^2}$$

$$= \lim_{\epsilon \to 0+} \left(\frac{1}{\epsilon} - 1 \right) + \lim_{\epsilon \to 0+} \left(-1 + \frac{1}{\epsilon} \right) = +\infty,$$

and the integral diverges.

Example 3.   For what values of p does $\int_0^1 \dfrac{dx}{x^p}$ converge?

Solution.   If $p \leqq 0$, the integral is proper, and therefore converges (Note 3). If $0 < p < 1$,

$$\int_0^1 x^{-p}\ dx = \lim_{\epsilon \to 0+} \left[\frac{x^{1-p}}{1-p} \right]_\epsilon^1 = \frac{1}{1-p},$$

and the integral converges.   If $p = 1$, $\displaystyle\lim_{\epsilon \to 0+} \left[\ln x \right]_\epsilon^1 = \lim_{\epsilon \to 0+} (-\ln \epsilon) = +\infty,$

and if $p > 1$, $\lim\limits_{\epsilon \to 0+} \left[\dfrac{x^{1-p}}{1-p} \right]_{\epsilon}^{1} = +\infty$. Therefore the given integral converges if and only if $p < 1$.

Example 4. Evaluate $\displaystyle\int_{-2}^{2} \dfrac{dx}{\sqrt{4 - x^2}}$.

Solution. The integrand becomes infinite at both end-points of the interval $[-2, 2]$, and we therefore evaluate according to Definition II, choosing some number c in the interior of this interval. The simplest value of c is 0. We find, then, that

$$\int_{-2}^{0} \dfrac{dx}{\sqrt{4 - x^2}} = \lim_{\epsilon \to 0+} \left[\operatorname{Arcsin} \dfrac{x}{2} \right]_{-2+\epsilon}^{0} = -\operatorname{Arcsin}(-1) = \dfrac{\pi}{2},$$

and

$$\int_{0}^{2} \dfrac{dx}{\sqrt{4 - x^2}} = \lim_{\epsilon \to 0+} \left[\operatorname{Arcsin} \dfrac{x}{2} \right]_{0}^{2-\epsilon} = \operatorname{Arcsin}(1) = \dfrac{\pi}{2},$$

and the value of the given integral is π. Notice that any other value of c between -2 and 2 could have been used (Note 2, above):

$$\int_{-2}^{c} \dfrac{dx}{\sqrt{4 - x^2}} + \int_{c}^{2} \dfrac{dx}{\sqrt{4 - x^2}} = \left(\operatorname{Arcsin} \dfrac{c}{2} + \dfrac{\pi}{2} \right) + \left(\dfrac{\pi}{2} - \operatorname{Arcsin} \dfrac{c}{2} \right) = \pi.$$

NOTE 4. Under certain circumstances a student may evaluate an improper integral on a finite interval, with correct result, without forming a limit, or even without recognizing that the given integral is improper. This would be the case with Example 1, above—but not with Example 2. The following theorem justifies such a method and simplifies many evaluations:

Theorem. *If $f(x)$ is continuous in the open interval (a, b), and if there exists a function $F(x)$ which is continuous over the closed interval $[a, b]$ and such that $F'(x) = f(x)$ in the open interval (a, b), then the integral $\displaystyle\int_{a}^{b} f(x)\, dx$, whether proper or improper, converges and*

$$\int_{a}^{b} f(x)\, dx = F(b) - F(a).$$

(Cf. Ex. 15, § 515.)

Proof. By the Fundamental Theorem of Integral Calculus, for any c between a and b, and sufficiently small positive ϵ and η,

$$\int_{a+\epsilon}^{c} f(x)\, dx + \int_{c}^{b-\eta} f(x)\, dx = F(b - \eta) - F(a + \epsilon),$$

and the result follows from the continuity of $F(x)$ at a and b.

Example 5. In Example 1, above, let $F(x) \equiv 2\sqrt{x - 4}$. Then

$$\int_{4}^{5} \dfrac{dx}{\sqrt{x - 4}} = \left[2\sqrt{x - 4} \right]_{4}^{5} = 2.$$

513. IMPROPER INTEGRALS, INFINITE INTERVAL

Definition I. *Let* $f(x)$ *be (Riemann-) integrable on the interval* $[a, u]$ *for every number* $u > a$, *and assume that* $\lim\limits_{u \to +\infty} \int_a^u f(x)\, dx$ *exists. Under these conditions the **improper integral*** $\int_a^{+\infty} f(x)\, dx$ *is defined to be this limit:*

(1)
$$\int_a^{+\infty} f(x)\, dx \equiv \lim_{u \to +\infty} \int_a^u f(x)\, dx.$$

If the limit in (1) *is finite the improper integral is **convergent** to this limit and the function* $f(x)$ *is said to be **improperly integrable** on the interval* $[a, +\infty)$; *if the limit in* (1) *is infinite or does not exist, the integral is **divergent**.*

A similar definition holds for the improper integral $\int_{-\infty}^a f(x)\, dx.$

Definition II. *Let* $f(x)$ *be (Riemann-) integrable on every finite closed interval, and assume that both improper integrals* $\int_0^{+\infty} f(x)\, dx$ *and* $\int_{-\infty}^0 f(x)\, dx$ *converge. Then the **improper integral*** $\int_{-\infty}^{+\infty} f(x)\, dx$ *is **convergent** and defined to be:*

(2)
$$\int_{-\infty}^{+\infty} f(x)\, dx \equiv \int_{-\infty}^0 f(x)\, dx + \int_0^{+\infty} f(x)\, dx.$$

If either integral on the right-hand side of (2) *diverges, so does* $\int_{-\infty}^{+\infty} f(x)\, dx.$

NOTE 1. The improper integral (2) could have been defined unambiguously: $\int_{-\infty}^{+\infty} f(x)\, dx = \int_{-\infty}^c f(x)\, dx + \int_c^{+\infty} f(x)\, dx$, where c is an arbitrary number. (Cf. Ex. 12, § 515.)

Improper integrals on finite and infinite intervals are often combined:

Definition III. *Let* $f(x)$ *be improperly integrable on the interval* $(a, c]$ *and on the interval* $[c, +\infty)$, *where* c *is any constant greater than* a. *Then the **improper integral*** $\int_a^{+\infty} f(x)\, dx$ *is **convergent** and defined to be:*

(3)
$$\int_a^{+\infty} f(x)\, dx \equiv \int_a^c f(x)\, dx + \int_c^{+\infty} f(x)\, dx.$$

If either integral on the right-hand side of (3) *diverges, so does* $\int_a^{+\infty} f(x)\, dx.$

Similar statements hold for a similarly improper integral $\int_{-\infty}^{a} f(x)\ dx$.

NOTE 2. The improper integral (3) is independent of c. (Cf. Ex. 12, § 515.)

Example 1. Evaluate $\int_{0}^{+\infty} e^{-ax}\ dx,\ a > 0$.

Solution. $\int_{0}^{+\infty} e^{-ax}\ dx = \lim_{u \to +\infty} \left[\dfrac{e^{-ax}}{-a} \right]_{0}^{u} = \lim_{u \to +\infty} \left[\dfrac{1}{a} - \dfrac{e^{-au}}{a} \right] = \dfrac{1}{a}$.

Example 2. Evaluate $\int_{-\infty}^{+\infty} \dfrac{dx}{a^2 + x^2},\ a > 0$.

Solution.

$$\int_{-\infty}^{+\infty} \frac{dx}{a^2 + x^2} = \lim_{u \to -\infty} \left[\frac{1}{a} \operatorname{Arctan} \frac{x}{a} \right]_{u}^{0} + \lim_{v \to +\infty} \left[\frac{1}{a} \operatorname{Arctan} \frac{x}{a} \right]_{0}^{v}$$

$$= \lim_{u \to -\infty} \left[-\frac{1}{a} \operatorname{Arctan} \frac{u}{a} \right] + \lim_{v \to +\infty} \left[\frac{1}{a} \operatorname{Arctan} \frac{v}{a} \right] = \frac{1}{a} \cdot \frac{\pi}{2} + \frac{1}{a} \cdot \frac{\pi}{2} = \frac{\pi}{a}.$$

Example 3. For what values of p does $\int_{1}^{+\infty} \dfrac{dx}{x^p}$ converge?

Solution. If $p \neq 1$, $\int_{1}^{u} x^{-p}\ dx = \left[\dfrac{x^{1-p}}{1 - p} \right]_{1}^{u}$, and the integral converges if $p > 1$ and diverges if $p < 1$. Similarly, $\int_{1}^{+\infty} \dfrac{dx}{x} = \lim_{u \to +\infty} \ln u = +\infty$. Therefore the given integral converges if and only if $p > 1$, and its value, for such p, is $1/(p - 1)$.

Example 4. For what values of p does $\int_{0}^{+\infty} \dfrac{dx}{x^p}$ converge?

Solution. For this improper integral to converge, both $\int_{0}^{1}$ and $\int_{1}^{+\infty}$ must converge. But they never converge for the same value of p. (Examples 3, §§ 512, 513.) Answer: none.

514. COMPARISON TESTS. DOMINANCE

For a nonnegative function, convergence of an improper integral means (in a sense determined by the definition of the improper integral concerned) that *the function is not too big*: on a finite interval the function does not become infinite too fast, and on an infinite interval the function does not approach 0 too slowly. This means that whenever a nonnegative function $g(x)$ has a convergent improper integral, any well-behaved nonnegative function $f(x)$ less than or equal to $g(x)$ also has a convergent improper integral. We make these ideas precise:

Definition I. *The statement that a function* $g(x)$ **dominates** *a function* $f(x)$ *on a set* A *means that both functions are defined for every member* x *of* A *and that for every such* x, $|f(x)| \leqq g(x)$.

NOTE 1. Any dominating function is automatically nonnegative, although a dominated function may have negative values.

Theorem I. Comparison Test. *If a function $g(x)$ dominates a nonnegative function $f(x)$ on the interval $[a, b)$ $([a, +\infty))$, if both functions are integrable on the interval $[a, c]$ for every c such that $a < c < b$ $(a < c)$, and if the improper integral $\int_a^b g(x)\,dx$ $\left(\int_a^{+\infty} g(x)\,dx\right)$ converges, then so does $\int_a^b f(x)\,dx$ $\left(\int_a^{+\infty} f(x)\,dx\right)$.*

Similar statements apply to other types of improper integrals defined in §§ 512-513.

Proof. Since the two functions are nonnegative, the two integrals $\int_a^c f(x)\,dx$ and $\int_a^c g(x)\,dx$ are monotonically increasing functions of c, and both have limits as $c \to b-$ $(c \to +\infty)$. (Cf. § 215.) The inequalities $0 \leq \int_a^c f(x)\,dx \leq \int_a^c g(x)\,dx$ imply, thanks to Theorem VII, § 207, the inequalities $0 \leq \int_a^b f(x)\,dx \leq \int_a^b g(x)\,dx$ $\left(0 \leq \int_a^{+\infty} f(x)\,dx \leq \int_a^{+\infty} g(x)\,dx\right)$, and the proof is complete.

Example 1. Since, for $x \geq 1$, $\dfrac{1}{x^2 + 5x + 17} < \dfrac{1}{x^2}$, the convergence of $\int_1^{+\infty} \dfrac{dx}{x^2}$ implies that of $\int_1^{+\infty} \dfrac{dx}{x^2 + 5x + 17}$.

NOTE 2. An interchange of the roles of $f(x)$ and $g(x)$ in Theorem I furnishes a comparison test for divergence.

Example 2. Since, for $0 < x \leq 1$, $\dfrac{1}{x^2 + 5x} \geq \dfrac{1}{6x}$, the divergence of $\int_0^1 \dfrac{dx}{x}$ implies that of $\int_0^1 \dfrac{dx}{x^2 + 5x}$.

A convenient method for establishing dominance, and hence the convergence of an improper integral, can be formulated in terms of the "big O" notation (this is an upper case letter O derived from the expression "order of magnitude"):

Definition II. *The notation $f = O(g)$ (read "f is big O of g"), or equivalently $f(x) = O(g(x))$, as x approaches some limit (finite or infinite), means that within some deleted neighborhood of that limit, $f(x)$ is dominated by some positive constant multiple of $g(x)$: $|f(x)| \leq K \cdot g(x)$. If simultaneously $f = O(g)$ and $g = O(f)$, the two functions $f(x)$ and $g(x)$ are said to be of the **same order of magnitude** as x approaches its limit.*†

---

† Similar to the "big O" notation is the "little o" notation: $f = o(g)$ means that within some deleted neighborhood of the limiting value of x, an inequality of the form $|f(x)| \leq K(x)\, g(x)$ holds, where $K(x) \geq 0$ and $K(x) \to 0$. Obviously $f = o(g)$ implies $f = O(g)$.

Example 3. As $x \to +\infty$, $\sin x = O(1)$ and $\ln x = O(x)$. (Cf. Ex. 26, § 515.)

Big O and order of magnitude relationships are usually established by taking limits:

Theorem II. *Let $f(x)$ and $g(x)$ be positive functions and assume that*
$\lim \dfrac{f(x)}{g(x)} = L$ *exists, in a finite or infinite sense. Then:*

(*i*) $0 \leq L < +\infty$ *implies* $f = O(g)$,

(*ii*) $0 < L \leq +\infty$ *implies* $g = O(f)$,

(*iii*) $0 < L < +\infty$ *implies that $f(x)$ and $g(x)$ are of the same order of magnitude.*

(Give the details of the proof in Ex. 25, § 515.)

Example 4. As $x \to +\infty$, $\dfrac{1}{x+1} - \dfrac{1}{x} = O\left(\dfrac{1}{x^2}\right)$, since $\left[\dfrac{1}{x+1} - \dfrac{1}{x}\right] \Big/ \left[\dfrac{1}{x^2}\right]$
$= \dfrac{-x^2}{x^2 + x}$, and $\lim\limits_{x \to +\infty} \left|\dfrac{-x^2}{x^2 + x}\right| = 1 < +\infty$.

NOTE 3. The "big O" notation is also used in the following sense: $f(x) = g(x) + O(h(x))$ means that $f(x) - g(x) = O(h(x))$. Thus, as $x \to +\infty$, $\dfrac{1}{x+1} = \dfrac{1}{x} + O\left(\dfrac{1}{x^2}\right)$, by Example 4.

Theorem III. *If $f(x)$ and $g(x)$ are nonnegative on $[a, b]$ and integrable on $[a, c]$ for every c such that $a < c < b$, and if $f = O(g)$ as $x \to b-$, then the convergence of $\displaystyle\int_a^b g(x)\,dx$ implies that of $\displaystyle\int_a^b f(x)\,dx$.*

Similar statements apply to other types of improper integrals defined in §§ 512-513.

Proof. The convergence of $\displaystyle\int_c^b K\, g(x)\,dx$ implies that of $\displaystyle\int_c^b f(x)\,dx$ by Theorem I.

NOTE 4. An interchange of the roles of $f(x)$ and $g(x)$ in Theorem III furnishes a test for divergence. If $f(x)$ and $g(x)$ are of the same order of magnitude, then their two integrals either both converge or both diverge.

Example 5. Test for convergence or divergence: $\displaystyle\int_0^1 \dfrac{dx}{1 - x^3}$.

Solution. The integrand, $f(x)$, becomes infinite at $x = 1$. Write
$$f(x) = \frac{1}{(1 - x)(1 + x + x^2)},$$
and compare it with $g(x) \equiv \dfrac{1}{1 - x}$. Since
$$\lim_{x \to 1-} \frac{f(x)}{g(x)} = \lim_{x \to 1-} \frac{1}{1 + x + x^2} = \tfrac{1}{3} > 0,$$
$g = O(f)$ as $x \to 1-$, and since $\displaystyle\int_0^1 g(x)\,dx$ diverges, $\displaystyle\int_0^1 f(x)\,dx$ diverges.

Example 6. Test for convergence or divergence· $\int_0^5 \dfrac{dx}{\sqrt[3]{7x + 2x^4}}$.

Solution. The integrand, $f(x)$, becomes infinite at $x = 0$. Write

$$f(x) = \frac{1}{\sqrt[3]{x}\sqrt[3]{7 + 2x^3}}$$

and compare it with $g(x) \equiv \dfrac{1}{\sqrt[3]{x}}$. Since

$$\lim_{x\to0+} \frac{f(x)}{g(x)} = \lim_{x\to0+} \frac{1}{\sqrt[3]{7 + 2x^3}} = \frac{1}{\sqrt[3]{7}} < +\infty,$$

$f = O(g)$ as $x \to 0+$, and since $\int_0^5 g(x)\, dx$ converges, $\int_0^5 f(x)\, dx$ converges.

Example 7. Test for convergence or divergence: $\int_1^{+\infty} \dfrac{dx}{\sqrt{x^3 + 2x + 2}}$.

Solution. The integrand, as $x \to +\infty$, is of the same order of magnitude as $x^{\frac{3}{2}}$. Therefore the given integral converges.

Example 8. (The *Beta Function*.) Determine the values of p and q for which

$$B(p, q) \equiv \int_0^1 x^{p-1}(1 - x)^{q-1}\, dx$$

converges.

Solution. The integrand $f(x)$ has possible discontinuities at $x = 0$ and $x = 1$. As $x \to 0+$, $f(x)$ is of the same order of magnitude as x^{p-1}, and as $x \to 1-$, $f(x)$ is of the same order of magnitude as $(1 - x)^{q-1}$. Therefore convergence of both $\int_0^c f(x)\, dx$ and $\int_c^1 f(x)\, dx$, for $0 < c < 1$, is equivalent to the two inequalities $p - 1 > -1$ and $q - 1 > -1$. Therefore $\int_0^1 f(x)\, dx$ converges if and only if both p and q are positive.

Example 9. (The *Gamma Function*.) Determine the values of α for which

$$\Gamma(\alpha) \equiv \int_0^{+\infty} x^{\alpha-1}e^{-x}\, dx$$

converges.

Solution. If $f(x)$ is the integrand, $f(x)$ is of the same order of magnitude as $x^{\alpha-1}$ as $x \to 0+$, and $f(x) = O\left(\dfrac{1}{x^2}\right)$ as $x \to +\infty$ (this is true by l'Hospital's Rule in case $\alpha > -1$). Since $\int_0^1 x^{\alpha-1}\, dx$ converges if and only if $\alpha > 0$, and $\int_1^{+\infty} \dfrac{dx}{x^2}$ converges, the given integral converges if and only if α is positive.

515. EXERCISES

In Exercises 1-10, evaluate every convergent improper integral and specify those that diverge.

1. $\displaystyle\int_0^3 \frac{dx}{\sqrt{9 - x^2}}.$

2. $\displaystyle\int_{-1}^1 \frac{dx}{\sqrt[3]{x}}.$

3. $\displaystyle\int_{-2}^2 \frac{dx}{x^3}.$

4. $\displaystyle\int_0^{\frac{\pi}{2}} \sqrt{\sin x \tan x}\, dx.$

5. $\displaystyle\int_0^{+\infty} \frac{dx}{\sqrt{e^x}}.$

6. $\displaystyle\int_0^{+\infty} \sin x\, dx.$

7. $\displaystyle\int_1^{+\infty} \frac{dx}{x\sqrt{x^2 - 1}}.$

8. $\displaystyle\int_2^{+\infty} \frac{dx}{x(\ln x)^k}.$

9. $\displaystyle\int_0^{+\infty} \frac{e^{-\sqrt{x}}}{\sqrt{x}}\, dx.$

10. $\displaystyle\int_{-\infty}^{+\infty} \frac{dx}{1 + 4x^2}.$

11. Prove that the existence and the value of the improper integral (2), § 512, does not depend on the value of c in case (iv) of Note 2, § 512. *Hint:* Let $a + \epsilon < c < d < b - \eta$. Then

$$\int_{a+\epsilon}^c + \int_c^{b-\eta} = \int_{a+\epsilon}^c + \int_c^d + \int_d^{b-\eta} = \int_{a+\epsilon}^d + \int_d^{b-\eta}.$$

12. Prove the independence of c of the improper integrals referred to in the two Notes of § 513. (Cf. Ex. 11.) Illustrate each by an example.

13. Let $f(v)$ be continuous for $c < v < d$, let $v(x)$ have values between c and d, and a continuous derivative $v'(x)$, for $a < x < b$, and assume that $v(x) \to c$ as $x \to a+$ and $v(x) \to d$ as $x \to b-$. Prove that if the integral $\displaystyle\int_c^d f(x)\, dv$ converges (whether proper or improper) then the left-hand member in the following integration by substitution formula also converges and

(1) $$\int_a^b f(v(x))\, v'(x)\, dx = \int_c^d f(v)\, dv.$$

Evaluate the integral of Example 4, § 512, by use of this formula and the substitution $x = 2 \sin v$. Illustrate with other examples. *Hint:* If $F(v)$ is a primitive of $f(v)$, $c < v < d$,

$$\int_{a+\epsilon}^{b-\eta} f(v(x))\, v'(x)\, dx = F(v(b - \eta)) - F(v(a + \epsilon)).$$

14. Discuss the integration by substitution formula (1) for cases involving infinite intervals. Illustrate with examples.

In Exercises 15-24, merely establish convergence or divergence. Do not try to evaluate.

15. $\displaystyle\int_0^{+\infty} \frac{dx}{\sqrt{1 + x^4}}.$

16. $\displaystyle\int_2^{+\infty} \frac{x\, dx}{\sqrt{x^4 - 1}}.$

17. $\displaystyle\int_{-\infty}^{+\infty} e^{-x^2}\, dx.$

18. $\displaystyle\int_0^1 \frac{\ln x\, dx}{\sqrt{x}}.$

19. $\displaystyle\int_0^1 \frac{dx}{\sqrt{x}\, \ln x}.$

20. $\displaystyle\int_{-\infty}^0 e^x \ln |x|\, dx.$

21. $\displaystyle\int_{-\infty}^{+\infty} \frac{2x\, dx}{e^x - e^{-x}}.$

22. $\displaystyle\int_0^1 \frac{\ln x\, dx}{1 - x}.$

23. $\int_{-1}^{1} e^{\frac{1}{x}} \, dx.$ **24.** $\int_{0}^{1} \sqrt[3]{x \ln (1/x)} \, dx.$

25. Prove Theorem II, § 514.

26. Prove that if p is an arbitrary positive number, then

(2) $\ln x = o(x^p), \quad x = o(e^{px}), \quad \text{as} \quad x \to +\infty \, ;$

(3) $\ln x = o(x^{-p}), \quad \frac{1}{x} = o(e^{\frac{p}{x}}), \quad \text{as} \quad x \to 0+.$

27. Show that the functions in any "big O" relationship can be multiplied or divided by any function whose values are positive: If $f(x) = O(g(x))$ and $h(x) > 0$, then $f(x) \, h(x) = O(g(x) \, h(x))$; conversely, if $f(x) \, h(x) = O(g(x) \, h(x))$, then $f(x) = O(g(x))$. Is the same thing true for the "little o" relation?

28. Prove that $\int_{2}^{+\infty} \dfrac{dx}{x(\ln x)^p}$ converges if and only if $p > 1$.

29. Prove that $\int_{3}^{+\infty} \dfrac{dx}{x(\ln x)(\ln \ln x)^p}$ converges if and only if $p > 1$. More generally, prove that $\int_{a}^{+\infty} \dfrac{dx}{x(\ln x)(\ln \ln x) \cdots (\ln \ln \cdots \ln x)^p}$, where a is sufficiently large, converges if and only if $p > 1$.

★30. The **Cauchy principal value** of the improper integral $\int_{-\infty}^{+\infty} f(x) \, dx$ is denoted and defined

$$(P) \int_{-\infty}^{+\infty} f(x) \, dx \equiv \lim_{u \to +\infty} \int_{-u}^{u} f(x) \, dx,$$

provided the integral $\int_{-u}^{u} f(x) \, dx$ and its limit exist. Prove that whenever the improper integral $\int_{-\infty}^{+\infty} f(x) \, dx$ converges, its Cauchy principal value exists and is equal to it. Give examples to show that the converse is false. (Cf. Ex. 31.)

★31. For each of the cases (*i*) and (*ii*), below, define a Cauchy principal value of the improper integral $\int_{-a}^{a} f(x) \, dx$ assuming $f(x)$ is integrable on $[u, v]$ for every u and v such that

    (i) $-a < u < v < a$;   (ii) $-a \leqq u < v < 0$ and $0 < u < v \leqq a$.

Give a sufficient condition for the existence of the integral in each case. (Cf. Ex. 30.)

In Exercises 32-35, establish the given relation.

★32. $\int_{0}^{1} \dfrac{x^{p-1}}{x+1} \, dx = \int_{1}^{+\infty} \dfrac{x^{-p} \, dx}{x+1}, \; p > 0.$

★33. $\int_{0}^{+\infty} \dfrac{x^{p-1} \, dx}{x+1} = \int_{0}^{+\infty} \dfrac{x^{-p} \, dx}{x+1}, \; 0 < p < 1.$

★34. $\int_{0}^{1} x^{p-1}(1-x)^q \, dx = \dfrac{q}{p} \int_{0}^{1} x^p (1-x)^{q-1} \, dx, \; p > 0, \, q > 0.$

★35. $\int_{0}^{+\infty} \dfrac{dx}{(x+p) \sqrt{x}} = \dfrac{\pi}{\sqrt{p}}, \; p > 0.$

In Exercises 36 and 37, use integration by parts and mathematical induction to verify the formulas.

★36. **Wallis's Formulas.**

$$\int_0^1 \frac{x^n \, dx}{\sqrt{1 - x^2}} = \int_0^{\frac{\pi}{2}} \sin^n x \, dx = \int_0^{\frac{\pi}{2}} \cos^n x \, dx$$

$$= \begin{cases} \dfrac{2 \cdot 4 \cdot 6 \cdots (n - 1)}{3 \cdot 5 \cdot 7 \cdots n}, \text{ if } n \text{ is an odd integer} > 1; \\ \dfrac{1 \cdot 3 \cdot 5 \cdots (n - 1)}{2 \cdot 4 \cdot 6 \cdots n} \cdot \dfrac{\pi}{2}, \text{ if } n \text{ is an even integer} > 0. \end{cases}$$

★37. $\displaystyle\int_0^{+\infty} x^n e^{-ax} \, dx = \dfrac{n \, !}{a^{n+1}}$ (n a positive integer, $a > 0$).

In Exercise 38-41, state and prove the analogue for improper integrals of the specified theorem of § 501.

★38. Theorem II.   ★39. Theorem III.

★40. Theorem IV.   ★41. Theorem V.

★42. Show by an example that a continuous function improperly integrable on $[0, +\infty)$ need not have a zero limit at $+\infty$, in contrast to the fact that the general term of a convergent infinite series must tend toward zero (§ 703). (For another example see Ex. 46.)   *Hint:* See Figure 513.

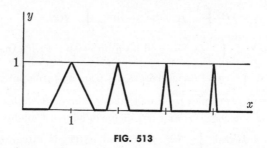

FIG. 513

★43. Prove the **Cauchy Criterion** for convergence of improper integrals: *If $f(x)$ is integrable on $[a, c]$ for every c such that $a < c < b$ $(a < c)$, then the improper integral $\displaystyle\int_a^b f(x) \, dx$ $\left(\displaystyle\int_a^{+\infty} f(x) \, dx \right)$ converges if and only if corresponding to $\epsilon > 0$ there exists a number $c = c(\epsilon)$ such that $a < c < b$ $(a < c)$ and such that $c < u < v < b$ $(c < u < v)$ implies $\left| \displaystyle\int_u^v f(x) \, dx \right| < \epsilon$.*

★44. If $f(x)$ is integrable on $[a, c]$ for every c such that $a < c < b$ $(a < c)$, then $\displaystyle\int_a^b f(x) \, dx$ $\left(\displaystyle\int_a^{+\infty} f(x) \, dx \right)$ is said to **converge absolutely** if and only if the improper integral $\displaystyle\int_a^b |f(x)| \, dx$ $\left(\displaystyle\int_a^{+\infty} |f(x)| \, dx \right)$ converges.   Prove that an absolutely convergent improper integral is convergent.

★45. An improper integral is said to be **conditionally convergent** if and only if it is convergent but not absolutely convergent.   Prove that $\int_0^{+\infty} \frac{\sin x}{x}\,dx$ is conditionally convergent.

★**46.** Prove that $\int_0^{+\infty} \cos x^2\,dx$ converges, by integrating $\int_u^v \cos x^2\,dx$ by parts to obtain $\frac{1}{2v}\sin v^2 - \frac{1}{2u}\sin u^2 + \frac{1}{2}\int_u^v \frac{\sin x^2}{x^2}\,dx$.   Also consider $\int_0^{+\infty} x\cos x^4\,dx$ (where the integrand is unbounded).   (Cf. Ex. 42.)

★★**47.** Prove the **Lebesgue Theorem on Dominated Convergence** for Improper Integrals: *If $\{f_n(x)\}$ is a sequence of functions improperly integrable on $[a, b)$ ($[a, +\infty)$) and converging there to an (improperly) integrable function $f(x)$, and if there exists a function $g(x)$ improperly integrable on that interval such that $|f_n(x)| \leq g(x)$ for $a \leq x < b$ ($a \leq x < +\infty$) and $n = 1, 2, \cdots$, then*

$$\lim_{n\to+\infty} \int_a^b f_n(x)\,dx = \int_a^b f(x)\,dx = \int_a^b \lim_{n\to+\infty} f_n(x)\,dx$$

$$\left(\lim_{n\to+\infty} \int_a^{+\infty} f_n(x)\,dx = \int_a^{+\infty} f(x)\,dx = \int_a^{+\infty} \lim_{n\to+\infty} f_n(x)\,dx \right).$$

(Similar statements apply to other types of improper integrals.)   *Hint:* For the interval $[a, b)$, and any $\epsilon > 0$, let c be a number between a and b such that $\int_c^b g(x)\,dx < \frac{1}{3}\epsilon$.   Then for any n,

$$\left| \int_a^b f_n(x)\,dx - \int_a^b f(x)\,dx \right| \leq \left| \int_a^c f_n(x)\,dx - \int_a^c f(x)\,dx \right|$$

$$+ \int_c^b |f_n(x)|\,dx + \int_c^b |f(x)|\,dx \leq \left| \int_a^c f_n(x)\,dx - \int_a^c f(x)\,dx \right| + \tfrac{2}{3}\epsilon.$$

Now use Ex. 49, § 503.

★★**48.** Prove that $\displaystyle\lim_{n\to+\infty} \sqrt[n]{\frac{n\,!}{n^n}} = \frac{1}{e}$, by adapting the technique of Exercises 24-27, § 503, to improper integrals.   (Cf. Ex. 36, § 711.)

★★516. BOUNDED VARIATION

The material of this section is presented primarily for its relation to the Riemann-Stieltjes integral defined in the following section, although it is also related to other topics in analysis, such as length of arc (not discussed in this book).   The first part of § 517 and the first exercises of § 518 do not depend on the present section.

Definition I.   *A function $f(x)$, defined on a closed interval $[a, b]$, is **of bounded variation** there if and only if, for all possible nets $\mathfrak{N}$, consisting of points $a = a_0 < a_1 < a_2 < \cdots < a_n = b$, the sums*

(1) $$\sum_{i=1}^{n} |f(a_i) - f(a_{i-1})|$$

*are bounded.   The **total variation** of a function $f(x)$ (of bounded variation)* *on the interval* $[a, b]$ *is defined to be the least upper bound of the set of all possible values of* (1), *and denoted:*

$$(2) \qquad V(f, [a, b]) \equiv \sup_{\mathfrak{N}} \sum_{i=1}^{n} |f(a_i) - f(a_{i-1})|.$$

Let us first show that the concept just introduced is far from a vacuous one by presenting two important classes of functions of bounded variation.

Theorem I. *Any function* $f(x)$ *defined and monotonic on a closed interval* $[a, b]$ *is of bounded variation there and*

$$V(f, [a, b]) = |f(b) - f(a)|.$$

Proof. Every sum (1) is equal to $|f(b) - f(a)|$.

Theorem II. *Any function* $f(x)$ *continuous on a closed interval* $[a, b]$ *and having a bounded derivative in the interior* (a, b) *is of bounded variation there.*

Proof. Let $|f'(x)| \leq K$ and use the Law of the Mean (§ 405) to obtain

$$\sum_{i=1}^{n} |f(a_i) - f(a_{i-1})| = \sum_{i=1}^{n} |f'(x_i)| \, \Delta x_i \leq K \, (b - a).$$

An explicit formulation for the total variation of a function is often possible:

Theorem III. *If* $f(x)$ *is differentiable on* $[a, b]$ *and if* $|f'(x)|$ *is integrable there, then* $f(x)$ *is of bounded variation there and*

$$(3) \qquad V(f, [a, b]) = \int_a^b |f'(x)| \, dx.$$

Proof: By the Law of the Mean (§ 405), the sums (1) have the form

$$(4) \qquad \sum_{i=1}^{n} |f(a_i) - f(a_{i-1})| = \sum_{i=1}^{n} |f'(x_i)| \, \Delta x_i,$$

and their least upper bound must be *at least* as large as $I \equiv \int_a^b |f'(x)| \, dx$. If a sum S of the form (1) *greater* than I were assumed to exist, a contradiction could be obtained as follows: Let $\epsilon \equiv S - I > 0$, and choose $\delta > 0$ so that $|\mathfrak{N}| < \delta$ implies $\left| \sum_{i=1}^{n} |f'(x_i)| \, \Delta x_i - I \right| < \epsilon$. Then add points to the net $\mathfrak{N}_1$ corresponding to the sum S until a net $\mathfrak{N}$ of norm less than δ is obtained. By the triangle inequality, each time such a point is added to the net, the sum (1) is either increased or unchanged. The final result, for the net $\mathfrak{N}$ of norm less than δ is the set of incompatible inequalities:

$$I + \epsilon = S \leq \sum_{i=1}^{n} |f(a_i) - f(a_{i-1})| = \sum_{i=1}^{n} |f'(x_i)| \, \Delta x_i < I + \epsilon.$$

Next we give a few statements to be used later, with references to the Exercises of § 518 for proofs:

Theorem IV. *If $f(x)$ is of bounded variation on $[a, b]$ and if*

$$a \leqq c < d \leqq b,$$

then $f(x)$ is of bounded variation on $[c, d]$ and

(5) $$V(f, [c, d]) \leqq V(f, [a, b]).$$

(Cf. Ex. 32, § 518.)

Theorem V. *If $f(x)$ is of bounded variation on $[a, b]$ and on $[b, c]$, then $f(x)$ is of bounded variation on $[a, c]$ and*

(6) $$V(f, [a, c]) = V(f, [a, b]) + V(f, [b, c]).$$

(Cf. Ex. 33, § 518.)

Theorem VI. *If $f(x)$ and $g(x)$ are of bounded variation on $[a, b]$, then so are $f(x) \pm g(x)$, $f(x)\, g(x)$, and $k\, f(x)$, where k is a constant, and*

(7) $$V(f \pm g, [a, b]) \leqq V(f, [a, b]) + V(g, [a, b]),$$

(8) $$V(kf, [a, b]) = |k| \cdot V(f, [a, b]).$$

(Cf. Ex. 34, § 518.)

We now introduce three new functions associated with a given function $f(x)$ of bounded variation on a given interval $[a, b]$:

Definition II. *The **total variation, positive variation,** and **negative variation functions,** and their symbols, are defined by the three equations, respectively:*

(9) $$v(x) \equiv V(f, [a, x]), a < x \leqq b; v(a) \equiv 0.$$

(10) $$p(x) \equiv \tfrac{1}{2}[v(x) + f(x) - f(a)], a \leqq x \leqq b.$$

(11) $$n(x) \equiv \tfrac{1}{2}[v(x) - f(x) + f(a)], a \leqq x \leqq b.$$

Theorem VII. *The three functions $v(x)$, $p(x)$, and $n(x)$ of Definition II are nonnegative monotonically increasing functions on the interval $[a, b]$, and*

(12) $$v(x) = p(x) + n(x),$$

(13) $$f(x) = p(x) - n(x) + f(a).$$

Proof. Formulas (12) and (13) follow immediately from (10) and (11). The total variation function is nonnegative by definition and monotonically increasing by Theorem IV. Since the negative variation of any function of bounded variation is the positive variation of the negative of that function, we need prove only the two statements regarding $p(x)$. The nonnegativeness of $p(x)$ follows from the inequality

$$V(f, [a, x]) \geq |f(x) - f(a)|,$$

while for $a \leqq c < d$, the inequality $p(c) \leqq p(d)$ reduces to the inequality

$$V(f, [c, d]) \geqq |f(d) - f(c)|,$$

thanks to Theorem V.

We are now in a position to establish a simple and useful criterion for bounded variation.

Theorem VIII. *A function $f(x)$ defined on an interval $[a, b]$ is of bounded variation there if and only if it can be represented as the difference between two monotonically increasing functions.*

Proof. If $f(x)$ is of bounded variation, equation (12) expresses $f(x)$ as the difference between the two monotonically increasing functions

$$(p(x) + f(a)) \quad \text{and} \quad n(x).$$

On the other hand, the difference between two monotonic functions is the difference between two functions of bounded variations (Theorem I) and is therefore of bounded variation (Theorem VI).

Example 1. The function $\sqrt{x}$ is of bounded variation on $[0, 1]$, by Theorem I.

Example 2. The function $y = x^2 \sin \frac{1}{x}$ $(y \equiv 0$ if $x = 0)$ (Example 3, § 403) is of bounded variation on $[0, 1]$, by Theorem II.

Example 3. Prove that the function $y = x \sin \frac{1}{x}$ $(y \equiv 0$ if $x = 0)$ (Example 2, § 403) is not of bounded variation on $[0, 1]$ (although it is continuous there).

Solution. Let $a_0 < a_1 < \cdots < a_n$ be the points

$$0, \frac{2}{\pi(2n - 3)}, \frac{2}{\pi(2n - 5)}, \cdots, \frac{2}{5\pi}, \frac{2}{3\pi}, \frac{2}{\pi}, 1.$$

Then

$$\sum_{i=1}^{n} |f(a_i) - f(a_{i-1})| = \left| \sin 1 - \frac{2}{\pi} \right| + \left(\frac{2}{\pi} + \frac{2}{3\pi} \right) + \left(\frac{2}{3\pi} + \frac{2}{5\pi} \right) + \cdots$$

$$+ \left(\frac{2}{\pi(2n - 5)} + \frac{2}{\pi(2n - 3)} \right) + \frac{2}{\pi(n - 3)} > \frac{1}{3} + \frac{1}{5} + \cdots + \frac{1}{2n - 3}.$$

Because of the divergence of the harmonic series $\sum \frac{1}{n}$ (Chapter 7), this expression can be made arbitrarily large.

Example 4. Find the total, positive, and negative variation functions for $f(x) = \sin x$ on the interval $[0, 2\pi]$.

Solution. By Theorem III, $v(x) = \int_0^x |\cos t|\, dt$, so that for

$$0 \leqq x \leqq \frac{\pi}{2}, \quad v(x) = \int_0^x \cos t\, dt = \sin x,$$

$$\frac{\pi}{2} \leqq x \leqq \frac{3\pi}{2}, \quad v(x) = 1 - \int_{\frac{\pi}{2}}^x \cos t\, dt = 2 - \sin x,$$

$$\frac{3\pi}{2} \leqq x \leqq 2\pi, \quad v(x) = 3 + \int_{\frac{\pi}{2}}^{x} \cos t \, dt = 4 + \sin x.$$

Similarly, in the ranges $\left[0, \frac{\pi}{2}\right], \left[\frac{\pi}{2}, \frac{3\pi}{2}\right]$, and $\left[\frac{3\pi}{2}, 2\pi\right]$, respectively, the function $p(x) = \sin x$, 1, and $2 + \sin x$, and the function $n(x) = 0$, $1 - \sin x$, and 2. The graphs are given in Figure 514.

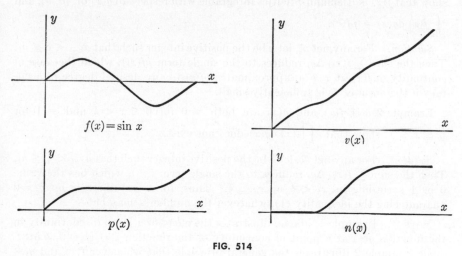

FIG. 514

★517. THE RIEMANN-STIELTJES INTEGRAL

A generalization of the definite integral, with useful applications in many applied fields including Physics and Statistics, is given in the following definition:

Definition I. *Let $f(x)$ and $g(x)$ be defined and bounded on a closed interval $[a, b]$. Then $f(x)$ is **Riemann-Stieltjes integrable** with respect to $g(x)$ on $[a, b]$, with **Riemann-Stieltjes integral I,** if and only if corresponding to $\epsilon > 0$ there exists $\delta > 0$ such that for any net*

$$\mathfrak{N} = \{a = a_0 < a_1 < \cdots < a_n = b\}$$

of norm $|\mathfrak{N}| < \delta$ and any choice of points $x_i, a_{i-1} \leqq x_i \leqq a_i, i = 1, 2, \cdots, n$:

(1)
$$\left| \sum_{i=1}^{n} f(x_i)[g(a_i) - g(a_{i-1})] - I \right| < \epsilon.$$

Letting $\Delta g_i \equiv g(a_i) - g(a_{i-1})$ and $\int_a^b f(x) \, dg(x) \equiv I$, we write (1) in limit notation:

(2)
$$\int_a^b f(x) \, dg(x) \equiv \lim_{|\mathfrak{N}| \to 0} \sum_{i=1}^{n} f(x_i) \, \Delta g_i.$$

NOTE 1. If $g(x) \equiv x$, the Riemann-Stieltjes integral (2) reduces to the Riemann or definite integral:

(3) $$\int_a^b f(x) \, dg(x) = \int_a^b f(x) \, dx, \quad \text{if} \quad g(x) \equiv x.$$

Example 1. If $f(x)$ is defined and bounded on $[a, b]$ and continuous at $x = c \; (a < c < b)$, and if $g(x) \equiv 0$ for $a \le x < c$ and $g(x) \equiv p$ for $c \le x \le b$, show that $f(x)$ is Riemann-Stieltjes integrable with respect to $g(x)$ on $[a, b]$, and $\int_a^b f(x) \, dg(x) = pf(c)$.

Solution. For any net $\mathfrak{N}$, let k be the positive integer such that $a_{k-1} < c \le a_k$. Then the sum $\sum f(x_i) \, \Delta g_i$ reduces to the single term $pf(x_k)$, which (because of continuity of $f(x)$ at $x = c$) approximates $pf(c)$ to any desired degree of accuracy if the norm of $\mathfrak{N}$ is sufficiently small.

Example 2. If $f(x)$ and $g(x)$ are both $\equiv 0$ for $0 \le x < \frac{1}{2}$ and $\equiv 1$ for $\frac{1}{2} \le x \le 1$, show that $\int_0^1 f(x) \, dg(x)$ does not exist.

Solution. For any net $\mathfrak{N}$, let k be the positive integer such that $a_{k-1} < \frac{1}{2} \le a_k$. Then the sum $\sum f(x_i) \, \Delta g_i$ reduces to the single term $f(x_k)$, which has the value 0 or 1 according as $x_k < \frac{1}{2}$ or $x_k \ge \frac{1}{2}$. Thus, for $\epsilon = \frac{1}{2}$ there is no $\delta > 0$ guaranteeing the inequality (1), whatever the number I may be!

NOTE 2. Example 1, above, illustrates the effect of a jump discontinuity in the function $g(x)$ at a point of continuity of the function $f(x)$ (Ex. 9, § 518), while Example 2 illustrates the general principle that whenever $f(x)$ and $g(x)$ have a common point of discontinuity the integral $\int_a^b f(x) \, dg(x)$ fails to exist (Ex. 10, § 518).

The following theorem establishes the differential nature of the symbol $dg(x)$, and shows how certain Riemann-Stieltjes integrals can be written as standard Riemann integrals.

Theorem I. *If $f(x)$ is defined and $g(x)$ is differentiable at every point of a closed interval $[a, b]$, and if $f(x)$ and $g'(x)$ are integrable there, then $f(x)$ is Riemann-Stieltjes integrable with respect to $g(x)$ there, and*

$$\int_a^b f(x) \, dg(x) = \int_a^b f(x) \, g'(x) \, dx.$$

Proof. If $I \equiv \int_a^b f(x) \, g'(x) \, dx$ (cf. Ex. 35, § 503), and $\epsilon > 0$, we wish to establish an inequality of the form (1), which can be rewritten with the aid of the Law of the Mean in the form

(4) $$\left| \sum_{i=1}^n f(x_i) \, g'(\xi_i) \, \Delta x_i - I \right| < \epsilon.$$

To this end we appeal to Bliss's Theorem (Ex. 41, § 503), and produce the required $\delta > 0$.

The following theorem shows the reciprocal relation between $f(x)$ and $g(x)$ in the definition of Riemann-Stieltjes integrability (cf. Ex. 11, § 518, for hints on a proof):

Theorem II. Integration by Parts. *If $f(x)$ is integrable with respect to $g(x)$ on $[a, b]$, then $g(x)$ is integrable with respect to $f(x)$ there and*

$$(5) \qquad \int_a^b f(x)\, dg(x) + \int_a^b g(x)\, df(x) = f(b)\, g(b) - f(a)\, g(a).$$

The question of existence of the integral of a function $f(x)$ with respect to a function $g(x)$ in case the function $g(x)$ is not differentiable, or possibly not even continuous, naturally arises. The simplest useful sufficient condition corresponds to the condition of continuity of $f(x)$ for the existence of the definite integral of $f(x)$:

Theorem III. *If, on the interval $[a, b]$, one of the functions $f(x)$ and $g(x)$ is continuous and the other monotonic, the integral $\int_a^b f(x)\, dg(x)$ exists.*

Proof. Thanks to Theorem II and the similarity in behavior of monotonically increasing and decreasing functions, we shall assume without loss of generality that $f(x)$ is continuous and $g(x)$ monotonically increasing (with $g(b) > g(a)$ since the case $g(b) = g(a)$ is trivial).

Our object is to find a number I which is approximated by all possible sums $\sum f(x_i)(g(a_i) - g(a_{i-1})) = \sum f(x_i)\, \Delta g_i$ associated with nets of sufficiently small norm. For a given net $\mathfrak{N}$, let m_i and M_i be the minimum and maximum values, respectively, of the continuous function $f(x)$ for $a_{i-1} \leq x \leq a_i$, $i = 1, 2, \cdots, n$. For any choice of x_i such that $a_{i-1} \leq x_i \leq a_i$, $i = 1, 2, \cdots, n$, $m_i \leq f(x_i) \leq M_i$, and since $g(x)$ is assumed to be monotonically increasing, $\Delta g_i \geq 0$, $i = 1, 2, \cdots, n$. Therefore

$$(6) \qquad \sum_{i=1}^n m_i\, \Delta g_i \leq \sum_{i=1}^n f(x_i)\, \Delta g_i \leq \sum_{i=1}^n M_i\, \Delta g_i.$$

The extreme left-hand and right-hand terms of (6) are called the **lower** and **upper sums** for the net $\mathfrak{N}$, and written $L(\mathfrak{N})$ and $U(\mathfrak{N})$, respectively.

In our quest for the desired number I, we shall define two numbers, I and J, and then prove that they are equal:

$$(7) \qquad \begin{cases} I \equiv \sup \sum_{i=1}^n m_i\, \Delta g_i = \sup \text{ (all lower sums)}, \\[2mm] J \equiv \inf \sum_{i=1}^n M_i\, \Delta g_i = \inf \text{ (all upper sums)}. \end{cases}$$

In order to establish the equality of the numbers I and J, we first affirm that $I \leq J$ and that this inequality is a consequence of the fact that *every* *lower sum is less than or equal to every upper sum: If $\mathfrak{M}$ and $\mathfrak{N}$ are any two nets on* $[a, b]$,

$$(8) \qquad\qquad L(\mathfrak{M}) \leqq U(\mathfrak{N}).$$

Reasonable though (8) may appear, it needs proof, and detailed hints are given in Exercise 12, § 518. In Exercise 13, § 518, the student is asked to prove that (8) implies $I \leqq J$.

Finally, with $I \leqq J$ established, we wish to show that $I = J$ and that if $\epsilon > 0$ there exists $\delta > 0$ such that

$$(9) \qquad\qquad \left| \sum_{i=1}^{n} f(x_i)\, \Delta g_i - I \right| < \epsilon$$

whenever $|\mathfrak{N}| < \delta$. By use of the inequalities (6) and

$$(10) \qquad\qquad L(\mathfrak{N}) \leqq I \leqq J \leqq U(\mathfrak{N}),$$

the desired equality $I = J$ and inequality (9) follow from the fact that if δ is chosen so small that (thanks to the uniform continuity of $f(x)$)

$$|x' - x''| < \delta \text{ implies } |f(x') - f(x'')| < \frac{\epsilon}{g(b) - g(a)},$$

then $|\mathfrak{N}| < \delta$ implies

$$U(\mathfrak{N}) - L(\mathfrak{N}) = \sum_{i=1}^{n} (M_i - m_i)\, \Delta g_i < \frac{\epsilon}{g(b) - g(a)} \sum_{i=1}^{n} \Delta g_i = \epsilon.$$

(Details are requested in Ex. 14, § 518.)

A few facts about the result of adding or subtracting functions or of multiplying by constants are herewith assembled (proofs are requested in Ex. 15, § 518):

Theorem IV. *If $f_i(x)$ is (Riemann-Stieltjes) integrable with respect to $g_j(x)$ for $i, j = 1, 2$, and if c is any constant, then $f_1(x) + f_2(x)$ is integrable with respect to $g_1(x)$, $f_1(x)$ is integrable with respect to $g_1(x) + g_2(x)$, $c f_1(x)$ is integrable with respect to $g_1(x)$, $f_1(x)$ is integrable with respect to $c\, g_1(x)$, and (with a simplified notation suggested by $\int f\, dg \equiv \int_a^b f(x)\, dg(x)$):*

$$(11) \qquad\qquad \int (f_1 + f_2)\, dg_1 = \int f_1\, dg_1 + \int f_2\, dg_2,$$

$$(12) \qquad\qquad \int f_1\, d(g_1 + g_2) = \int f_1\, dg_1 + \int f_1\, dg_2,$$

$$(13) \qquad\qquad \int c f_1\, dg_1 = \int f_1\, d(cg_1) = c \int f_1\, dg_1.$$

Definition II. *If $b < a$,*

$$(14) \qquad\qquad \int_a^b f(x)\, dg(x) \equiv -\int_b^a f(x)\, dg(x),$$

in case the latter integral exists. Furthermore,

(15) $$\int_a^a f(x) \, dg(x) \equiv 0.$$

For integrals over adjoining intervals we have:

Theorem V.   *For any three numbers a, b, and c,*

(16) $$\int_a^c f(x) \, dg(x) = \int_a^b f(x) \, dg(x) + \int_b^c f(x) \, dg(x),$$

provided the three integrals exist.

Proof.   We shall assume $a < b < c$ (cf. Exs. 16-17, § 518).   For $\epsilon > 0$, let $\delta > 0$ be such that $|\mathfrak{N}| < \delta$ implies that any sum corresponding to any of the three integrals approximates that integral within $\frac{1}{3}\epsilon$.   Then the sum of two such approximating sums for the two integrals on the right-hand side of (16) must approximate the left-hand side within $\frac{1}{3}\epsilon$.   Therefore the two sides of (16) are constants differing by less than ϵ, and must consequently be equal.

★★Finally, a simple application of Theorems II-IV and the fact (Theorem VIII, § 516) that any function of bounded variation can be represented as the difference between two monotonically increasing functions yields the following generalization of Theorem III:

★★**Theorem VI.**   *If, on the interval* $[a, b]$, *one of the functions* $f(x)$ *and* $g(x)$ *is continuous and the other of bounded variation, the integral* $\int_a^b f(x) \, dg(x)$ *exists.*

Example 3.   Evaluate the Riemann-Stieltjes integral $\int_0^{\frac{\pi}{2}} x \, d \sin x$.

Solution.   By Theorem I, this integral is equal to $\int_0^{\frac{\pi}{2}} x \cos x \, dx$.   However, it is simpler to use the integration by parts formula (Theorem II) directly:

$$\int_0^{\frac{\pi}{2}} x \, d \sin x = \frac{\pi}{2} \sin \frac{\pi}{2} - 0 \sin 0 - \int_0^{\frac{\pi}{2}} \sin x \, dx = \frac{\pi}{2} - 1.$$

Example 4.   Evaluate the Riemann-Stieltjes integral $\int_0^3 e^{2x} \, d \, [x]$, where x is the bracket function of § 201.

Solution.   The integration by parts formula gives

$$\int_0^3 e^{2x} \, d \, [x] = 3e^6 - 0 \, e^0 - \int_0^3 [x] \, d \, e^{2x},$$

which, by Theorem I, is equal to

$$3e^6 - 2 \int_1^2 e^{2x} \, dx - 4 \int_2^3 e^{2x} \, dx = e^2 + e^4 + e^6.$$

The result could be obtained directly by using the fact that the function $[x]$ in the original form of the integral makes contributions only at its jumps, of amounts determined by the values of e^{2x} and the size of the jumps (cf. Example 1, and Exs. 8-9, § 518.)

★518. EXERCISES

The notation $[x]$ indicates the bracket function of § 201.

In Exercises 1-6, evaluate the Riemann-Stieltjes integral.

★1. $\displaystyle\int_0^1 x \, dx^2.$ ★2. $\displaystyle\int_0^2 x \, d\,[x].$

★3. $\displaystyle\int_0^{\frac{\pi}{2}} \cos x \, d \sin x.$ ★4. $\displaystyle\int_0^3 e^x \, d\{x - [x]\}.$

★5. $\displaystyle\int_{-1}^1 e^x \, d\,|x|.$ ★6. $\displaystyle\int_0^\pi x \, d\,|\cos x|.$

★7. Prove that if $g(x)$ is defined on $[a, b]$, then $\displaystyle\int_a^b dg(x)$ exists and is equal to $g(b) - g(a)$.

★8. Prove that if $f(x)$ is continuous on $[0, n]$, then $\displaystyle\int_0^n f(x) \, d\,[x] = f(1) + f(2) + \cdots + f(n)$.

★9. For a net $\mathfrak{N}: a = a_0 < a_1 < \cdots < a_n = b$, let $g(x)$ be a step-function constant for $a_{i-1} < x < a_i$, $i = 1, 2, \cdots, n$, and having jumps $J_0 \equiv g(a+) - g(a)$, $J_i \equiv g(a_i+) - g(a_i-)$, $i = 1, 2, \cdots, n - 1$, and $J_n \equiv g(b) - g(b-)$. If $f(x)$ is continuous on $[a, b]$, prove that

(1) $$\int_a^b f(x) \, dg(x) = \sum_{i=0}^n J_i f(a_i).$$

Hint: Since the integral exists (Theorem VI, § 517) choose a net of arbitrarily small norm such that each a_i, $i = 1, 2, \cdots, n - 1$, is interior to some subinterval. Then let each a_i, $i = 0, 1, \cdots, n$, be a point chosen for evaluating $f(x)$.

★10. Prove that if $f(x)$ and $g(x)$ are both discontinuous at a point c, where $a \leqq c \leqq b$, then $\displaystyle\int_a^b f(x) \, dg(x)$ does not exist. *Hint:* For $a < c < b$, consider any net $\mathfrak{N}$, of arbitrarily small norm, not containing c and let $a_{k-1} < c < a_k$. Then $|\Delta g_k|$ can always be made $\geqq \eta$, a fixed positive number. Also, for two suitable numbers, x_k and x_k', in $[a_{k-1}, a_k]$, $|f(x_k) - f(x_k')| \geqq \xi$, a fixed positive number. Hence, for any $\delta > 0$, there is a net $\mathfrak{N}$ of norm $< \delta$, and two sums $\sum f(x_i) \Delta g_i$ which differ numerically by at least $\eta \xi$ (for $i \neq k$, let $x_i = x_i'$).

★11. Prove Theorem II, § 517. *Hint:* Expansion of $\displaystyle\sum_{i=1}^n g(x_i)[f(a_i) - f(a_{i-1})]$ and rearrangement of terms leads to the following identical formulation, where $x_0 \equiv a$ and $x_{n+1} \equiv b$:

$$f(b) \, g(b) - f(a) \, g(a) - \sum_{i=0}^n f(a_i) \, (g(x_{i+1}) - g(x_i)).$$

★**12.** Prove (8), § 517. *Hint:* If $\mathfrak{M}$ and $\mathfrak{N}$ are arbitrary nets on $[a, b]$, let $\mathcal{P}$ be the net consisting of all points appearing in either $\mathfrak{M}$ or $\mathfrak{N}$ (or both). Then, since $\mathcal{P}$ contains both $\mathfrak{M}$ and $\mathfrak{N}$,

$$L(\mathfrak{M}) \leqq L(\mathcal{P}) \leqq U(\mathcal{P}) \leqq U(\mathfrak{N}).$$

★**13.** Prove that (8), § 517, implies $I \leqq J$.

★**14.** Supply the details requested at the end of the proof of Theorem III, § 517.

★**15.** Prove Theorem IV, § 517.

★**16.** Show that formula (16), Theorem V, § 517, holds whatever the order relation between a, b, and c may be.

★**17.** Show by the example

$$f(x) \equiv 0 \quad \text{for} \quad 0 \leqq x < 1, \quad f(x) \equiv 1 \quad \text{for} \quad 1 \leqq x \leqq 2,$$
$$g(x) \equiv 0 \quad \text{for} \quad 0 \leqq x \leqq 1, \quad g(x) \equiv 1 \quad \text{for} \quad 1 < x \leqq 2$$

that the existence of the integrals on the right-hand side of (16), Theorem V, § 517, do not imply the existence of the integral on the left-hand side.

★**18.** Prove the *integration by substitution* formula for Riemann-Stieltjes integrals: If $\phi(t)$ is continuous and strictly monotonic on $[a, b]$, and if $\phi(a) = c$ and $\phi(b) = d$, then the equality

(2)
$$\int_c^d f(x) \, d\, g(x) = \int_a^b f(\phi(t)) \, dg(\phi(t))$$

holds, the existence of either integral implying that of the other. (Cf. Exs. 19-21.)

★★**19.** Prove that if the assumption in Exercise 18 that $\phi(t)$ is strictly monotonic on $[a, b]$ is replaced by the assumption that $\phi(t)$ is monotonic on $[a, b]$, then the existence of the left-hand integral of (2) implies that of the right-hand integral, and their equality. (Cf. Exs. 20-21.)

★★**20.** Show by means of the following example that under the assumptions of Exercise 19, the existence of the right-hand integral of (2) does not imply that of the left-hand integral:

$f(x) \equiv 0$ for $0 \leqq x < \frac{1}{2}$, $f(x) \equiv 1$ for $\frac{1}{2} \leqq x \leqq 1$;

$g(x) \equiv 0$ for $0 \leqq x \leqq \frac{1}{2}$, $g(x) \equiv 1$ for $\frac{1}{2} < x \leqq 1$;

$\phi(t) \equiv \frac{3}{2}t$ for $0 \leqq t \leqq \frac{1}{3}$, $\phi(t) \equiv \frac{1}{2}$ for $\frac{1}{3} < t < \frac{2}{3}$, $\phi(t) \equiv \frac{1}{2}(3x - 1)$ for $\frac{2}{3} \leqq t \leqq 1$.

★★**21.** Prove that if the assumption in Exercise 18 that $\phi(t)$ is strictly monotonic is dropped, then formula (2) holds whenever both integrals exist. *Hint:* Use Theorem IV, § 213, to show that by introducing appropriate points between those of a given net on $[a, b]$, a net $\mathfrak{N}: a = a_0 < a_1 < \cdots < a_n = b$ can be obtained such that with an appropriate choice of $t_1, t_2, \cdots, t_n$ all terms of

$$\sum_{i=1}^n f(\phi(t_i)) \, [g(\phi(t_i)) - g(\phi(t_{i-1}))]$$ cancel except those corresponding to a monotonic sequence of points $\{\phi(t_{i_k})\}$.

★**22.** Prove that if $f(x) \geqq 0$ and $g(x)$ monotonically increasing on $[a, b]$, then the integral $\int_a^b f(x) \, dg(x)$, if it exists, is nonnegative. State and prove a generalization of this for which $f_1(x) \leqq f_2(x)$ implies $\int_a^b f_1(x) \, dg(x) \leqq \int_a^b f_2(x) \, dg(x)$

★**23.** Prove that if $f(x)$ is continuous and nonnegative on $[a, b]$ but not identically 0 there, and if $g(x)$ is strictly increasing on $[a, b]$, then

$$\int_a^b f(x) \, dg(x) > 0.$$

State and prove a generalization of this for which $f_1(x) \leq f_2(x)$ implies

$$\int_a^b f_1(x) \, dg(x) < \int_a^b f_2(x) \, dg(x)$$

(Cf. Ex. 22.)

★**24.** Prove the analogue of Exercise 23 for the case $f(x)$ continuous and positive on $[a, b]$, and $g(x)$ monotonically increasing but nonconstant there. Also generalize to $f_1(x)$ and $f_2(x)$.

★**25.** Prove the **First Mean Value Theorem** for Riemann-Stieltjes integrals (cf. Exs. 5-6, § 503): *If $f(x)$ is continuous and $g(x)$ is monotonic (strictly monotonic) on $[a, b]$, then there exists a point ξ such that $a \leq \xi \leq b$ ($a < \xi < b$), and such that*

$$(3) \qquad \int_a^b f(x) \, dg(x) = f(\xi) \, [g(b) - g(a)].$$

Hint: Assume $g(x)$ increasing, and let $M \equiv \sup f(x)$ and $m \equiv \inf f(x)$ for $a \leq x \leq b$. Then

$$m[g(b) - g(a)] \leq \int_a^b f(x) \, dg(x) \leq M \, [g(b) - g(a)].$$

(See Ex. 23 for the strict inequalities.)

★**26.** Show by an example that equation (3) may not hold for $a < \xi < b$ if $g(x)$ is not *strictly* monotonic. *Hint:* Let $g(x) \equiv [x]$ on $[0, 1]$.

★**27.** Prove the **Second Mean Value Theorem** for Riemann-Stieltjes integrals (cf. Ex. 14, § 506): *If $f(x)$ is monotonic (strictly monotonic) and $g(x)$ is continuous on $[a, b]$, then there exists a point ξ such that $a \leq \xi \leq b$ ($a < \xi < b$) and such that*

$$(4) \qquad \int_a^b f(x) \, dg(x) = f(a) \, [g(\xi) - g(a)] + f(b) \, [g(b) - g(\xi)].$$

Hint: Use (3), Ex. 25, and the integration by parts formula (Theorem II, § 517).

★**28.** Prove the following form of the second Mean Value Theorem for Riemann integrals (cf. Ex. 14, § 506): *If $f(x)$ is monotonic (strictly monotonic) and if $h(x)$ is continuous on $[a, b]$, then there exists a point ξ such that $a \leq \xi \leq b$ ($a < \xi < b$) such that*

$$(5) \qquad \int_a^b f(x) \, h(x) \, dx = f(a) \int_a^\xi h(x) \, dx + f(b) \int_\xi^b h(x) \, dx.$$

Hint: Let $g(x)$ be a primitive of $h(x)$, and use (4).

★**29.** Prove the following Bonnet form of the Second Mean Value Theorem for Riemann integrals: *If $f(x) \geq 0$ and monotonically decreasing (or, alternatively, $f(x) \leq 0$ and monotonically increasing) and if $h(x)$ is continuous on $[a, b]$, then there exists a point ξ of $[a, b]$ such that*

$$(6) \qquad \int_a^b f(x) \, h(x) \, dx = f(a) \int_a^\xi h(x) \, dx.$$

If $f(x) \geq 0$ and monotonically increasing (or, alternatively, $f(x) \leq 0$ and monotonically decreasing) and if $h(x)$ is continuous on $[a, b]$, then there exists a point ξ

of $[a, b]$ *such that*

(7) $$\int_a^b f(x)\, h(x)\, dx = f(b) \int_\xi^b h(x)\, dx.$$

Hint: Use (5), redefining $f(x)$ to be 0 at either b or a.

★**30.** It is trivial (is it not?) that if $g(x)$ is a constant then $\int_a^b f(x)\, dg(x) = 0$. Prove the following converse: If $f(x)$ and $g(x)$ are bounded on $[a, b]$, and if $\int_a^b f(x)\, dg(x)$ exists and is equal to 0 for all monotonic functions $f(x)$, then $g(x)$ is a constant. *Hint:* By Ex. 10, $g(x)$ is continuous, and by Theorem II, § 517, $\int_a^b g(x)\, df(x) = f(b)\, g(b) - f(a)\, g(a)$. Let $f(x)$ be a step-function with one jump.

★★**31.** Prove that $\sin x^2$ is of bounded variation on every finite interval.

★★**32.** Prove Theorem IV, § 516.

★★**33.** Prove Theorem V, § 516.

★★**34.** Prove Theorem VI, § 516.

In Exercises 35–36, find the total, positive, and negative variation functions for the given function on the given interval.

★★**35.** $x - [x]$; $[0, 4]$.

★★**36.** $2x - x^2$; $[-1, 2]$.

★★**37.** Prove that any function of bounded variation on an interval is bounded there.

★★**38.** Prove that a function of bounded variation has only jump or removable discontinuities. *Hint:* Cf. Theorem VIII, § 516, and Ex. 28, § 216.

★★**39.** Prove that the set of points of discontinuity of a function of bounded variation is either finite or denumerable. *Hint:* Cf. Ex. 29, § 216.

★★**40.** Prove that a function of bounded variation on $[a, b]$ is integrable there. *Hint:* Four proofs are available (Theorem VIII, § 516; Theorem VI, § 517; Ex. 34, § 503; Ex. 54, § 503).

★★**41.** Prove that the total, positive, and negative variation functions of a function of bounded variation $f(x)$ are continuous wherever $f(x)$ is continuous.

★★**42.** Let $f(x)$ be continuous and $g(x)$ be of bounded variation on $[a, b]$, and let $v(x)$ be the total variation function of $g(x)$. Prove that

$$\left| \int_a^b f(x)\, dg(x) \right| \leq \int_a^b |f(x)|\, dv(x).$$

6

Some Elementary Functions

~~~~~~

★601. THE EXPONENTIAL AND LOGARITHMIC FUNCTIONS

The function x^n has been defined for integral exponents and arbitrary x in Chapter 1, and for positive rational exponents and nonnegative x in Chapter 2. In this section and the Exercises of the next, we study the expression a^b ($a > 0$, b real) and the logarithmic function.

One method of procedure is to define the exponential function a^x, first for integral exponents, then for all rational exponents, and finally by a limiting process, for all real exponents. Having defined the exponential function one can then define and study its inverse, the logarithmic function. For simplicity, we have chosen to reverse the order and define the logarithmic function first, by means of an integral, and then the exponential function as its inverse. We finally show that the exponential expression thus obtained agrees with the special cases previously studied. All of this is presented in the following section, by means of exercises arranged in logical order.

★602. EXERCISES

★1. Prove that the logarithmic function *defined* by the equation

$$(1) \qquad \ln x \equiv \int_1^x \frac{dt}{t}, \quad x > 0,$$

has the following five properties:

  (*i*) $\ln 1 = 0$;

  (*ii*) $\ln x$ is strictly increasing;

  (*iii*) $\ln x$ is continuous and, in fact, differentiable, with derivative $\dfrac{1}{x}$;

  (*iv*) $\lim\limits_{x \to +\infty} \ln x = +\infty$;

  (*v*) $\lim\limits_{x \to 0+} \ln x = -\infty$.

Hints for (iv) and (v):

$$\int_1^{2^n} \frac{dt}{t} = \int_1^2 \frac{dt}{t} + \int_2^4 \frac{dt}{t} + \int_4^3 \frac{dt}{t} + \cdots + \int_{2^{n-1}}^{2^n} \frac{dt}{t}$$

$$> \int_1^2 \frac{dt}{2} + \int_2^4 \frac{dt}{4} + \cdots + \int_{2^{n-1}}^{2^n} \frac{dt}{2^n} = \frac{n}{2}.$$

$$\int_{1/n}^1 \frac{dt}{t} = \int_n^1 \frac{d\,(1/u)}{1/u} = \int_1^n \frac{du}{u}.$$

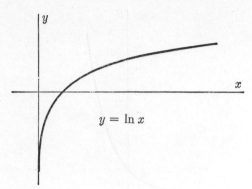

$$y = \ln x$$

FIG. 601

★**2.** Prove the following laws for ln x:

(i) $\ln (xy) = \ln x + \ln y$, $x > 0$, $y > 0$;

(ii) $\ln \left(\dfrac{x}{y}\right) = \ln x - \ln y$, $x > 0$, $y > 0$;

(iii) $\ln (x^n) = n \ln x$, $x > 0$, n an integer;

(iv) $\ln (\sqrt[n]{x}) = \dfrac{1}{n} \ln x$, $x > 0$, n a positive integer;

(v) $\ln (x^r) = r \ln x$, $x > 0$, r rational.

(Cf. § 214 and Exs. 21-22, § 216.) It follows from Exercise 6, below, that (v) holds for any real r. *Hints:*

(i): $\displaystyle\int_1^{xy} \frac{dt}{t} = \int_1^x \frac{dt}{t} + \int_x^{xy} \frac{dt}{t} = \int_1^x \frac{dt}{t} + \int_x^{xy} \frac{d\,(t/x)}{t/x};$

(ii): use (i) with $x = y \cdot \dfrac{x}{y};$

(iv): use (iii) with $x = (\sqrt[n]{x})^n.$

★**3.** Let the function $e^x = \exp (x)$ be *defined* as the inverse of the logarithmic function:

$$y = e^x = \exp (x) \quad \text{if and only if} \quad x = \ln y.$$

Prove that e^x has the following three properties:

(i) e^x is defined, positive, and strictly increasing for all real x;

(ii) $e^0 = 1$, $\displaystyle\lim_{x \to +\infty} e^x = +\infty$, $\displaystyle\lim_{x \to -\infty} e^x = 0$;

(iii) e^x is continuous and, in fact, differentiable, with derivative e^x.

★**4.** Prove the following laws for e^x:

(*i*) $e^x e^y = e^{x+y}$,

(*ii*) $\dfrac{e^x}{e^y} = e^{x-y}$,

(*iii*) if r is rational, $(e^x)^r = e^{rx}$.

Hints: (*i*): let $a \equiv e^x$, $b \equiv e^y$, $c \equiv e^{x+y}$; then $x = \ln a$, $y = \ln b$, $x + y = \ln c = \ln (ab)$; (*ii*): use (*i*) with e^{x-y} and e^y.

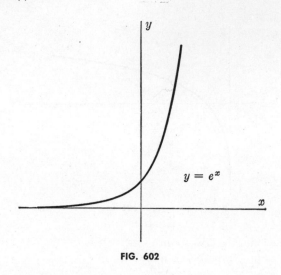

FIG. 602

★**5.** Define the number e as the value of e^x, for $x = 1$, $e \equiv \exp(1)$, or, equivalently, as the number whose (natural) logarithm is 1.   Prove that if x is rational, then the exponential function e^x, defined in Exercise 3, is identical with the function e^x previously defined in Exercise 22, § 216.

★**6.** For an arbitrary positive base a, define the exponential function:

$$a^x \equiv e^{x \ln a}.$$

Prove the following ten properties of a^x:

(*i*) a^x is defined and positive for all real x;

(*ii*) if $a = 1$, $a^x = 1$ for all x;

(*iii*) if $a = e$, $a^x = e^x$ (Ex. 3), for all x;

(*iv*) if x is rational, a^x, as defined here, is identical with the function a^x previously defined in Exercise 22, § 216;

(*v*) if $a > 1$ ($a < 1$), a^x is strictly increasing (decreasing);

(*vi*) $a^x a^y = a^{x+y}$;

(*vii*) $\dfrac{a^x}{a^y} = a^{x-y}$;

(*viii*) $(a^x)^y = a^{xy}$;

(*ix*) $a^x b^x = (ab)^x$, $a > 0$, $b > 0$;

(*x*) a^x is continuous and, in fact, differentiable, with derivative $\ln a \cdot a^x$.

★7. The function x^a, for $x > 0$ and arbitrary real a, is defined as in Exercise 6:

$$x^a \equiv e^{a \ln x}.$$

Prove the following properties of x^a:

(i) If $a > 0$ ($a < 0$), x^a is strictly increasing (decreasing);

(ii) if $a > 0$ ($a < 0$), $\lim\limits_{x \to +\infty} x^a = +\infty$ (0) and $\lim\limits_{x \to 0+} x^a = 0$ ($+\infty$);

(iii) x^a is continuous and, in fact, differentiable, with derivative ax^{a-1}.

★8. If $a > 0$, prove that the function x^a, defined as in Exercise 7 for $x > 0$, and defined to be 0 when $x = 0$, has the three properties stated in Exercise 7, except that if $0 < a < 1$, the derivative of x^a at $x = 0$ is $+\infty$.

★9. Prove that $e = \lim\limits_{x \to 0} (1 + x)^{\frac{1}{x}}$. *Hint:* At $x = 1$,

$$\frac{d}{dx} \ln x = \lim_{h \to 0} \frac{\ln (1 + h) - \ln (1)}{h} = \lim_{h \to 0} \ln (1 + h)^{\frac{1}{h}} = 1.$$

★10. Prove that $\lim\limits_{x \to 0} (1 + ax)^{\frac{1}{x}} = e^a$.

★11. Define $\log_a x$, where $a > 0$ and $a \neq 1$, $x > 0$, as the inverse of the function a^x. That is, $\log_a x$ is that unique number y such that $a^y = x$. Prove the standard laws of logarithms, and the change of base formulas:

$$\log_a x = \log_a b \log_b x = \frac{\log_b x}{\log_b a}.$$

Prove that $a^{\log_a x} = \log_a (a^x) = x$.

★★12. Show that the function $\log_a x$ *defined* as $\ln x/\ln a$ is the inverse of the function a^x and hence identical with the function of Exercise 11. Derive its other properties from this definition alone.

★603. THE TRIGONOMETRIC FUNCTIONS

In a first course in Trigonometry the six basic trigonometric functions are defined. Their definitions there and their subsequent treatment in Calculus, however, are usually based on geometric arguments and intuitive appeal unfortified by a rigorous analytic background. It is the purpose of this section and the following section of exercises to present purely analytic definitions and discussion of the trigonometric functions. That these definitions correspond to those of the reader's previous experience is easily shown after the concept of arc length is available.

The development here is restricted to the sine and cosine functions, since the remaining four trigonometric functions are readily defined in terms of those two. Furthermore, the calculus properties of the other four are immediately obtainable, once they are established for $\sin x$ and $\cos x$. These properties, as well as those of the inverse trigonometric functions will be assumed without specific formulation here.

★604. EXERCISES

★1. Prove that the function defined by the equation

$$\text{Arcsin } x \equiv \int_0^x \frac{dt}{\sqrt{1 - t^2}}, \quad -1 < x < 1,$$

is strictly increasing, continuous, and, in fact, differentiable with derivative $(1 - x^2)^{-\frac{1}{2}}$. (Fig. 603.)

★2. Let the function $\sin x$ be *defined* as the inverse of the function prescribed in Exercise 1:

$y = \sin x$ if and only if $x = \text{Arcsin } y$, for $-\text{Arcsin } \frac{3}{4} < x < \text{Arcsin } \frac{3}{4}$.

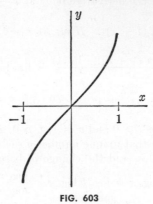

FIG. 603

If the number π is defined: $\pi \equiv 4 \text{ Arcsin } \frac{1}{2}\sqrt{2}$, and if the number b is defined: $b \equiv \text{Arcsin } \frac{3}{4}$, prove that over the interval $(-b, b)$, containing π, $\sin x$ is strictly increasing, continuous, and, in fact, differentiable with derivative $(1 - \sin^2 x)^{\frac{1}{2}}$ $\equiv [1 - (\sin x)^2]^{\frac{1}{2}}$. (Fig. 604.) Also, $\sin 0 = 0$, $\sin \frac{1}{4}\pi = \frac{1}{2}\sqrt{2}$.

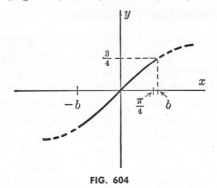

FIG. 604

★3. Let the function $\cos x$ be *defined*, on the interval $(-b, b)$ of Exercise 2, as the positive square root of $1 - \sin^2 x$. Prove that $\cos x$ is differentiable and that the derivatives of $\sin x$ and $\cos x$ are $\cos x$ and $-\sin x$, respectively. Also, $\cos 0 = 1$ and $\cos \frac{1}{4}\pi = \frac{1}{2}\sqrt{2}$. *Hint:* If $y = \cos x \neq 0$, $y^2 = 1 - \sin^2 x$, $2 \cos x \, dy/dx = -2 \sin x \cos x$.

★4. Let $s(x)$ and $c(x)$ be any two functions defined and differentiable on an open interval $(-a, a)$, $a > 0$, and possessing there the following four properties:

(1) $$(s(x))^2 + (c(x))^2 = 1,$$

(2) $$\frac{d}{dx}(s(x)) = c(x),$$

(3) $$\frac{d}{dx}(c(x)) = -s(x),$$

(4) $$c(0) = 1.$$

Prove that if α and β are any two numbers which, together with their sum $\alpha + \beta$, belong to the interval $(-a, a)$, then the following two identities hold:

(5) $$s(\alpha + \beta) = s(\alpha)\, c(\beta) + c(\alpha)\, s(\beta),$$

(6) $$c(\alpha + \beta) = c(\alpha)\, c(\beta) - s(\alpha)\, s(\beta).$$

Hence prove that if α and 2α belong to $(-a, a)$, then

(7) $$s(2\alpha) = 2s(\alpha)\, c(\alpha),$$

(8) $$c(2\alpha) = (c(\alpha))^2 - (s(\alpha))^2.$$

Hint: For (5), let $\gamma \equiv \alpha + \beta$, and prove that the function $s(x)\, c(\gamma - x) + c(x)\, s(\gamma - x)$ has an identically vanishing derivative and is therefore a constant. Then let $x = \alpha$ and $x = 0$, in turn.

★5. Let $s(x)$ and $c(x)$ be any two functions satisfying (1)-(4) of Exercise 4, on the open interval $(-a, a)$, $a > 0$. Define two new functions in the open interval $(-2a, 2a)$ by means of the formulas

(9) $$S(x) \equiv 2s(\tfrac{1}{2}x)\, c(\tfrac{1}{2}x),$$

(10) $$C(x) \equiv (c(\tfrac{1}{2}x))^2 - (s(\tfrac{1}{2}x))^2.$$

Prove that $S(x) = s(x)$ and $C(x) = c(x)$ on $(-a, a)$, and that properties (1)-(4), and therefore also (5)-(8), hold for $S(x)$ and $C(x)$ on $(-2a, 2a)$ (where s and c are replaced by S and C, respectively).

★6. Prove that a repeated application of the extension definitions of Exercise 5 provide two functions, $\sin x$ and $\cos x$, defined and differentiable for all real numbers, possessing properties (1)-(8) (where $s(x)$ and $c(x)$ are replaced by $\sin x$ and $\cos x$, respectively), and agreeing with the originally defined $\sin x$ and $\cos x$ on the interval $(-b, b)$ of Exercise 2.

★7. Prove that $\sin x$ and $\cos x$, as defined for all real numbers x, are odd and even functions, respectively. (Cf. Exs. 7-8, § 503.)

★8. Prove that $\sin \tfrac{1}{2}\pi = 1$, and $\cos \tfrac{1}{2}\pi = 0$, and that $\tfrac{1}{2}\pi$ is the smallest positive number whose sine is 1 and also the smallest positive number whose cosine is 0. Hence show that in the closed interval $[0, \tfrac{1}{2}\pi]$, $\sin x$ and $\cos x$ are strictly increasing and decreasing, respectively. Hint: If $2k \leq \tfrac{1}{2}\pi$, and if $\sin 2k = 1$, then $\cos 2k = \cos^2 k - \sin^2 k = 0$, and $\cos k = \sin k = \tfrac{1}{2}\sqrt{2}$, and $k = \tfrac{1}{4}\pi$.

★9. Prove that $\sin \pi = 0$ and $\cos \pi = -1$, and that π is the smallest positive number whose sine is 0 and also the smallest positive number whose cosine is -1.

★10. Prove that $\sin 2\pi = 0$ and $\cos 2\pi = 1$, and that 2π is the smallest positive number whose cosine is 1.

★**11.** Prove that $\sin x$ and $\cos x$ are periodic with period 2π. That is, $\sin (x + 2\pi) = \sin x$ and $\cos (x + 2\pi) = \cos x$ for all x, and if either $\sin (x + k) = \sin x$ or $\cos (x + k) = \cos x$ for all x, then $k = 2n\pi$, for some integer n.

★**12.** Prove that $\sin x$ and $\cos x$ have the familiar signs in the appropriate "quadrants"; namely, $+$, $+$, $-$, $-$, and $+$, $-$, $-$, $+$, respectively, for x in the ranges $(0, \frac{1}{2}\pi)$, $(\frac{1}{2}\pi, \pi)$, $(\pi, \frac{3}{2}\pi)$, $(\frac{3}{2}\pi, 2\pi)$.

★**13.** Prove that if λ and μ are any two real numbers such that $\lambda^2 + \mu^2 = 1$, then there is a unique value of x in the half open interval $[0, 2\pi)$ such that $\sin x = \lambda$ and $\cos x = \mu$. *Hint:* Let x_0 be the unique number in the closed interval $[0, \frac{1}{2}\pi]$ whose sine is $|\lambda|$, and choose for x the appropriate number according to Ex. 12: $x_0, \pi - x_0, \pi + x_0, 2\pi - x_0$.

★**14.** Prove that $-1 \leqq \sin x \leqq 1$ and $-1 \leqq \cos x \leqq 1$ for all x.

★**15.** Prove that $\sin x$ and $\cos x$ have, everywhere, continuous derivatives of all orders.

★**16.** Prove that $\lim\limits_{x\to 0} \dfrac{\sin x}{x} = 1$.

Hint: Let $f(x) \equiv \sin x$. Then $f'(0) = \lim\limits_{h\to 0} \dfrac{f(0 + h) - f(0)}{h}$.

★★**17.** Prove that the function $f(x) \equiv \dfrac{\sin x}{x}$, $x \neq 0$, $f(0) \equiv 1$, (i) is everywhere continuous; (ii) is everywhere differentiable; (iii) has everywhere a continuous nth derivative for all positive integers n.

605. SOME INTEGRATION FORMULAS

We start by asking two questions. (i) If $\displaystyle\int \frac{dx}{x} = \ln x + C$, and if $\ln x$ is defined only for $x > 0$, how does one evaluate the simple integral $\displaystyle\int_{-3}^{-2} \frac{dx}{x}$?

(ii) If $\displaystyle\int \frac{dx}{a^2 - x^2} = \frac{1}{2a} \ln \frac{a + x}{a - x} + C$ and $\displaystyle\int \frac{dx}{x^2 - a^2} = \frac{1}{2a} \ln \frac{x - a}{x + a} + C'$,

where $a > 0$, why cannot each of these integration formulas be obtained from the other by a mere change in sign? In other words, why does their sum, which should be a constant, give formally the result

$$\frac{1}{2a} \ln \left(\frac{a + x}{a - x} \cdot \frac{x - a}{x + a}\right) + C + C' \text{ or } \frac{1}{2a} \ln (-1) + C + C'$$

which does not even exist!

The answers to these questions lie most simply in the use of absolute values. We know that if $x > 0$, then $\dfrac{d}{dx} (\ln (x)) = \dfrac{1}{x}$ and that if $x < 0$, then $\dfrac{d}{dx} (\ln (-x)) = \dfrac{1}{-x} (-1) = \dfrac{1}{x}$. That is, $\ln x$ and $\ln (-x)$ both have the same derivative, formally, but have completely distinct domains of definition, $\ln x$ being defined for $x > 0$ and $\ln (-x)$ for $x < 0$. The function $\ln |x|$ encompasses both and is defined for any nonzero x. Thus the single integration formula

(1)
$$\int \frac{dx}{x} = \ln |x| + C$$

is applicable under all possible circumstances. The integration of question (i) is therefore simple: $\int_{-3}^{-2} \frac{dx}{x} = \left[\ln |x| \right]_{-3}^{-2} = \ln |-2| - \ln |-3| = \ln \frac{2}{3}$.

For similar reasons the formulas of question (ii) are only apparently incompatible, since they apply to different domains of definition. The first is applicable if $x^2 < a^2$ and the second if $x^2 > a^2$. (Ex. 11, § 606.) However, again a single integration formula is available which is universally applicable, and can be written alternatively in the two forms:

(2)
$$\int \frac{dx}{a^2 - x^2} = \frac{1}{2a} \ln \left| \frac{a + x}{a - x} \right| + C;$$

(2′)
$$\int \frac{dx}{x^2 - a^2} = \frac{1}{2a} \ln \left| \frac{x - a}{x + a} \right| + C.$$

The seeming paradox is resolved by the fact that $|-1| = 1$, whose logarithm certainly exists (although it vanishes).

More generally, any of the standard integration formulas that involve logarithms become universally applicable when absolute values are inserted. The student should establish this fact in detail for the following formulas (Ex. 12, § 606). (In formulas (7)-(14), a represents a positive constant.)

(3) $\int \tan x \, dx = -\ln |\cos x| + C = \ln |\sec x| + C;$

(4) $\int \cot x \, dx = \ln |\sin x| + C = -\ln |\csc x| + C;$

(5) $\int \sec x \, dx = \ln |\sec x + \tan x| + C;$

(6) $\int \csc x \, dx = \ln |\csc x - \cot x| + C;$

(7) $\int \frac{dx}{\sqrt{x^2 \pm a^2}} = \ln |x + \sqrt{x^2 \pm a^2}| + C, \; |x| > a$ for the $-$ case;

(8) $\int \sqrt{x^2 \pm a^2} \, dx = \frac{1}{2}[x\sqrt{x^2 \pm a^2} \pm a^2 \ln |x + \sqrt{x^2 \pm a^2}|] + C, \; |x| > a$
       for the $-$ case;

(9) $\int \frac{dx}{x\sqrt{a^2 \pm x^2}} = \frac{1}{a} \ln \left| \frac{\sqrt{a^2 \pm x^2} - a}{x} \right| + C, \; |x| < a$ for the $-$ case.

Since the derivative of $\sec x \tan x$ is

$$\sec^3 x + \sec x \tan^2 x = \sec^3 x + \sec x \, (\sec^2 x - 1) = 2 \sec^3 x - \sec x,$$

and since by (5), above, the derivative of $\ln |\sec x + \tan x|$ is $\sec x$, we have, by addition,

(10) $$\int \sec^3 x \, dx = \tfrac{1}{2} \sec x \tan x + \tfrac{1}{2} \ln |\sec x + \tan x| + C.$$

Finally, we give four more integration formulas, which involve inverse trigonometric functions. These are valid for the principal value ranges specified. The student should draw the graphs of the functions involved and verify the statements just made, as well as show that the formulas that follow are not all valid if the range of the inverse function is unrestricted (Ex. 13, § 606).

(11) $$\int \frac{dx}{\sqrt{a^2 - x^2}} = \operatorname{Arcsin} \frac{x}{a} + C, \ -a < x < a, \ -\frac{\pi}{2} \leqq \operatorname{Arcsin} \frac{x}{a} \leqq \frac{\pi}{2};$$

(12) $$\int \frac{dx}{a^2 + x^2} = \frac{1}{a} \operatorname{Arctan} \frac{x}{a} + C, \ -\frac{\pi}{2} < \operatorname{Arctan} \frac{x}{a} < \frac{\pi}{2};$$

(13) $$\int \sqrt{a^2 - x^2} \, dx = \tfrac{1}{2} x \sqrt{a^2 - x^2} + \tfrac{1}{2} a^2 \operatorname{Arcsin} \frac{x}{a} + C, \ |x| < a;$$

(14) $$\int \frac{dx}{x\sqrt{x^2 - a^2}} = \begin{cases} -\dfrac{1}{a} \operatorname{Arcsin} \left(\dfrac{a}{x} \right) + C, \ x > a, \\[2ex] \dfrac{1}{a} \operatorname{Arcsin} \left(\dfrac{a}{x} \right) + C, \ x < -a. \end{cases}$$

606. EXERCISES

In Exercises 1-10, perform the integration, and specify any limitations on the variable x.

1. $\displaystyle \int \tan 5x \, dx.$

2. $\displaystyle \int \sec 4x \, dx.$

3. $\displaystyle \int \frac{dx}{\sqrt{2 - x^2}}.$

4. $\displaystyle \int \sqrt{x^2 + 4x} \, dx.$

5. $\displaystyle \int \frac{dx}{\sqrt{4x^2 - 4x + 5}}.$

6. $\displaystyle \int \sqrt{x - 3x^2} \, dx.$

7. $\displaystyle \int \frac{dx}{x\sqrt{5 - 2x^2}}.$

8. $\displaystyle \int \frac{\sec^3 \sqrt{x}}{\sqrt{x}} \, dx.$

9. $\displaystyle \int \frac{dx}{3x^2 + 5x - 7}.$

10. $\displaystyle \int \frac{dx}{3x^2 + 5x + 7}.$

11. Show that in formula (2), § 605, the absolute value signs can be removed if $|x| < a$, and similarly for formula (2'), § 605, if $|x| > a$. *Hints:* The quotient of $a + x$ and $a - x$ is positive if and only if their product is positive.

12. Establish formulas (3)-(9), § 605, by direct evaluation rather than mere differentiation of the right-hand members. *Hints:* For (3)-(6) express the functions in terms of sines and cosines. For (7)-(9) make trigonometric substitutions and, if necessary, use (10), § 605.

13. Establish formulas (11)-(14), § 605, by direct evaluation. (Cf. Ex. 12.)

607. HYPERBOLIC FUNCTIONS

The hyperbolic functions, called *hyperbolic sine, hyperbolic cosine,* etc., are defined:

(1)
$$\sinh x \equiv \frac{e^x - e^{-x}}{2}, \qquad \coth x \equiv \frac{1}{\tanh x},$$

$$\cosh x \equiv \frac{e^x + e^{-x}}{2}, \qquad \operatorname{sech} x \equiv \frac{1}{\cosh x},$$

$$\tanh x \equiv \frac{\sinh x}{\cosh x}, \qquad \operatorname{csch} x \equiv \frac{1}{\sinh x}.$$

These six functions bear a close resemblance to the trigonometric functions. For example, $\sinh x$, $\tanh x$, $\coth x$, and $\operatorname{csch} x$ are odd functions and $\cosh x$ and $\operatorname{sech} x$ are even functions. (Ex. 21, § 609.) Furthermore, the hyperbolic functions satisfy identities that are similar to the basic trigonometric identities (verify the details in Ex. 22, § 609):

(2)　$\cosh^2 x - \sinh^2 x = 1;$

(3)　$1 - \tanh^2 x = \operatorname{sech}^2 x;$

(4)　$\coth^2 x - 1 = \operatorname{csch}^2 x;$

(5)　$\sinh (x \pm y) = \sinh x \cosh y \pm \cosh x \sinh y;$

(6)　$\cosh (x \pm y) = \cosh x \cosh y \pm \sinh x \sinh y;$

(7)　$\tanh (x \pm y) = \dfrac{\tanh x \pm \tanh y}{1 \pm \tanh x \tanh y};$

(8)　$\sinh 2x = 2 \sinh x \cosh x;$

(9)　$\cosh 2x = \cosh^2 x + \sinh^2 x = 2 \cosh^2 x - 1 = 2 \sinh^2 x + 1.$

The differentiation formulas (and therefore the corresponding integration formulas, which are omitted here) also have a familiar appearance (Ex. 23, § 609):

(10)　$d(\sinh x)/dx = \cosh x;$

(11)　$d(\cosh x)/dx = \sinh x;$

(12)　$d(\tanh x)/dx = \operatorname{sech}^2 x;$

(13)　$d(\coth x)/dx = -\operatorname{csch}^2 x;$

(14)　$d(\operatorname{sech} x)/dx = -\operatorname{sech} x \tanh x;$

(15)　$d(\operatorname{csch} x)/dx = -\operatorname{csch} x \coth x.$

The graphs of the first four hyperbolic functions are given in Figure 605.

A set of integration formulas (omitting those that are mere reformulations of the differentiation formulas (10)-(15) follows (Ex. 24, § 609):

(16) $$\int \tanh x \, dx = \ln \cosh x + C;$$

(17) $$\int \coth x \, dx = \ln |\sinh x| + C;$$

(18) $$\int \operatorname{sech} x \, dx = \operatorname{Arctan}(\sinh x) + C;$$

(19) $$\int \operatorname{csch} x \, dx = \ln \left| \tanh \frac{x}{2} \right| + C.$$

NOTE. The trigonometric functions are sometimes called the **circular functions** because of their relation to a circle. For example, the parametric equations of the circle $x^2 + y^2 = a^2$ can be written $x = a \cos \theta$, $y = a \sin \theta$. In analogy with this, the hyperbolic functions are related to a hyperbola. For example, the parametric equations of the rectangular hyperbola $x^2 - y^2 = a^2$ can be written $x = a \cosh \theta$, $y = a \sinh \theta$. In this latter case, however, the parameter θ does not represent the polar coordinate angle for the point (x, y).

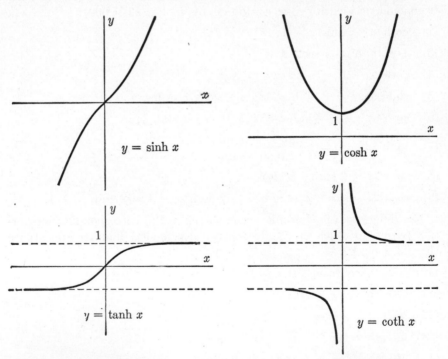

FIG. 605

608. INVERSE HYPERBOLIC FUNCTIONS

The integrals of certain algebraic functions are expressed in terms of inverse trigonometric functions (§ 605). In a similar fashion, the integrals of certain other algebraic functions can be expressed in terms of inverse hyperbolic functions. The four hyperbolic functions whose inverses are the most useful in this connection are the first four, sinh x, cosh x, tanh x, and coth x. The graphs and notation are given in Figure 606. For simplicity, by analogy with the principal value ranges for the inverse trigonometric functions, we choose only the nonnegative values of $\cosh^{-1} x$, and write for these principal values $\text{Cosh}^{-1} x$.

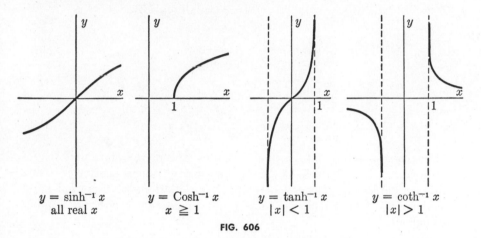

$$y = \sinh^{-1} x \qquad y = \text{Cosh}^{-1} x \qquad y = \tanh^{-1} x \qquad y = \coth^{-1} x$$
$$\text{all real } x \qquad x \geq 1 \qquad |x| < 1 \qquad |x| > 1$$

FIG. 606

The inverse hyperbolic functions can be expressed in terms of functions discussed previously:

(1) $\qquad \sinh^{-1} x = \ln (x + \sqrt{x^2 + 1})$, all real x;

(2) $\qquad \text{Cosh}^{-1} x = \ln (x + \sqrt{x^2 - 1})$, $x \geq 1$;

(3) $\qquad \tanh^{-1} x = \tfrac{1}{2} \ln \dfrac{1 + x}{1 - x}$; $|x| < 1$;

(4) $\qquad \coth^{-1} x = \tfrac{1}{2} \ln \dfrac{x + 1}{x - 1}$; $|x| > 1$.

We prove (2) and leave the rest for the student (Ex. 25, § 609). If $x = \dfrac{e^y + e^{-y}}{2}$, let the positive quantity e^y be denoted by p. Then $2x = p + \dfrac{1}{p}$, or $p^2 - 2xp + 1 = 0$. Solving this equation we get $p = x \pm \sqrt{x^2 - 1}$. Since y is to be chosen nonnegative, $p = e^y \geq 1$. If

$x > 1$, $x + \sqrt{x^2 - 1} > 1$, and since the product of this and $x - \sqrt{x^2 - 1}$ is equal to 1, $x - \sqrt{x^2 - 1} < 1$. We therefore reject the minus sign and have $p = x + \sqrt{x^2 - 1}$, or equation (2). Notice that the expressions in (3) and (4) exist for the specified values of x. For example, in (3), $(1 + x)$ and $(1 - x)$ have a positive quotient if and only if they have a positive product, and $1 - x^2 > 0$ if and only if $|x| < 1$.

The derivatives of the four inverse hyperbolic functions considered here can either be obtained from the derivatives of the corresponding hyperbolic functions (Ex. 26, § 609) or from formulas (1)-(4) (Ex. 27, § 609). They are:

(5)
$$\frac{d}{dx} \sinh^{-1} x = \frac{1}{\sqrt{1 + x^2}}, \text{ all real } x;$$

(6)
$$\frac{d}{dx} \text{Cosh}^{-1} x = \frac{1}{\sqrt{x^2 - 1}}, x > 1;$$

(7)
$$\frac{d}{dx} \tanh^{-1} x = \frac{1}{1 - x^2}, |x| < 1;$$

(8)
$$\frac{d}{dx} \coth^{-1} x = \frac{1}{1 - x^2}, |x| > 1.$$

The corresponding integration formulas are mere reformulations of formulas (2) and (7) of § 605, with appropriate ranges specified. They can be established independently by differentiations of the right-hand members (Ex. 28, § 609). The letter a represents a positive number throughout.

(9)
$$\int \frac{dx}{\sqrt{a^2 + x^2}} = \sinh^{-1} \frac{x}{a} + C, \text{ all real } x;$$

(10)
$$\int \frac{dx}{\sqrt{x^2 - a^2}} = \text{Cosh}^{-1} \frac{x}{a} + C, x > a;$$

(11)
$$\int \frac{dx}{a^2 - x^2} = \frac{1}{a} \tanh^{-1} \frac{x}{a} + C, |x| < a;$$

(12)
$$\int \frac{dx}{x^2 - a^2} = -\frac{1}{a} \coth^{-1} \frac{x}{a} + C, |x| > a.$$

609. EXERCISES

In Exercises 1-10, differentiate the given function.

1. $\cosh 3x$.

2. $\sinh^2 x$.

3. $\tanh (2 - x)$.

4. $x \coth x^2$.

5. $\ln \sinh 2x$.

6. $e^{ax} \cosh bx$.

7. $\sinh^{-1} 4x$.

8. $\text{Cosh}^{-1} e^x$.

9. $\tanh^{-1} x^2$.

10. $\coth^{-1} (\sec x)$.

In Exercises 11-20, perform the indicated integration, expressing your answer in terms of hyperbolic functions or their inverses.

11. $\int \tanh 6x \, dx.$ **12.** $\int e^x \coth e^x \, dx.$

13. $\int \cosh^3 x \, dx.$ **14.** $\int \tanh^2 10x \, dx.$

15. $\int \sinh^2 x \, dx.$ **16.** $\int x^3 \tanh^{-1} x \, dx.$

17. $\int \dfrac{dx}{\sqrt{x^2 - 2}}.$ **18.** $\int \dfrac{dx}{\sqrt{4x^2 - 4x + 5}}.$

19. $\int \dfrac{dx}{3x^2 + 5x - 7},$ **20.** $\int \dfrac{dx}{7 - 5x - 3x^2},$

$(3x^2 + 5x - 7 > 0).$ $(7 - 5x - 3x^2 > 0).$

21. Prove that $\cosh x$ and $\operatorname{sech} x$ are even functions and that the other four hyperbolic functions are odd (cf. Exs. 7-8, § 503).

22. Establish the identities (2)-(9), § 607.

23. Establish the differentiation formulas (10)-(15), § 607.

24. Establish the integration formulas (16)-(19), § 607. *Hint for* (19): $\int \dfrac{dx}{\sinh x} = \int \dfrac{du}{u^2 - 1},$ where $u = \cosh x,$ and $\dfrac{\cosh x - 1}{\cosh x + 1} = \dfrac{2 \sinh^2 \frac{1}{2}x}{2 \cosh^2 \frac{1}{2}x}.$

25. Establish formulas (1), (3), (4), § 608.

26. Establish formulas (5)-(8), § 608, by use of (10)-(13), § 607. *Hint for* (5): Let $y = \sinh^{-1} x.$ Then $x = \sinh y,$ $dx/dy = \cosh y,$ and $dy/dx = 1/\sqrt{1 + \sinh^2 y}.$

27. Establish formulas (5)-(8), § 608, by use of (1)-(4), § 608.

28. Establish formulas (9)-(12), § 608.

★29. Show that $\int \operatorname{csch} x \, dx = -\coth^{-1}(\cosh x) + C.$

★30. Establish formulas (7)-(9), § 605, by means of hyperbolic substitutions.

★610. CLASSIFICATION OF NUMBERS AND FUNCTIONS

Certain classes of numbers (integers, rational numbers, and irrational numbers) were defined in Chapter 1. Another important class of numbers is the algebraic numbers, an **algebraic number** being defined to be a root of a **polynomial equation**

(1) $$a_0 x^n + a_1 x^{n-1} + \cdots + a_n = 0,$$

where the coefficients $a_0, a_1, \cdots, a_n$ are integers. Examples of algebraic numbers are $\frac{3}{4}$ (a root of the equation $4x - 3 = 0$) (in fact, *every rational number is algebraic*), $-\sqrt[3]{5}$ (a root of the equation $x^3 + 5 = 0$), and $\sqrt[3]{5} + \sqrt{3}$ (a root of the equation $x^6 - 9x^4 - 10x^3 + 27x^2 - 90x - 2 = 0$). It can be shown† that any number that is the sum, difference, product, or

† Cf. Birkhoff and MacLane, *A Survey of Modern Algebra* (New York, The Macmillan Company, 1944).

quotient of algebraic numbers is algebraic, and that any (real) root of an algebraic number is an algebraic number. Therefore any number (like $\sqrt{3} - \sqrt[6]{8/9} / 4\sqrt[7]{61}$) that can be obtained from the integers by a finite sequence of sums, differences, products, quotients, powers, and roots is algebraic. However, it should be appreciated that not every algebraic number is of the type just described. In fact, it is shown in Galois Theory (cf. the Birkhoff and MacLane book just referred to) that the general equation of degree 5 or higher cannot be solved in terms of radicals. In particular, the real root of the equation $x^5 - x - 1 = 0$ (this number is algebraic by definition) cannot be expressed in the finite form described above.

A **transcendental number** is any number that is not algebraic. The most familiar transcendental numbers are e and π. The transcendental character of e was established by Hermite in 1873, and that of π by Lindemann in 1882.† For a discussion of the transcendance of these two numbers see Felix Klein, *Elementary Mathematics from an Advanced Standpoint* (New York, Dover Publications, 1945). The first number to be proved transcendental was neither e nor π, but a number constructed artificially for the purpose by Liouville in 1844. (Cf. the Birkhoff and MacLane reference, page 413.) The existence of a vast infinite supply of transcendental numbers was provided by Cantor in 1874 in his theory of transfinite cardinal numbers. This amounts to showing (Ex. 10, § 612) that the algebraic numbers are denumerable (Ex. 12, § 113) and that the real numbers are not (Ex. 30, § 711). This method, however, merely establishes existence without specifically producing examples.

Functions are classified in a manner similar to that just outlined for numbers. The role played by integers above is now played by polynomials. A **rational function** is any function that can be expressed as the quotient of two polynomials, an **algebraic function** is any function $f(x)$ that satisfies (identically in x) a polynomial equation

$$(2) \qquad a_0(x)(f(x))^n + a_1(x)(f(x))^{n-1} + \cdots + a_n(x) = 0,$$

where $a_0(x)$, $a_1(x)$, $\cdots$, $a_n(x)$ are polynomials, and a **transcendental function** is any function that is not algebraic.

Examples of polynomials are $2x - \sqrt{3}$ and $\pi x^5 + \sqrt{e}$. Examples of rational functions that are not polynomials are $1/x$ and $(x + \sqrt{3})/(5x - 6)$. Examples of algebraic functions that are not rational are $\sqrt{x}$ and $1/\sqrt{x^2 + \pi}$. Examples of transcendental functions are e^x, $\ln x$, $\sin x$, and $\cos x$. (Cf. Exs. 11-13, § 612.)

---

† It is easy to show that e is irrational (Ex. 34, § 811). A proof of the irrationality of π was given in 1761 by Lambert. For an elementary proof, given in 1947 by Niven, see Trygve Nagell, *Introduction to Number Theory* (New York, John Wiley and Sons, Inc., 1951).

★611. THE ELEMENTARY FUNCTIONS

Most of the familiar functions which one encounters at the level of elementary calculus, like $\sin 2x$, e^{-x^2}, and $\frac{1}{2}$ Arctan $\frac{1}{2}x$, are examples of what are called *elementary functions*. In order to define this concept, we describe first the elementary operations on functions. The **elementary operations** on functions $f(x)$ and $g(x)$ are those that yield any of the following: $f(x) \pm g(x)$, $f(x)\, g(x)$, $f(x)/g(x)$, $\{f(x)\}^a$, $a^{f(x)}$, $\log_a f(x)$, and $T(f(x))$, where T is any trigonometric or inverse trigonometric function. The **elementary functions** are those generated by constants and the independent variable by means of a finite sequence of elementary operations. Thus

$$(x^2 + 17\pi)^e \text{ Arcsin } [(\log_3 \cos x)(e^{\sqrt{x}})]$$

is an elementary function. Its derivative is also an elementary function. In fact (cf. Ex. 9, § 612), the derivative of any elementary function is an elementary function. Reasonable questions to be asked at this point are, "Is there ever any occasion to study functions that are *not* elementary? What are some examples?" The answer is that nonelementary functions arise in connection with infinite series, differential equations, integral equations, and equations defining functions implicitly. For example, the differential equation $\dfrac{dy}{dx} = \dfrac{\sin x}{x}$ ($=1$ if $x = 0$) has a nonelementary solution

$$(1) \qquad \int_0^x \frac{\sin t}{t}\, dt$$

whose power series expansion (cf. Chapter 7) is

$$x - \frac{x^3}{3\cdot 3\,!} + \frac{x^5}{5\cdot 5\,!} - \frac{x^7}{7\cdot 7\,!} + \cdots.$$

Other examples of nonelementary functions which are integrals of elementary functions are the *probability integral*,

$$(2) \qquad \int_0^x e^{-t^2}\, dt,$$

the *Fresnel sine integral* and *cosine integral*,

$$(3) \qquad \int_0^x \sin t^2\, dt \quad \text{and} \quad \int_0^x \cos t^2\, dt,$$

and the *elliptic integrals of the first and second kind*,

$$(4) \qquad \int_0^x \frac{dt}{\sqrt{1 - k^2 \sin^2 t}} \quad \text{and} \quad \int_0^x \sqrt{1 - k^2 \sin^2 t}\, dt.$$

Extensive tables for these and other nonelementary functions exist.†

† Cf. Eugen Jahnke and Fritz Emde, *Tables of Functions* (New York, Dover Publications, 1943).

Proofs that these functions are not elementary are difficult and will not be given in this book.†

The inverse of an elementary function need not be elementary. For example, the inverse of the function $x - a \sin x$ $(a \neq 0)$, the function defined implicitly by *Kepler's equation*

$$(5) \qquad\qquad y - a \sin y - x = 0,$$

is not elementary.† Again, the proof is omitted.

An important lesson to be extracted from the above considerations is that inability to integrate an elementary function in terms of elementary functions does not mean that the integral fails to exist. In fact, many important nonelementary functions owe their existence to the (Riemann) integration process. This is somewhat similar to the position of the logarithmic, exponential, and trigonometric functions as developed in this chapter, which were defined, ultimately, in terms of Riemann integrals of algebraic functions.

One more final remark. The reader might ask, "Apart from the importance of the functions defined above, if all we seek is an example of a nonelementary function, isn't the bracket function $[x]$ of § 201 one such?" Perhaps the most satisfactory reply is that whereas $[x]$ is elementary in intervals, the functions presented above might be described as "nowhere elementary." A behind-the-scenes principle here is that of analytic continuation, important in the theory of analytic functions of a complex variable. (Cf. § 815.)

★612. EXERCISES

★1. Prove that $\sqrt{5} - \sqrt{2}$ is algebraic by finding a polynomial equation with integral coefficients of which it is a root.

★2. Prove that $1/x$ is not a polynomial. *Hint:* It is not sufficient to remark that it does not *look* like one. Show that $1/x$ has some property that no polynomial can have, such as a certain kind of limit as $x \to \infty$. (Cf. Ex. 4.)

★3. Prove that $\dfrac{x^2}{x+1}$ is not a polynomial (cf. Ex. 2).

★4. Prove that $\sqrt{x^2 + 1}$ is not a polynomial. *Hint:* Differentiate the function a large number of times.

★5. Prove that $\sqrt{x^2 + 1}$ is not rational. (Cf. Ex. 4.)

★6. Prove that the hyperbolic functions and their inverses are elementary.

★7. Prove that x^x is elementary.

★8. Prove that $\displaystyle\int_0^x t^n \sin t \, dt$, where n is a positive integer, is elementary.

★9. Prove that the derivative of any elementary function is elementary.

† Cf. J. F. Ritt, *Integration in Finite Terms* (New York, Columbia University Press, 1948).

★**10.** Prove that the algebraic numbers are denumerable (cf. Ex. 12, § 113). *Hint:* A useful device of Cantor was to let $p(x) = a_0 x^n + \cdots + a_n = 0$ be the (unique!) polynomial equation of lowest degree and smallest positive leading coefficient a_0 ($a_0, \cdots, a_n$ being integers) satisfied by a given algebraic number a and to define the **height** of a to be the positive integer $n - 1 + |a_0| + \cdots |a_n|$. Show that there are only finitely many algebraic numbers having a given height.

★**11.** Prove that e^x is transcendental. *Hint:* Let
$$a_0(x)\, e^{nx} + a_1(x)\, e^{(n-1)x} + \cdots + a_{n-1}(x)\, e^x + a_n(x) = 0,$$
where $a_0(x), \cdots, a_n(x)$ are polynomials and $a_n(x)$ is not identically 0. Form the limit as $x \to -\infty$. Then $\lim\limits_{x \to -\infty} a_n(x) = 0$ (!).

★**12.** Prove that $\ln x$ is transcendental. *Hint:* Let $y \equiv \ln x$, and assume that y satisfies identically a polynomial equation, arranged in the form
$$b_0(y)\, x^n + b_1(y)\, x^{n-1} + \cdots + b_{n-1}(y)\, x + b_n(y) = 0,$$
where $b_0(y)$ is not identically 0. Divide every term by x^n, and let $x \to +\infty$.

★**13.** Prove that $\sin x$ and $\cos x$ are transcendental. *Hint for* $\sin x$: Let
$$a_0(x)\, \sin^n x + a_1(x)\, \sin^{n-1} x + \cdots + a_{n-1}(x)\, \sin x + a_n(x) = 0,$$
where $a_0(x), \cdots, a_n(x)$ are polynomials and $a_n(x)$ is not identically 0. Let $x = k\pi$, where k is so large that $a_n(x) \neq 0$.

7

Infinite Series of Constants

~~~~~~

701. BASIC DEFINITIONS

If $a_1, a_2, \cdots, a_n, \cdots$ is a sequence of numbers, the expression

$$(1) \qquad \sum_{n=1}^{+\infty} a_n = a_1 + a_2 + \cdots + a_n + \cdots$$

(also written $\sum a_n$ if there is no possible misinterpretation) is called an **infinite series** or, in brief, a **series**. The numbers $a_1, a_2, \cdots, a_n, \cdots$ are called **terms,** and the number a_n is called the **nth term** or **general term.**

The sequence $\{S_n\}$, where

$$S_1 \equiv a_1, \ S_2 \equiv a_1 + a_2, \ \cdots, \ S_n \equiv a_1 + a_2 + \cdots + a_n,$$

is called the **sequence of partial sums** of the series (1). An infinite series **converges** or **diverges** according as its sequence of partial sums converges or diverges. In case of convergence, the series (1) is said to have a **sum** equal to the limit of the sequence of partial sums, and if $S \equiv \lim_{n \to +\infty} S_n$, we write

$$(2) \qquad \sum a_n = \sum_{n=1}^{+\infty} a_n = a_1 + \cdots + a_n + \cdots = S,$$

and say that the series **converges to S.**

In case $\lim_{n \to +\infty} S_n$ exists and is infinite the series $\sum a_n$, although divergent, is said to have an **infinite sum**:

$$(3) \qquad \sum a_n = \sum_{n=1}^{+\infty} a_n = a_1 + \cdots + a_n + \cdots = +\infty, \ -\infty, \text{ or } \infty,$$

and the series is said to **diverge to** $+\infty$, $-\infty$, or ∞.

Example 1. $\frac{1}{2} + \frac{1}{4} + \cdots + \frac{1}{2^n} + \cdots = 1$, since the sum of the first n terms is

$$S_n = \frac{1}{2} + \frac{1}{4} + \cdots + \frac{1}{2^n} = 1 - \frac{1}{2^n},$$

and $S_n \to 1$ (cf. Example 3, § 202).

Example 2. The series whose general term is $2n$ diverges to $+\infty$:
$$2 + 4 + 6 + \cdots + 2n + \cdots = +\infty.$$

Example 3. The series
$$1 - 1 + 1 - 1 + \cdots + (-1)^{n+1} + \cdots$$
diverges since its sequence of partial sums is
$$1, 0, 1, 0, 1, 0, 1, \cdots.$$
This sequence diverges since, if it converged to S, every subsequence would also converge to S, and S would equal both 0 and 1, in contradiction to the uniqueness of the limit of a sequence.   (Cf. § 204; also Example 4, § 202.)

702. THREE ELEMENTARY THEOREMS

Direct consequences of Theorems I, II, and X, § 204, are the following:

Theorem I.   *The alteration of a finite number of terms of a series has no effect on convergence or divergence (although it will in general change the sum in case of convergence).*

Theorem II.   *If a series converges or has an infinite sum, this sum is unique.*

Theorem III.   *Multiplication of the terms of a series by a nonzero constant k does not affect convergence or divergence.   If the original series converges, the new series converges to k times the sum of the original, for any constant k:*

(1)
$$\sum_{n=1}^{+\infty} k\, a_n = k \sum_{n=1}^{+\infty} a_n.$$

(Cf. Ex. 27, § 707.)

703. A NECESSARY CONDITION FOR CONVERGENCE

Theorem.   *If a series converges, its general term tends toward zero as n becomes infinite.   Equivalently, if the general term of a series does not tend toward zero as n becomes infinite, the series diverges.*

Proof.   Assume the series, $a_1 + a_2 + \cdots$, converges to S. Then $S_n = S_{n-1} + a_n$, or $a_n = S_n - S_{n-1}$. Since the sequence of partial sums converges to S, both S_n and S_{n-1} tend toward S as n becomes infinite. Hence (Theorem VII, § 204),

$$\lim_{n \to +\infty} a_n = \lim_{n \to +\infty} (S_n - S_{n-1}) = S - S = 0.$$

Example.   Show that the series $2 + 4 + \cdots + 2n + \cdots$ and $0 + 1 + 0 + 1 + \cdots$ diverge.

Solution.   In neither case does the general term tend toward zero, although the second series contains a subsequence converging to zero.

NOTE. The condition of the theorem is necessary but *not sufficient* for convergence. It will be shown later (Theorem IV, § 708) that the *harmonic series* $1 + \frac{1}{2} + \frac{1}{3} + \cdots$ diverges, although the general term, $\frac{1}{n}$, converges to zero.

704. THE GEOMETRIC SERIES

The series

$$(1) \qquad a + ar + ar^2 + \cdots + ar^{n-1} + \cdots$$

is known as a **geometric series**.

Theorem. *The geometric series* (1), *where $a \neq 0$, converges if $|r| < 1$, with $\frac{a}{1-r}$ as its sum, and diverges if $|r| \geqq 1$.*

Proof. By use of the formula of algebra for the sum of the terms of a finite geometric progression, the sum of the first n terms of (1) can be written

$$S_n = \frac{a - ar^n}{1 - r} = \frac{a}{1 - r} - \frac{a}{1 - r} r^n.$$

If $|r| < 1$, $\lim\limits_{n \to +\infty} r^n = 0$ (Theorem XIII, § 204), and therefore

$$\lim_{n \to +\infty} S_n = \frac{a}{1 - r} - \frac{a}{1 - r} \lim_{n \to +\infty} r^n = \frac{a}{1 - r}.$$

If $|r| \geqq 1$, $|ar^{n-1}| = |a| \cdot |r|^{n-1} \geqq |a|$, and the general term of (1) does not tend toward zero. Therefore, by the Theorem of § 703, the series (1) diverges.

Example. Determine for each of the following series whether the series converges or diverges. In case of convergence, find the sum:

(a) $\frac{1}{2} + \frac{1}{4} + \frac{1}{8} + \frac{1}{16} + \cdots$;   (b) $2 + 3 + \frac{9}{2} + \frac{27}{4} + \cdots$;

(c) $3 - 2 + \frac{4}{3} - \frac{8}{9} + \cdots$.

Solution. (a) The series converges since $r = \frac{1}{2} < 1$, and the sum is $\dfrac{\frac{1}{2}}{1 - \frac{1}{2}} = 1$.

(b) The series diverges since $r = \frac{3}{2} > 1$.   (c) The series converges since $r = -\frac{2}{3}$, and $|r| < 1$. The sum is $\dfrac{3}{1 - (-\frac{2}{3})} = \dfrac{9}{5}$.

705. POSITIVE SERIES

For a **positive series** (a series whose terms are positive) or, more generally, a **nonnegative series** (a series whose terms are nonnegative), there is a simple criterion for convergence.

Theorem.   *The series* $\sum\limits_{n=1}^{+\infty} a_n$, *where* $a_n \geqq 0$, *converges if and only if the sequence of partial sums is bounded; that is, if and only if there is a number* A *such that* $a_1 + \cdots + a_n \leqq A$ *for all values of* n. *If this condition is satisfied, the sum of the series is less than or equal to* A. *A series of nonnegative terms either converges, or diverges to* $+\infty$.

Proof.   Since $S_{n+1} = S_n + a_n$, the condition $a_n \geqq 0$ is equivalent to the condition $S_n \uparrow$, that is, that the sequence $\{S_n\}$ is monotonically increasing. The Theorem of this section is therefore a direct consequence of the Note following Theorem XIV, § 204.

706. THE INTEGRAL TEST

A convenient test for establishing convergence or divergence for certain series of positive terms makes use of the technique of integration.

Theorem.   **Integral Test.**   *If* $\sum a_n$ *is a positive series and if* $f(x)$ *is a positive monotonically decreasing function, defined for* $x \geqq a$, *where* a *is some real number, and if (for integral values of* n) $f(n) = a_n$ *for* $n > a$, *then the improper integral*

$$(1) \qquad\qquad \int_a^{+\infty} f(x) \, dx$$

and the infinite series

$$(2) \qquad\qquad \sum_{n=1}^{+\infty} a_n$$

either both converge, or both diverge to $+\infty$.

Proof.   Let us observe that both (1) and (2) always exist, in the finite or $+\infty$ sense. (Why? Supply details in Ex. 28, § 707.) We wish to show that the finiteness of either implies the finiteness of the other. With the aid of results given in §§ 511, 702, and 705, we have only to show that if K is a fixed positive integer $\geqq a$ and if N is an arbitrary integer $> K$, then the boundedness (as a function of N) of either

$$(3) \qquad\qquad I(N) \equiv \int_K^N f(x) \, dx$$

or

$$(4) \qquad\qquad J(N) \equiv \sum_{n=K}^N a_n$$

implies that of the other. (Cf. Ex. 29, § 707). Let us look at the geometric representations of (3) and (4) given in Figure 701. Each term of (4) is the area of a rectangle of width 1 and height a_n. This suggests that if (3) is written as the sum

(5) $$I(N) = \int_K^N f(x)\,dx = \sum_{n=K}^{N-1} \int_n^{n+1} f(x)\,dx,$$

then each term of (5) is trapped between successive terms of (4). Indeed, for the interval $n \leq x \leq n+1$, since $f(x)$ is monotonically decreasing,

$$a_n = f(n) \geq f(x) \geq f(n+1) = a_{n+1},$$

so that

$$a_n = \int_n^{n+1} a_n\,dx \geq \int_n^{n+1} f(x)\,dx \geq \int_n^{n+1} a_{n+1}\,dx = a_{n+1}.$$

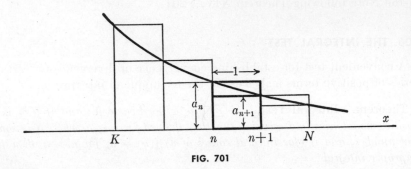

FIG. 701

Therefore

$$\sum_{n=K}^{N-1} a_n \geq \int_K^N f(x)\,dx \geq \sum_{n=K}^{N-1} a_{n+1}.$$

Consequently (in the notation of (3) and (4)), since

$$\sum_{n=K}^{N-1} a_{n+1} = \sum_{n=K+1}^{N} a_n = J(N) - a_K,$$

$$J(N-1) \geq I(N) \geq J(N) - a_K.$$

These two inequalities show that the boundedness of either $J(N)$ or $I(N)$ implies that of the other (Ex. 30, § 707) and the proof is complete.

Example 1. Show that the *p*-series

$$\sum_{n=1}^{+\infty} \frac{1}{n^p}$$

converges if $p > 1$ and diverges if $p \leq 1$.

Solution. This follows immediately from Example 3, § 511, if $p \geq 0$. If $p < 0$, the conclusion is trivial.

Example 2. Show that $\sum_{n=2}^{+\infty} \dfrac{1}{n(\ln n)^p}$ converges if and only if $p > 1$.

Solution. The integral $\int_2^{+\infty} \dfrac{dx}{x(\ln x)^p}$ converges if and only if $p > 1$. (Ex. 28, § 513.)

707. EXERCISES

In Exercises 1-4, find an expression for the sum of the first n terms of the series. Thus find the sum of the series, if it exists.

1. $\dfrac{1}{1 \cdot 2} + \dfrac{1}{2 \cdot 3} + \dfrac{1}{3 \cdot 4} + \cdots$.   *Hint:* $\dfrac{1}{n(n+1)} = \dfrac{1}{n} - \dfrac{1}{n+1}$.

2. $\dfrac{1}{1 \cdot 3} + \dfrac{1}{3 \cdot 5} + \dfrac{1}{5 \cdot 7} + \cdots$.

3. $\frac{1}{3} + \frac{2}{9} + \frac{4}{27} + \frac{8}{81} + \cdots$.   **4.** $1 + 2 + 3 + 4 + \cdots$.

In Exercises 5-8, write down the first four terms and the general term of the series whose sequence of partial sums is given.

5. $2, 2\frac{1}{2}, 2\frac{2}{3}, 2\frac{3}{4}, \cdots$.   **6.** $1, 3, 1, 3, 1, 3, \cdots$.

7. $1.3, 0.91, 1.027, 0.9919, \cdots, 1 - (-.3)^n, \cdots$.

8. $2, 1.3, 1.09, 1.027, \cdots, 1 + (.3)^{n-1}, \cdots$.

In Exercises 9-12, determine whether the given geometric series is convergent or not, and find its sum in case of convergence.

9. $12 - 8 + \cdots$.   **10.** $8 - 12 + \cdots$.

11. $0.27 + 0.027 + \cdots$.   **12.** $101 - 100 + \cdots$.

In Exercises 13-16, find as a quotient of integers the rational number represented by the repeating decimal, by means of geometric series.

13. $0.5555 \cdots$.   *Hint:* $0.5555 \cdots$ means $0.5 + 0.05 + 0.005 + \cdots$.

14. $3.285555 \cdots$.   *Hint:* Write the number $3.28 + 0.005555 \cdots$.

15. $6.1727272 \cdots$.   **16.** $0.428571428571428571 \cdots$.

In Exercises 17-26, establish convergence or divergence by the integral test of § 506.

17. $\sum \dfrac{1}{2n+1}$.   **18.** $\sum \dfrac{n}{n^2+3}$.

19. $\sum \dfrac{1}{n^2+4}$,   **20.** $\sum \dfrac{n}{e^n}$.

21. $\displaystyle\sum_{n=3}^{+\infty} \dfrac{1}{n^2-4}$.   **22.** $\displaystyle\sum_{n=4}^{+\infty} \dfrac{1}{\sqrt{n^2-9}}$.

23. $\sum \dfrac{\ln n}{n}$.   **24.** $\displaystyle\sum_{n=3}^{+\infty} \dfrac{1}{n(\ln n)(\ln \ln n)^2}$.

25. $\sum \dfrac{1}{(n+1)^3}$.   **26.** $\sum \dfrac{1}{n^3+1}$.

27. Establish formula (1) of Theorem III, § 702, for the case of an infinite sum ($+\infty$, $-\infty$, or ∞).

28. Explain why both (1) and (2), § 706 must exist, as either finite or infinite limits. (Cf. Theorem X, § 501.)

29. For the Theorem of § 706 prove that it is sufficient to show that the boundedness of either (3) or (4) implies that of the other. In particular, explain why we may use K in place of a in (3) and K in place of 1 in (4).

30. Supply the details needed in the last sentence of the proof of § 706.

31. Prove that $\sum\limits_{n=3}^{+\infty} \dfrac{1}{n(\ln n)(\ln \ln n)^p}$ converges if and only if $p > 1$. More

generally, prove that $\sum\limits_{n=N}^{+\infty} \dfrac{1}{n(\ln n)(\ln \ln n) \cdots (\ln \ln \cdots \ln n)^p}$, where N is suf-

ficiently large for $(\ln \ln \cdots \ln n)$ to be defined, converges if and only if $p > 1$.
(Cf. Ex. 29, § 513.)

★32. Indicate by a graph how you could define a function $f(x)$ having the

properties: $f(x)$ is positive, continuous, defined for $x \geqq 0$, $\displaystyle\int_0^{+\infty} f(x)\, dx$ con-

verges, and $\sum\limits_{n=1}^{+\infty} f(n)$ diverges.   (Cf. Ex. 40, § 513.)

★33. Indicate by a graph how you could define a function $f(x)$ having the

properties: $f(x)$ is positive, continuous, defined for $x \geqq 0$, $\displaystyle\int_0^{+\infty} f(x)\, dx$ diverges,

and $\sum\limits_{n=1}^{+\infty} f(n)$ converges.

708. COMPARISON TESTS. DOMINANCE

In establishing the integral test of § 706 we have already made use of the fact that a series of positive terms converges if and only if its sequence of partial sums is *bounded*. In order to prove convergence for a series of positive terms it is necessary to show only that the terms *approach zero fast enough* to keep the partial sums bounded. One of the simplest and most useful ways of doing this is to compare the terms of the given series with those of a series whose behavior is known. The ideas are similar to those relevant to comparison tests for improper integrals (§ 512).

Definition I. *The statement that a series $\sum b_n$ **dominates** a series $\sum a_n$ means that $|a_n| \leqq b_n$ for every positive integer n.*

NOTE 1. Any dominating series consists automatically of nonnegative terms, although a dominated series may have negative terms.

Theorem I. Comparison Test. *Any nonnegative series dominated by a convergent series converges. Equivalently, any series that dominates a divergent nonnegative series diverges.*

Proof.   We shall prove only the first form of the statement (cf. Ex. 21, § 711).   Assume $0 \leqq a_n \leqq b_n$ and that $\sum b_n$ converges.   The convergence of $\sum b_n$ implies the boundedness of the partial sums $\sum\limits_{n=1}^{N} b_n$, which implies

the boundedness of the partial sums $\sum\limits_{n=1}^{N} a_n$.   By the Theorem of § 705, the proof is complete.

Example 1. Prove that the series

$$1 + \frac{1}{2^2} + \frac{1}{3^3} + \cdots \frac{1}{n^n} + \cdots$$

converges.

Solution. Since $\frac{1}{n^n} \leqq \frac{1}{2^n}$, for $n > 1$, the given series is dominated by a convergent geometric series (except for the first term).

Example 2. Prove that the series

$$\frac{1}{2} + \frac{1}{3} + \frac{1}{2^2} + \frac{1}{3^2} + \frac{1}{2^3} + \frac{1}{3^3} + \cdots$$

converges.

Solution. This series is dominated by

$$\frac{1}{2} + \frac{1}{2} + \frac{1}{2^2} + \frac{1}{2^2} + \frac{1}{2^3} + \frac{1}{2^3} + \cdots,$$

whose partial sums are bounded by twice the sum of the convergent geometric series $\sum \frac{1}{2^n}$.

Let us adapt the "big O" notation of § 512 to the present topic:†

Definition II. *If $\{a_n\}$ and $\{b_n\}$ are two sequences, the notation $a_n = O(b_n)$ (read "a sub n is big O of b sub n"), means that there exist a positive integer N and a positive number K such that $n > N$ implies $|a_n| \leqq K\, b_n$. If simultaneously $a_n = O(b_n)$ and $b_n = O(a_n)$, the two sequences (and also the two series $\sum a_n$ and $\sum b_n$) are said to be of the **same order of magnitude** at $+\infty$.*

NOTE 2.   As in § 512, the "big O" notation is also used in the following sense: $a_n = b_n + O(c_n)$ means $a_n - b_n = O(c_n)$.

Big O and order of magnitude relationships are usually established by taking limits:

Theorem II. *Let $\{a_n\}$ and $\{b_n\}$ be sequences of positive terms and assume that $\lim\limits_{n \to +\infty} \frac{a_n}{b_n} = L$ exists, in a finite or infinite sense. Then:*

(i) $0 \leqq L < +\infty$ implies $a_n = O(b_n)$,

(ii) $0 < L \leqq +\infty$ implies $b_n = O(a_n)$,

(iii) $0 < L < +\infty$ implies that $\{a_n\}$ and $\{b_n\}$ are of the same order of magnitude at $+\infty$.

(Give the details of the proof in Ex. 22, § 711.   Cf. Theorem II, § 512.)

---

† The "little o" notation of § 512 takes the form for sequences: $a_n = o(b_n)$ means that there exist a positive integer N and a sequence of nonnegative terms K_n such that $K_n \to 0$ and such that $n > N$ implies $|a_n| \leqq K_n b_n$.   Obviously $a_n = o(b_n)$ implies $a_n = O(b_n)$.

Theorem III. *If $\sum a_n$ and $\sum b_n$ are series of nonnegative terms and if $a_n = O(b_n)$, then the convergence of $\sum b_n$ implies that of $\sum a_n$. Equivalently, the divergence of $\sum a_n$ implies that $\sum b_n$.*

Proof. The convergence of $\displaystyle\sum_{n=N+1}^{+\infty} K b_n$ implies that of $\displaystyle\sum_{n=N+1}^{+\infty} a_n$ by Theorem I.

Corollary. *Two positive series that have the same order of magnitude either both converge or both diverge.*

Because of the usefulness of the p-series, $\sum \dfrac{1}{n^p}$, given in Example 1, § 706, as a "test series," we restate here the facts established in that Example.

Theorem IV. *The **p-series** $\displaystyle\sum_{n=1}^{+\infty} \dfrac{1}{n^p}$ converges if $p > 1$ and diverges if $p \leqq 1$. As a special case, the **harmonic series,** $\displaystyle\sum_{n=1}^{+\infty} \dfrac{1}{n}$, diverges.†*

(Cf. Ex. 29, § 707, for a sequence of test series similar to the p-series, each converging more slowly than the preceding.)

The technique of the comparison test for positive series, particularly in the form of Theorem III, consists usually of four steps:

(*i*) get a "feeling" for how rapidly the terms of the given series are approaching zero;

(*ii*) construct a new test-series of positive terms which dominates, is dominated by, or is of the same order of magnitude as the original series;

(*iii*) establish the necessary inequalities, or the limit of the quotient of the general terms;

(*iv*) infer convergence if the dominating series converges, and divergence if the dominated series diverges.

In practice, one frequently postpones applying a comparison test to a given series until after one has tried one of the more automatic tests (like the ratio test) given in subsequent sections.

Example 3. Test for convergence or divergence:

$$\frac{1}{1\cdot 3} + \frac{2}{5\cdot 7} + \frac{3}{9\cdot 11} + \frac{4}{13\cdot 15} + \cdots .$$

† The function defined by the convergent p-series is called the **Riemann Zeta-function:**

$$(1) \qquad\qquad \zeta(z) \equiv \sum_{n=1}^{+\infty} \frac{1}{n^z}.$$

This function is defined for complex values of z, by (1) if the real part of $z > 1$, and by other means (infinite products, improper integrals) for other values of z. Its values have been tabulated (cf. Fugen Jahnke and Fritz Emde, *Tables of Functions* (New York, Dover Publications, 1943).

Solution. The general term is $\dfrac{n}{(4n-3)(4n-1)}$, which evidently is of the same order of magnitude at $+\infty$ as $\dfrac{1}{n}$ (the limit of the quotient is $\frac{1}{16}$). Since the test series $\sum \dfrac{1}{n}$ diverges, so does the given series.

Example 4. Prove that if $a_n = O(c_n)$ and $b_n = O(d_n)$, then $a_n + b_n = O(c_n + d_n)$ and $a_n b_n = O(c_n d_n)$. Prove that if $a_n = O(c_n)$ and b_n and d_n are sequences of positive numbers which are of the same order of magnitude at $+\infty$, then $\dfrac{a_n}{b_n} = O\left(\dfrac{c_n}{d_n}\right)$.

Solution. For the first part, if $|a_n| \leq K_1 c_n$ and $|b_n| \leq K_2 d_n$, then $|a_n + b_n| \leq \max(K_1, K_2)(c_n + d_n)$ and $|a_n b_n| \leq K_1 K_2 c_n d_n$. For the second part, since $1/b_n = O(1/d_n)$, the result follows from the product form of the first part.

Example 5. Test for convergence or divergence:

$$\frac{\ln 5}{1 \cdot 2} + \frac{\sqrt{3}\,\ln 9}{2 \cdot 3} + \frac{\sqrt{5}\,\ln 13}{3 \cdot 4} + \cdots .$$

Solution. The general term is $\dfrac{\sqrt{2n-1}\,\ln(4n+1)}{n(n+1)}$. Inasmuch as $\sqrt{2n-1} = O(n^{\frac{1}{2}})$ and $\ln(4n+1) = O(n^p)$ for every $p > 0$ (by l'Hospital's Rule), the numerator $= O(n^q)$ for every $q > \frac{1}{2}$ (cf. Example 4). Since the denominator is of the same order of magnitude as n^2 at $+\infty$, the general term $= O(n^r)$ for every $r > -\frac{3}{2}$. Finally, since $\sum n^r$ converges for every $r < -1$, we have only to choose r between $-\frac{3}{2}$ and -1 to establish the convergence of the given series.

709. THE RATIO TEST

One of the most practical routine tests for convergence of a positive series makes use of the ratio of consecutive terms.

Theorem. Ratio test. *Let $\sum a_n$ be a positive series, and define the* **test ratio**

$$r_n \equiv \frac{a_{n+1}}{a_n}.$$

Assume that the limit of this test ratio exists:

$$\lim_{n \to +\infty} r_n = \rho,$$

where $0 \leq \rho \leq +\infty$. Then

   (*i*) *if $0 \leq \rho < 1$, $\sum a_n$ converges;*

   (*ii*) *if $1 < \rho \leq +\infty$, $\sum a_n$ diverges;*

   (*iii*) *if $\rho = 1$, $\sum a_n$ may either converge or diverge, and the test fails.*

Proof of (*i*). Assume $\rho < 1$, and let r be any number such that $\rho < r < 1$. Since $\lim_{n \to +\infty} r_n = \rho < r$, we may choose a neighborhood of ρ that excludes r.

Since every r_n, for n greater than or equal to some N, lies in this neighborhood of ρ, we have:

$$n \geqq N \text{ implies } r_n < r.$$

This gives the following sequence of inequalities:

$$\frac{a_{N+1}}{a_N} < r, \text{ or } a_{N+1} < ra_N,$$

$$\frac{a_{N+2}}{a_{N+1}} < r, \text{ or } a_{N+2} < ra_{N+1} < r^2 a_N,$$

$$\frac{a_{N+3}}{a_{N+2}} < r, \text{ or } a_{N+3} < ra_{N+2} < r^3 a_N,$$
$$\cdots\cdots \qquad \cdots\cdots .$$

Thus, each term of the series

$$(1) \qquad\qquad a_{N+1} + a_{N+2} + a_{N+3} + \cdots$$

is less than the corresponding term of the series

$$(2) \qquad\qquad ra_N + r^2 a_N + r^3 a_N + \cdots .$$

But the series (2) is a geometric series with common ratio $r < 1$, and therefore converges. Since (2) dominates (1), the latter series also converges. Therefore (Theorem I, § 702), the original series $\sum a_n$ converges.

Proof of (ii). By reasoning analogous to that employed above, we see that since $\lim_{n \to +\infty} r_n > 1$, whether the limit is finite or infinite, there must be a number N such that $r_n \geqq 1$ whenever $n \geqq N$. In other words,

$$(3) \qquad\qquad n \geqq N \text{ implies } \frac{a_{n+1}}{a_n} \geqq 1, \text{ or } a_{n+1} \geqq a_n.$$

The inequalities (3) state that beyond the first N terms, each term is at least as large as the preceding term. Since these terms are positive, the limit of the general term cannot be 0 (take $\epsilon \equiv a_N > 0$), and therefore (§ 703) the series $\sum a_n$ diverges.

Proof of (iii). For any p-series the test ratio is $r_n = \dfrac{a_{n+1}}{a_n} = \left(\dfrac{n}{n+1}\right)^p$, and since the function x^p is continuous at $x = 1$ (Ex. 7, § 602),

$$\lim_{n \to +\infty} r_n = \lim_{n \to +\infty} \left(\frac{n}{n+1}\right)^p = \left[\lim_{n \to +\infty} \frac{n}{n+1}\right]^p = 1^p = 1.$$

If $p > 1$ the p-series converges and if $p \leqq 1$ the p-series diverges, but in either case $\rho = 1$.

NOTE 1. For convergence it is important that the *limit* of the test ratio be less than 1. It is not sufficient that the test ratio itself be always less than 1. This is shown by the harmonic series, which diverges, whereas the test ratio $n/(n+1)$ is always less than 1. However, if an inequality of the form

$\frac{a_{n+1}}{a_n} \leq r < 1$ holds for all sufficiently large n (whether the limit ρ exists or not), the series $\sum a_n$ converges.

NOTE 2. For divergence it is sufficient that the test ratio itself be greater than 1. In fact, if $r_n \geq 1$ for all sufficiently large n, the series $\sum a_n$ diverges, since this inequality is the inequality (3) upon which the proof of (ii) rests.

NOTE 3. The ratio test may fail, not only by the equality of ρ and 1, but by the failure of the limit ρ to exist, finitely or infinitely. For example, the series of Example 2, § 708, converges, although the test ratio $r_n = a_{n+1}/a_n$ has no limit, since $r_{2n-1} = 2^n/3^n \to 0$ and $r_{2n} = 3^n/2^{n+1} \to +\infty$.

NOTE 4. The ratio test provides a simple proof that certain limits are zero. That is, if $\lim_{n \to +\infty} a_{n+1}/a_n$, where $a_n > 0$ for all n, exists and is less than 1, then $a_n \to 0$. This is true because a_n is the general term of a convergent series.

Example 1. Prove that $\lim_{n \to +\infty} \dfrac{x^n}{n\,!} = 0$, for every real number x.

Solution. Without loss of generality we can assume $x > 0$ (take absolute values). Then $\dfrac{x^{n+1}}{(n+1)\,!} \div \dfrac{x^n}{n\,!} = \dfrac{x}{n+1} \to 0.$

Example 2. Use the ratio test to establish convergence of the series

$$1 + \frac{1}{1\,!} + \frac{1}{2\,!} + \frac{1}{3\,!} + \cdots + \frac{1}{(n-1)\,!} + \cdots .$$

Solution. Since $a_n = \dfrac{1}{(n-1)\,!}$, $a_{n+1} = \dfrac{1}{n\,!}$ and

$$r_n = \frac{a_{n+1}}{a_n} = \frac{(n-1)\,!}{n\,!} = \frac{1}{n}.$$

Therefore $\rho = \lim_{n \to +\infty} r_n = 0 < 1$.

Example 3. Use the ratio test to establish convergence of the series

$$\frac{1}{2} + \frac{2^2}{2^2} + \frac{3^2}{2^3} + \frac{4^2}{2^4} + \cdots + \frac{n^2}{2^n} + \cdots .$$

Solution. Since $a_n = \dfrac{n^2}{2^n}$, $a_{n+1} = \dfrac{(n+1)^2}{2^{n+1}}$ and

$$r_n = \frac{a_{n+1}}{a_n} = \left(\frac{n+1}{n}\right)^2 \cdot \frac{2^n}{2^{n+1}} = \frac{1}{2}\left(\frac{n+1}{n}\right)^2.$$

Therefore $\rho = \lim_{n \to +\infty} r_n = \frac{1}{2} \lim_{n \to +\infty} \left(1 + \frac{1}{n}\right)^2 = \frac{1}{2} < 1$.

Example 4. Test for convergence or divergence:

$$\frac{1}{3} + \frac{2\,!}{3^2} + \frac{3\,!}{3^3} + \cdots + \frac{n\,!}{3^n} + \cdots .$$

Solution. Since $a_n = \dfrac{n\,!}{3^n}$, $a_{n+1} = \dfrac{(n+1)\,!}{3^{n+1}}$ and

$$r_n = \frac{(n+1)\,!}{n\,!} \cdot \frac{3^n}{3^{n+1}} = \frac{n+1}{3}.$$

Therefore $\rho = \lim\limits_{n \to +\infty} \dfrac{n+1}{3} = +\infty$, and the series diverges.

NOTE 5.   Experience teaches us that if the general term of a series involves the index n either exponentially or factorially (as in the preceding Examples) the ratio test can be expected to answer the question of convergence or divergence, while if the index n is involved only algebraically or logarithmically (as in the p-series and Examples 3 and 5, § 708), the ratio test can be expected to fail.

710. THE ROOT TEST

A test somewhat similar to the ratio test is the following, whose proof is requested in Exercise 23, § 711:

Theorem.   Root Test. *Let $\sum a_n$ be a nonnegative series, and assume the existence of the following limit:*

$$\lim_{n \to +\infty} \sqrt[n]{a_n} = \sigma,$$

where $0 \leqq \sigma \leqq +\infty$.   Then

(*i*) *if $0 \leqq \sigma < 1$, $\sum a_n$ converges;*
(*ii*) *if $1 < \sigma \leqq +\infty$, $\sum a_n$ diverges;*
(*iii*) *if $\sigma = 1$, $\sum a_n$ may either converge or diverge, and the test fails.*

NOTE 1.   The inequality $\sqrt[n]{a_n} < 1$, for all n, is not sufficient for convergence, although an inequality of the form $\sqrt[n]{a_n} \leqq r < 1$, for $n > N$, does guarantee convergence.

NOTE 2.   For divergence it is sufficient to have an inequality of the form $\sqrt[n]{a_n} \geqq 1$, for $n > N$, since this precludes $\lim\limits_{n \to +\infty} a_n = 0$.

NOTE 3.   The ratio test is usually easier to apply than the root test, but the latter is more powerful.   (Cf. Exs. 34-35, § 711.)

Example.   Use the root test to establish convergence of the series

$$1 + \frac{2}{2^1} + \frac{3}{2^2} + \frac{4}{2^3} + \cdots .$$

Solution.   Since $\sqrt[n]{a_n} = \sqrt[n]{\dfrac{n}{2^{n-1}}} = \dfrac{\sqrt[n]{n}}{2^{\frac{n-1}{n}}}$, the problem of finding $\lim\limits_{n \to +\infty} \sqrt[n]{a_n}$

can be reduced to that of finding the two limits $\lim\limits_{n \to +\infty} \sqrt[n]{n}$ and $\lim\limits_{n \to +\infty} 2^{1-\frac{1}{n}}$.
The second of these is not indeterminate, owing to the continuity of the function 2^x at $x = 1$, and has the value $2^1 = 2$.   To evaluate $\lim\limits_{n \to +\infty} \sqrt[n]{n}$, or $\lim\limits_{x \to +\infty} x^{\frac{1}{x}}$,

let $y \equiv x^{\frac{1}{x}}$, and take logarithms: (cf. § 416): $\ln y = \dfrac{\ln x}{x}$.   Then, by l'Hospital's

Rule (§ 415), $\lim\limits_{x \to +\infty} \ln y = \lim\limits_{x \to +\infty} \dfrac{1/x}{1} = 0,$ and $y \to e^0 = 1.$ Therefore

$\lim\limits_{n \to +\infty} \sqrt[n]{a_n} = \frac{1}{2} < 1,$ and $\sum a_n$ converges.

711. EXERCISES

In Exercises 1-20, establish convergence or divergence of the given series.

1. $\dfrac{1}{3} + \dfrac{\sqrt{2}}{5} + \dfrac{\sqrt{3}}{7} + \dfrac{\sqrt{4}}{9} + \cdots .$

2. $\dfrac{1}{\sqrt{1 \cdot 2}} + \dfrac{1}{\sqrt{2 \cdot 3}} + \dfrac{1}{\sqrt{3 \cdot 4}} + \dfrac{1}{\sqrt{4 \cdot 5}} + \cdots .$

3. $\dfrac{\sqrt{3}}{2 \cdot 4} + \dfrac{\sqrt{5}}{4 \cdot 6} + \dfrac{\sqrt{7}}{6 \cdot 8} + \dfrac{\sqrt{9}}{8 \cdot 10} + \cdots .$

4. $\dfrac{\sqrt{2} + 1}{3^3 - 1} + \dfrac{\sqrt{3} + 1}{4^3 - 1} + \dfrac{\sqrt{4} + 1}{5^3 - 1} + \dfrac{\sqrt{5} + 1}{6^3 - 1} + \cdots .$

5. $\dfrac{1}{3} + \dfrac{1 \cdot 2}{3 \cdot 5} + \dfrac{1 \cdot 2 \cdot 3}{3 \cdot 5 \cdot 7} + \dfrac{1 \cdot 2 \cdot 3 \cdot 4}{3 \cdot 5 \cdot 7 \cdot 9} + \cdots .$

6. $\dfrac{1!}{2^5} + \dfrac{2!}{2^6} + \dfrac{3!}{2^7} + \dfrac{4!}{2^8} + \cdots .$

7. $\dfrac{1}{\ln 2} + \dfrac{1}{\ln 3} + \dfrac{1}{\ln 4} + \dfrac{1}{\ln 5} + \cdots .$

8. $\dfrac{2!}{4!} + \dfrac{3!}{5!} + \dfrac{4!}{6!} + \dfrac{5!}{7!} + \cdots .$

9. $\sum\limits_{n=1}^{+\infty} \dfrac{\sqrt{n}}{n^2 + 4}.$

10. $\sum\limits_{n=1}^{+\infty} \dfrac{\ln n}{n \sqrt[3]{n + 1}}.$

11. $\sum\limits_{n=1}^{+\infty} \dfrac{n^4}{n!}.$

12. $\sum\limits_{n=1}^{+\infty} \dfrac{3^{2n-1}}{n^2 + 1}.$

13. $\sum\limits_{n=1}^{+\infty} e^{-n^2}.$

14. $\sum\limits_{n=2}^{+\infty} \dfrac{1}{(\ln n)^n}.$

15. $\sum\limits_{n=1}^{+\infty} \dfrac{\sqrt{n + 1} - \sqrt{n}}{n^\alpha}.$

16. $\sum\limits_{n=1}^{+\infty} \dfrac{n!}{n^n}.$

17. $\sum\limits_{n=2}^{+\infty} \dfrac{1}{(\ln n)^\alpha}.$

18. $\sum\limits_{n=1}^{+\infty} \dfrac{1}{1 + \alpha^n}, \alpha > -1.$

19. $\sum\limits_{n=1}^{+\infty} (\sqrt[n]{n} - 1)^n.$

20. $\sum\limits_{n=1}^{+\infty} r^n |\sin n\alpha|, \alpha > 0, r > 0.$

21. Prove the comparison test (Theorem I, § 708) for divergence.
22. Prove Theorem II, § 708.
23. Prove the root test, § 710.
24. Prove that if $a_n \geqq 0$ and there exists a number $k > 1$ such that $\lim\limits_{n \to +\infty} n^k a_n$

exists and is finite, then $\sum a_n$ converges.

25. Prove that if $a_n \geqq 0$ and $\lim\limits_{n \to +\infty} n\, a_n$ exists and is positive, then $\sum a_n$ diverges.

★**26.** Prove the *Schwarz* (or *Cauchy*) *inequality* for nonnegative series: If $a_n \geqq 0$ and $b_n \geqq 0$, $n = 1, 2, \cdots$, then

(1)
$$\left(\sum_{n=1}^{+\infty} a_n b_n \right)^2 \leqq \sum_{n=1}^{+\infty} a_n{}^2 \sum_{n=1}^{+\infty} b_n{}^2,$$

with the following interpretations: (*i*) if both series on the right-hand side of (1) converge, then the series on the left-hand side also converges and (1) holds; (*ii*) if either series on the right-hand side of (1) has a zero sum, then so does the series on the left. (Cf. Ex. 43, § 107, Ex. 29, § 503, Ex. 14, § 717.)

★**27.** Prove that if $\sum a_n{}^2$ is a convergent series, then $\sum |a_n|/n$ is also convergent. (Cf. Ex. 26.)

★**28.** Prove that any series of the form $\sum\limits_{n=1}^{+\infty} \dfrac{d_n}{10^n}$, where $d_n = 0, 1, 2, \cdots, 9$, converges. Hence show that any decimal expansion $0.d_1 d_2 \cdots$ represents some real number r, where $0 \leqq r \leqq 1$.

★**29.** Prove the converse of Exercise 28: If $0 \leqq r \leqq 1$, then there exists a decimal expansion $0.d_1 d_2 \cdots$ representing r. Show that this decimal expansion is unique unless r is positive and representable by a (unique) terminating decimal (cf. Ex. 5, § 113), in which case r is also representable by a (unique) decimal composed, from some point on, of repeating 9's.

★**30.** Show that Exercise 29 establishes a one-to-one correspondence between the points of the half-open interval $(0, 1]$ and all nonterminating decimals $0.d_1 d_2 \cdots$. Prove that any subset of a denumerable set (cf. Ex. 12, § 113) is either finite or denumerable, and hence in order to establish that the real numbers are **nondenumerable** (neither finite nor denumerable) it is sufficient to show that the set S of nonterminating decimals $0.d_1 d_2 \cdots$ is nondenumerable. Finally, prove that the set S is nondenumerable by assuming the contrary and obtaining a contradiction, as follows: Assume S is made up of the sequence $\{x_n\}$:

$$
\begin{array}{lllllll}
x_1: & .d_{11} & d_{12} & d_{13} & d_{14} & \cdots \\
x_2: & .d_{21} & d_{22} & d_{23} & d_{24} & \cdots \\
x_3: & .d_{31} & d_{32} & d_{33} & d_{34} & \cdots \\
\cdots\cdots & \cdots\cdots
\end{array}
$$

Construct a new sequence $\{a_n\}$, where a_n is one of the digits $1, 2, \cdots, 9$, and $a_n \neq d_{nn}$, for $n = 1, 2, \cdots$. Finally, show that the decimal $0.a_1 a_2 a_3 \cdots$ simultaneously must and cannot belong to S.

★**31.** Establish the following form of the ratio test: The positive series $\sum a_n$ converges if $\overline{\lim\limits_{n \to +\infty}} \dfrac{a_{n+1}}{a_n} < 1$, and diverges if $\underline{\lim\limits_{n \to +\infty}} \dfrac{a_{n+1}}{a_n} > 1$. (Cf. Ex. 16, § 305.)

★**32.** Establish the following form of the root test: If $\sum a_n$ is a nonnegative series and if $\sigma \equiv \overline{\lim\limits_{n \to +\infty}} \sqrt[n]{a_n}$, then $\sum a_n$ converges if $\sigma < 1$ and diverges if $\sigma > 1$. (Cf. Ex. 31.)

★**33.** Apply Exercises 31 and 32 to the series $\dfrac{1}{2} + \dfrac{1}{3} + \dfrac{1}{2^2} + \dfrac{1}{3^2} + \cdots$ of Example 2, § 708, and show that $\overline{\lim} \dfrac{a_{n+1}}{a_n} = +\infty$, $\underline{\lim} \dfrac{a_{n+1}}{a_n} = 0$, $\overline{\lim} \sqrt[n]{a_n} = 1/\sqrt{2}$,

and $\underline{\lim} \sqrt[n]{a_n} = 1/\sqrt{3}$. Thus show that the ratio test of § 709 and that of Exercise 31 both fail, that the root test of § 710 fails, and that the root test of Exercise 32 succeeds in establishing convergence of the given series.

★**34.** Prove that if $\lim\limits_{n \to +\infty} \dfrac{a_{n+1}}{a_n}$ exists, then $\lim\limits_{n \to +\infty} \sqrt[n]{a_n}$ also exists and is equal

to it.   *Hints:* For the case $\lim\limits_{n \to +\infty} \dfrac{a_{n+1}}{a_n} = L$, where $0 < L < +\infty$, let α and β be arbitrary numbers such that $0 < \alpha < L < \beta$.   Then for $n \geqq$ some N, $\alpha\, a_n < a_{n+1} < \beta\, a_n$.   Hence

$$\alpha\, a_N < a_{N+1} < \beta\, a_N$$
$$\alpha^2 a_N < \alpha\, a_{N+1} < a_{N+2} < \beta\, a_{N+1} < \beta^2 a_N$$
$$\cdot \qquad \cdot \qquad \cdot \qquad \cdot \qquad \cdot$$
$$\alpha^p a_N < a_{N+p} < \beta^p u_N.$$

Thus, for $n > N$,

$$\alpha^n \frac{a_N}{\alpha^N} < a_n < \beta^n \frac{a_N}{\beta^N},$$

and

$$\alpha \leqq \left\{ \begin{array}{c} \overline{\lim\limits_{n \to +\infty}} \sqrt[n]{a_n} \\[4pt] \underline{\lim\limits_{n \to +\infty}} \sqrt[n]{a_n} \end{array} \right\} \leqq \beta.$$

★**35.** The example $1, 2, 1, 2, \cdots$ shows that $\lim\limits_{n \to +\infty} \sqrt[n]{a_n}$ may exist when

$\lim\limits_{n \to +\infty} \dfrac{a_{n+1}}{a_n}$ does not.   Find an example of a convergent positive series $\sum a_n$ for which this situation is also true.

★**36.** Prove that $\lim\limits_{n \to +\infty} \sqrt[n]{\dfrac{n^n}{n\,!}} = e$.   (Cf. Ex. 34, above; also Ex. 48, § 515.)

★712. MORE REFINED TESTS

The tests discussed in preceding sections are those most commonly used in practice.   There are occasions, however, when such a useful test as the ratio test fails, and it is extremely difficult to devise an appropriate test series for the comparison test.   We give now some sharper criteria which

may sometimes be used in the event that $\lim\limits_{n \to +\infty} \dfrac{a_{n+1}}{a_n} = 1$.

Theorem I.   Kummer's Test.   *Let $\sum a_n$ be a positive series, and let $\{p_n\}$ be a sequence of positive constants such that*

(1)
$$\lim_{n \to +\infty} \left[p_n \frac{a_n}{a_{n+1}} - p_{n+1} \right] = L$$

exists and is positive $(0 < L \leqq +\infty)$.   *Then $\sum a_n$ converges.*

If the limit (1) *exists and is negative* $(-\infty \leq L < 0)$ *(or, more generally, if*
$p_n \dfrac{a_n}{a_{n+1}} - p_{n+1} \leq 0$ *for* $n \geq N$), *and if* $\sum \dfrac{1}{p_n}$ *diverges, then* $\sum a_n$ *diverges.*

Proof. Let r be any number such that $0 < r < L$. Then (cf. the proof of the ratio test) there must exist a positive integer N such that $n \geq N$ implies $p_n \dfrac{a_n}{a_{n+1}} - p_{n+1} > r$. For any positive integer m, then, we have the sequence of inequalities:

$$p_N a_N - p_{N+1} a_{N+1} > r a_{N+1},$$

$$p_{N+1} a_{N+1} - p_{N+2} a_{N+2} > r a_{N+2},$$

$$\cdot \quad \cdot \quad \cdot \quad \cdot \quad \cdot$$

$$p_{N+m-1} a_{N+m-1} - p_{N+m} a_{N+m} > r a_{N+m}.$$

Adding on both sides we have, because of cancellations by pairs on the left:

(2) $p_N a_N - p_{N+m} a_{N+m} > r(a_{N+1} + \cdots + a_{N+m}).$

Using the notation S_n for the partial sum $a_1 + \cdots + a_n$, we can write the sum in parentheses of (2) as $S_{N+m} - S_N$, and obtain by rearrangement of terms:

$$r S_{N+m} < r S_N + p_N a_N - p_{N+m} a_{N+m} < r S_N + p_N a_N.$$

Letting B denote the constant $(r S_N + p_N a_N)/r$, we infer that $S_n < B$ for $n > N$. In other words, the partial sums of $\sum a_n$ are bounded and hence (§ 705) the series converges.

To prove the second part we infer from the inequality $p_n \dfrac{a_n}{a_{n+1}} - p_{n+1} \leq 0$, which holds for $n \geq N$, the sequence of inequalities

$$p_N a_N \leq p_{N+1} a_{N+1} \leq \cdots \leq p_n a_n,$$

for any $n > N$. Denoting by A the positive constant $p_N a_N$, we conclude from the comparison test, the inequality

$$a_n \geq A \cdot \frac{1}{p_n}, \text{ for } n > N,$$

and the divergence of $\sum \dfrac{1}{p_n}$, that $\sum a_n$ also diverges.

Theorem II.   Raabe's Test.   *Let $\sum a_n$ be a positive series and assume that*

$$\lim_{n \to +\infty} n\left(\frac{a_n}{a_{n+1}} - 1\right) = L$$

exists (finite or infinite).   Then
  (i) if $1 < L \leq +\infty$, $\sum a_n$ converges;
  (ii) if $-\infty \leq L < 1$, $\sum a_n$ diverges;
  (iii) if $L = 1$, $\sum a_n$ may either converge or diverge, and the test fails.

Proof. The first two parts are a consequence of Kummer's Test with $p_n \equiv n$. (Cf. Ex. 5, § 713, for further suggestions.)

In case the limit L of Raabe's Test exists and is equal to 1, a refinement is possible:

Theorem III. *Let $\sum a_n$ be a positive series and assume that*

$$\lim_{n \to +\infty} \ln n \left[n \left(\frac{a_n}{a_{n+1}} - 1 \right) - 1 \right] = L$$

exists (finite or infinite). Then

    (i) if $1 < L \leq +\infty$, $\sum a_n$ converges;
    (ii) if $-\infty \leq L < 1$, $\sum a_n$ diverges;
    (iii) if $L = 1$, $\sum a_n$ may either converge or diverge, and the test fails.

Proof. The first two parts are a consequence of Kummer's Test with $p_n \equiv n \ln n$. (Cf. Exs. 9-10, § 713, for further suggestions.)

Example 1. Test for convergence or divergence:

$$\left(\frac{1}{2} \right)^p + \left(\frac{1 \cdot 3}{2 \cdot 4} \right)^p + \left(\frac{1 \cdot 3 \cdot 5}{2 \cdot 4 \cdot 6} \right)^p + \cdots .$$

Solution. Since $\lim_{n \to +\infty} \frac{a_{n+1}}{a_n} = 1$, the ratio test fails, and we turn to Raabe's test. We find

$$n \left(\frac{a_n}{a_{n+1}} - 1 \right) = n \left[\left(\frac{2n}{2n-1} \right)^p - 1 \right] = \frac{2n}{2n-1} \cdot \frac{(1+x)^p - 1}{2x},$$

where $x \equiv (2n - 1)^{-1}$. The limit of this expression, as $n \to +\infty$, is (by l'Hospital's Rule):

$$\lim_{x \to 0} \frac{(1+x)^p - 1}{2x} = \lim_{x \to 0} \frac{p(1+x)^{p-1}}{2} = \frac{p}{2}.$$

Therefore the given series converges for $p > 2$ and diverges for $p < 2$. For the case $p = 2$, see Example 2.

Example 2. Test for convergence or divergence

$$\left(\frac{1}{2} \right)^2 + \left(\frac{1 \cdot 3}{2 \cdot 4} \right)^2 + \left(\frac{1 \cdot 3 \cdot 5}{2 \cdot 4 \cdot 6} \right)^2 + \cdots .$$

Solution. Both the ratio test and Raabe's test fail (cf. Example 1). Preparing to use Theorem III, we simplify the expression

$$n \left(\frac{a_n}{a_{n+1}} - 1 \right) - 1 = n \frac{4n - 1}{4n^2 - 4n + 1} - 1 = \frac{3n - 1}{(2n-1)^2}.$$

Since $\lim_{n \to +\infty} \ln n \frac{3n - 1}{(2n-1)^2} = 0 < 1$, the given series diverges.

★713. EXERCISES

In Exercises 1-4, test for convergence or divergence.

★1. $\displaystyle\sum_{n=1}^{+\infty} \frac{2 \cdot 4 \cdot 6 \cdots 2n}{1 \cdot 3 \cdot 5 \cdots (2n+1)}$. (Cf. Ex. 4.)

★2. $\displaystyle\sum_{n=1}^{+\infty} \frac{1\cdot 3 \cdots (2n-1)}{2\cdot 4 \cdots 2n} \cdot \frac{1}{2n+1}$.

★3. $\displaystyle\sum_{n=1}^{+\infty} \frac{1\cdot 3 \cdots (2n-1)}{2\cdot 4 \cdots 2n} \cdot \frac{4n+3}{2n+2}$.

★4. $\displaystyle\sum_{n=1}^{+\infty} \left[\frac{2\cdot 4\cdot 6 \cdots 2n}{1\cdot 3\cdot 5 \cdots (2n+1)} \right]^{p}$.

★5. Prove Theorem II, § 712. *Hint:* For examples for part (*iii*), define the terms of $\displaystyle\sum_{n=1}^{+\infty} a_n$ inductively, with $a_1 \equiv 1$, and $\dfrac{a_n}{a_{n+1}} \equiv 1 + \dfrac{1}{n} + \dfrac{k}{n \ln n}$. Then use Theorem III, § 712.

★6. Prove that the **hypergeometric series**

$$1 + \frac{\alpha \cdot \beta}{1 \cdot \gamma} + \frac{\alpha(\alpha+1)\beta(\beta+1)}{1 \cdot 2 \cdot \gamma \cdot (\gamma+1)} + \cdots$$
$$+ \frac{\alpha(\alpha+1) \cdots (\alpha+n-1) \cdot \beta(\beta+1) \cdots (\beta+n-1)}{n! \, \gamma(\gamma+1) \cdots (\gamma+n-1)} + \cdots$$

converges if and only if $\gamma - \alpha - \beta > 0$ (n not 0 or a negative integer).

★7. Prove **Gauss's Test:** *If the positive series $\sum a_n$ is such that*

$$\frac{a_n}{a_{n+1}} = 1 + \frac{h}{n} + O\left(\frac{1}{n^2}\right),$$

then $\sum a_n$ converges if $h > 1$, and diverges if $h \leq 1$. Show that $O(1/n^2)$ could be replaced by the weaker condition $O(1/n^\alpha)$, where $\alpha > 1$.

★8. State and prove limit superior and limit inferior forms for the Theorems of § 712. (Cf. Exs. 31-32, § 711.)

★9. Prove the first two parts of Theorem III, § 712. (Cf. Ex. 11.) *Hint:* This is equivalent to showing (using Kummer's test with $p_n \equiv n \ln n$) that

$$\ln n \left[n \left(\frac{a_n}{a_{n+1}} - 1 \right) - 1 \right] - \left\{ n \ln n \, \frac{a_n}{a_{n+1}} - (n+1) \ln (n+1) \right\} \to 1,$$

or

$$(n+1) \ln (n+1) - [n \ln n + \ln n] = (n+1) \ln \left(\frac{n+1}{n} \right) \to 1.$$

★★10. Prove the following refinement of Theorem III, § 712: Let $\sum a_n$ be a positive series such that

$$\lim_{n \to +\infty} \ln \ln n \left\{ \ln n \left[n \left(\frac{a_n}{a_{n+1}} - 1 \right) - 1 \right] - 1 \right\} = L$$

exists (finite or infinite). Then (*i*) if $1 < L \leq +\infty$, $\sum a_n$ converges, and (*ii*) if $-\infty \leq L < 1$, $\sum a_n$ diverges. *Hint:* The problem is to show (cf. Ex. 9) that

(1) $(n+1) \ln (n+1) \ln \ln (n+1)$
$$- \{ n \ln n \ln \ln n + \ln n \ln \ln n + \ln \ln n \} \to 1.$$

To establish this limit, show first that if $\epsilon_n \to 0$, then $\ln (1 + \epsilon_n) = \epsilon_n + O(\epsilon_n^2)$ (cf. Ex. 21, § 408), and, more generally, if $\{\alpha_n\}$ is a sequence of positive numbers and if $\epsilon_n/\alpha_n \to 0$, then $\ln (\alpha_n + \epsilon_n) = \ln (\alpha_n) + \dfrac{\epsilon_n}{\alpha_n} + O\left(\dfrac{\epsilon_n^2}{\alpha_n^2}\right)$. Thus

$$\ln(n+1) = \ln n + \frac{1}{n} + O\left(\frac{1}{n^2}\right)$$

and

$$\ln \ln n = \ln\left[\ln n + \frac{1}{n} + O\left(\frac{1}{n^2}\right)\right] = \ln \ln n + \frac{1}{\ln n}\left[\frac{1}{n} + O\left(\frac{1}{n^2}\right)\right]$$

$$+ O\left(\left[\frac{1}{n} + O\left(\frac{1}{n^2}\right)\right]^2\right) = \ln \ln n + \frac{1}{n \ln n} + O\left(\frac{1}{n^2}\right).$$

Now form the product $(n+1)\ln(n+1)\ln\ln(n+1)$, subtract the terms in the braces of (1), and take a limit.

★★11. Prove the third part of Theorem III, § 712. *Hint:* Cf. Exs. 5 and 10.

714. SERIES OF ARBITRARY TERMS

If a series has terms of one sign, as we have seen for nonnegative series, there is only one kind of divergence—to infinity—and convergence of the series is equivalent to the boundedness of the partial sums. We wish to turn our attention now to series whose terms may be either positive or negative—or zero. The behavior of such series is markedly different from that of nonnegative series, but we shall find that we can make good use of the latter to clarify the former.

715. ALTERNATING SERIES

An **alternating series** is a series of the form

(1) $$c_1 - c_2 + c_3 - c_4 + \cdots,$$

where $c_n > 0$ for every n.

Theorem. *An alternating series (1) whose terms satisfy the two conditions*
   (i) $c_{n+1} < c_n$ *for every* n,
   (ii) $c_n \to 0$ *as* $n \to +\infty$,
converges. If S and S_n denote the sum, and the partial sum of the first n terms, respectively, of the series (1),

(2) $$|S_n - S| < c_{n+1}.$$

Proof. We break the proof into six parts (cf. Fig. 702.):
   A. The partial sums S_{2n} (consisting of an even number of terms) form an increasing sequence.
   B. The partial sums S_{2n-1} (consisting of an odd number of terms) form a decreasing sequence.
   C. For every m and every n, $S_{2m} < S_{2n-1}$.
   D. S exists.
   E. For every m and every n, $S_{2m} < S < S_{2n-1}$.
   F. The inequality (2) holds.

A: Since $S_{2n+2} = S_{2n} + (c_{2n+1} - c_{2n+2})$, and since $c_{2n+2} < c_{2n+1}$, $S_{2n+2} > S_{2n}$.

B: Since $S_{2n+1} = S_{2n-1} - (c_{2n} - c_{2n+1})$, and since $c_{2n+1} < c_{2n}$, $S_{2n+1} < S_{2n-1}$.

C: If $2m < 2n - 1$,
$$S_{2n-1} - S_{2m} = (c_{2m+1} - c_{2m+2}) + \cdots + (c_{2n-3} - c_{2n-2}) + c_{2n-1} > 0,$$
and $S_{2m} < S_{2n-1}$. If $2m > 2n - 1$,
$$S_{2m} - S_{2n-1} = -(c_{2n} - c_{2n+1}) - \cdots - (c_{2m-2} - c_{2m-1}) - c_{2m} < 0,$$
and $S_{2m} < S_{2n-1}$.

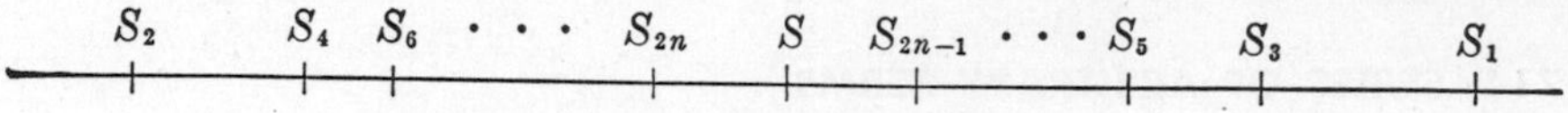

FIG. 702

D: From A, B, and C it follows that $\{S_{2n}\}$ and $\{S_{2n-1}\}$ are bounded monotonic sequences and therefore converge. We need only show that their limits are equal. But this is true, since

$$\lim_{n \to +\infty} S_{2n+1} - \lim_{n \to +\infty} S_{2n} = \lim_{n \to +\infty} (S_{2n+1} - S_{2n}) = \lim_{n \to +\infty} c_{2n+1} = 0.$$

E: By the fundamental theorem on convergence of monotonic sequences (Theorem XIV, § 204), for an arbitrary fixed n and variable m, $S_{2m} < S_{2n+1}$ implies $S \leqq S_{2n+1} < S_{2n-1}$. Similarly, for an arbitrary fixed m and variable n, $S_{2m+2} < S_{2n+1}$ implies $S_{2m} < S_{2m+2} \leqq S$.

F: On the one hand,

$$0 < S_{2n-1} - S < S_{2n-1} - S_{2n} = c_{2n},$$

while, on the other hand

$$0 < S - S_{2n} < S_{2n+1} - S_{2n} = c_{2n+1}.$$

Example 1. The **alternating harmonic series**
$$1 - \tfrac{1}{2} + \tfrac{1}{3} - \tfrac{1}{4} + \cdots$$
converges, since the conditions of the Theorem above are satisfied.

Example 2. Prove that the series $\sum\limits_{n=1}^{+\infty} (-1)^n \dfrac{\ln n}{n}$ converges.

Solution. All of the conditions of the alternating series test are obvious except for the inequality $\dfrac{\ln (n + 1)}{n + 1} < \dfrac{\ln n}{n}$. The simplest way of establishing this is to show that $f(x) \equiv \dfrac{\ln x}{x}$ is strictly decreasing since its derivative is

$$f'(x) = \frac{1 - \ln x}{x^2} < 0, \quad \text{for} \quad x > e.$$

716. ABSOLUTE AND CONDITIONAL CONVERGENCE

We introduce some notation.   Let $\sum\limits_{n=1}^{+\infty} a_n$ be a given series of arbitrary terms.   For every positive integer n we define p_n to be the larger of the two numbers a_n and 0, and q_n to be the larger of the two numbers $-a_n$ and 0 (in case $a_n = 0$, $p_n = q_n = 0$):

(1) $$p_n \equiv \max\,(a_n, 0), \; q_n \equiv \max\,(-a_n, 0).$$

Then p_n and q_n are nonnegative numbers (at least one of them being zero) satisfying the two equations

(2) $$p_n - q_n = a_n, \; p_n + q_n = |a_n|,$$

and the two inequalities

(3) $$0 \le p_n \le |a_n|,\, 0 \le q_n \le |a_n|.$$

The two nonnegative series $\sum p_n$ and $\sum q_n$ are called the **nonnegative** and **nonpositive parts,** respectively, of the series $\sum a_n$.   A third nonnegative series related to the original is $\sum |a_n|$, called the **series of absolute values** of $\sum a_n$.

We now assign labels to the partial sums of the series considered:

$$S_n \equiv a_1 + \cdots + a_n, \qquad A_n \equiv |a_1| + \cdots + |a_n|,$$
$$P_n \equiv p_1 + \cdots + p_n, \qquad Q_n \equiv q_1 + \cdots + q_n.$$

From (1) and (2) we deduce:

(4) $$P_n - Q_n = S_n, \qquad P_n + Q_n = A_n,$$

and are ready to draw some conclusions about convergence.

From the first equation of (4) we can solve for either P_n or Q_n

$$(P_n = Q_n + S_n \quad \text{and} \quad Q_n = P_n - S_n),$$

and conclude (with the aid of a limit theorem) that the convergence of any two of the three series $\sum a_n$, $\sum p_n$, and $\sum q_n$ implies the convergence of the third.   This means that if *both* the nonnegative and nonpositive parts of a series converge the series itself must also converge.   It also means that if a series converges, then the nonnegative and nonpositive parts must either *both converge* or *both diverge.*   (Why?)   The alternating harmonic series of § 715 is an example of a convergent series whose nonnegative and nonpositive parts both diverge.

The inequalities (3) and the second equation of (4) imply (by the comparison test and a limit theorem) that the series of absolute values, $\sum |a_n|$ converges if and only if *both* the nonnegative and nonpositive parts of the series converge.   Furthermore, in case the series $\sum |a_n|$ converges, if we define $P \equiv \lim\limits_{n \to +\infty} P_n$, $Q \equiv \lim\limits_{n \to +\infty} Q_n$, $S \equiv \lim\limits_{n \to +\infty} S_n$, and $A \equiv \lim\limits_{n \to +\infty} A_n$, we have from (4), $P - Q = S$, $P + Q = A$.

We give a definition and a theorem embodying some of the results just obtained:

Definition. *A series $\sum a_n$ **converges absolutely** (or is **absolutely convergent**) if and only if the series of absolute values, $\sum |a_n|$ converges. A series **converges conditionally** (or is **conditionally convergent**) if and only if it converges and does not converge absolutely.*

Theorem I. *An absolutely convergent series is convergent. In case of absolute convergence, $|\sum a_n| \leq \sum |a_n|$.*

NOTE 1. For an absolutely convergent series, the nonnegative and nonpositive parts both converge. For a conditionally convergent series, the nonnegative and nonpositive parts both diverge.

NOTE 2. An alternative proof of Theorem I is provided by the Cauchy Criterion (cf. Exs. 17–21, § 717 for a discussion).

NOTE 3. The tests established for convergence of nonnegative series are of course immediately available for absolute convergence of arbitrary series. We state here the ratio test for arbitrary series, of nonzero terms, both because of its practicality and because the conclusion for $\rho > 1$ is not simply that the series fails to converge absolutely but that it *diverges* (cf. Ex. 12, § 717).

Theorem II. Ratio Test. *Let $\sum a_n$ be a series of nonzero terms, and define the test ratio $r_n \equiv a_{n+1}/a_n$. Assume that the limit of the absolute value of this test ratio exists:*

$$\lim_{n \to +\infty} \left| \frac{a_{n+1}}{a_n} \right| = \rho,$$

where $0 \leq \rho \leq +\infty$. Then
- *(i) if $0 \leq \rho < 1$, $\sum a_n$ converges absolutely;*
- *(ii) if $1 < \rho \leq +\infty$, $\sum a_n$ diverges;*
- *(iii) if $\rho = 1$, $\sum a_n$ may converge absolutely, or converge conditionally, or diverge, and the test fails.*

NOTE 4. The ratio test never establishes convergence in the case of a conditionally convergent series.

Example 1. The alternating p-series,

$$1 - \frac{1}{2^p} + \frac{1}{3^p} - \frac{1}{4^p} + \cdots,$$

converges absolutely if $p > 1$, converges conditionally if $0 < p \leq 1$, and diverges if $p \leq 0$.

★Example 2. Show that the series $\dfrac{1}{2} - \dfrac{1\cdot 3}{2\cdot 4} + \dfrac{1\cdot 3\cdot 5}{2\cdot 4\cdot 6} - \dfrac{1\cdot 3\cdot 5\cdot 7}{2\cdot 4\cdot 6\cdot 8} + \cdots$

converges conditionally.

Solution. By Example 1, § 712, the series fails to converge absolutely. In order to prove that the series converges, we can use the alternating series test to reduce the problem to showing that the general term tends toward 0 (clearly $c_n \downarrow$). Letting $p = 3$ in Example 1, § 712, we know that $c_n{}^3 \to 0$. Therefore $c_n \to 0$.

717. EXERCISES

In Exercises 1-10, test for absolute convergence, conditional convergence, or divergence.

1. $\displaystyle\sum_{n=1}^{+\infty} \frac{(-1)^{n-1}}{2n+3}$.

2. $\displaystyle\sum_{n=1}^{+\infty} \frac{(-1)^n n}{n+2}$.

3. $\displaystyle\sum_{n=1}^{+\infty} \frac{(-1)^n \sqrt[3]{n^2+5}}{\sqrt[4]{n^3+n+1}}$.

4. $\displaystyle\sum_{n=1}^{+\infty} (-1)^{n-1} \frac{n^4}{(n+1)!}$.

5. $\displaystyle\sum_{n=1}^{+\infty} (-1)^n \frac{n \ln n}{e^n}$.

6. $\displaystyle\sum_{n=1}^{+\infty} (-1)^n \frac{\cos n\,\alpha}{n^2}$.

7. $e^{-x} \cos x + e^{-2x} \cos 2x + e^{-3x} \cos 3x + \cdots$.

8. $1 + r \cos \theta + r^2 \cos 2\theta + r^3 \cos 3\theta + \cdots$.

9. $\dfrac{1}{2(\ln 2)^p} - \dfrac{1}{3(\ln 3)^p} + \dfrac{1}{4(\ln 4)^p} - \cdots$.

★10. $\left(\dfrac{1}{2}\right)^p - \left(\dfrac{1\cdot 3}{2\cdot 4}\right)^p + \left(\dfrac{1\cdot 3\cdot 5}{2\cdot 4\cdot 6}\right)^p - \cdots$.

11. Prove that if the condition (i) of § 715 is replaced by $c_{n+1} \leqq c_n$, the conclusion is altered only by replacing (2), § 715, by $|S_n - S| \leqq c_{n+1}$.

12. Prove the ratio test (Theorem II) of § 716.

13. Show by three counterexamples that each of the three conditions of the alternating series test, § 715, is needed in the statement of that test (that is, the alternating of signs, the decreasing nature of c_n, and the limit of c_n being 0).

★14. Prove the **Schwarz (or Cauchy)** and the **Minkowski inequalities** for series:

If $\displaystyle\sum_{n=1}^{+\infty} a_n^2$ and $\displaystyle\sum_{n=1}^{+\infty} b_n^2$ converge, then so do $\displaystyle\sum_{n=1}^{+\infty} a_n b_n$ and $\displaystyle\sum_{n=1}^{+\infty} (a_n + b_n)^2$, and

$$\left[\sum_{n=1}^{+\infty} a_n b_n\right]^2 \leqq \sum_{n=1}^{+\infty} a_n^2 \sum_{n=1}^{+\infty} b_n^2,$$

$$\left[\sum_{n=1}^{+\infty} (a_n + b_n)^2\right]^{\frac{1}{2}} \leqq \left[\sum_{n=1}^{+\infty} a_n^2\right]^{\frac{1}{2}} + \left[\sum_{n=1}^{+\infty} b_n^2\right]^{\frac{1}{2}}.$$

(Cf. Exs. 43-44, § 107, Exs. 29-30, § 503, Ex. 26, § 711.)

★★15. Let $\displaystyle\sum_{n=1}^{+\infty} a_n$ be a given series, with partial sums $S_n \equiv a_1 + \cdots + a_n$. Define the sequence of *arithmetic means*

$$\sigma_n \equiv \frac{S_1 + \cdots + S_n}{n}.$$

The series $\sum a_n$ is said to be **summable** *by Cesàro's method of arithmetic means of order* 1 (for short, *summable* $(C, 1)$) if and only if $\displaystyle\lim_{n\to+\infty} \sigma_n$ exists and is finite. Show that Exercises 16-19, § 205, prove that summability $(C, 1)$ is a generalization of convergence: that any convergent series is summable $(C, 1)$ with $\displaystyle\lim_{n\to+\infty} \sigma_n = \lim_{n\to+\infty} S_n$, that for nonnegative series summability $(C, 1)$ is identical with convergence, and that there are divergent series (whose terms are not of one sign) which are summable $(C, 1)$. *Hint:* Consider $1 - 1 + 1 - 1 + \cdots$.

★★**16.** A series $\sum a_n$ is *summable by Cesàro's method of arithmetic means of order* 2 (*for short,* summable $(C, 2)$) if and only if

$$\lim_{n \to +\infty} \frac{\sigma_1 + \cdots + \sigma_n}{n}$$

(in the notation of Exercise 15) exists and is finite. Show that summability $(C, 1)$ implies summability $(C, 2)$, but not conversely. Generalize to summability (C, r).

★**17.** Prove the **Cauchy criterion** for convergence of an infinite series: *An infinite series* $\sum\limits_{n=1}^{+\infty} a_n$ *converges if and only if corresponding to* $\epsilon > 0$ *there exists a number* N *such that* $n > m > N$ *implies* $|a_m + a_{m+1} + \cdots + a_n| < \epsilon$. (Cf. § 302.)

★**18.** Prove that an infinite series $\sum\limits_{n=1}^{+\infty} a_n$ converges if and only if corresponding to $\epsilon > 0$ there exists a number N such that $n > N$ and $p > 0$ imply $|a_n + a_{n+1} + \cdots + a_{n+p}| < \epsilon$. (Cf. Ex. 17.)

★**19.** Prove that an infinite series $\sum\limits_{n=1}^{+\infty} a_n$ converges if and only if corresponding to $\epsilon > 0$ there exists a positive integer N such that $n > N$ implies $|a_N + a_{N+1} + \cdots + a_n| < \epsilon$. (Cf. Ex. 2, § 305.)

★**20.** Show by an example that the condition of Exercise 18 is not equivalent to the following: $\lim\limits_{n \to +\infty} (a_n + \cdots + a_{n+p}) = 0$ for every $p > 0$. (Cf. Ex. 4, § 305, Ex. 43, § 904.)

★**21.** Use the Cauchy criterion of Exercise 17 to prove that an absolutely convergent series is convergent.

★★**22.** Prove the following **Abel test:** *If the partial sums of a series* $\sum\limits_{n=1}^{+\infty} a_n$ *are bounded and if* $\{b_n\}$ *is a monotonically decreasing sequence of nonnegative numbers whose limit is* 0, *then* $\sum a_n b_n$ *converges.* Use this fact to establish the convergence in the alternating series test as phrased in Exercise 11. *Hint:* Let $S_n \equiv a_1 + \cdots + a_n$, and assume $|S_n| < K$ for all n. Then

$$\left| \sum_{i=m}^{n} a_i b_i \right| = \left| \sum_{i=m}^{n} (S_i - S_{i-1}) b_i \right| = \left| \sum_{i=m}^{n-1} S_i(b_i - b_{i+1}) + S_n b_n - S_{m-1} b_m \right|$$

$$\leq K \left[\sum_{i=m}^{n} (b_i - b_{i+1}) + b_n + b_m \right] = 2K\, b_m.$$

★★**23.** Prove the following **Abel test:** *If* $\sum a_n$ *converges and if* $\{b_n\}$ *is a bounded monotonic sequence, then* $\sum a_n b_n$ *converges.* *Hint:* Assume for definiteness that $b_n \downarrow$, let $b_n \to b$, write $a_n b_n = a_n(b_n - b) + a_n b$, and use Ex. 22.

★★**24.** Start with the harmonic series, and introduce $+$ and $-$ signs according to the following patterns:

   (i) in pairs: $1 + \frac{1}{2} - \frac{1}{3} - \frac{1}{4} + \frac{1}{5} + \frac{1}{6} - - \cdots$;
   (ii) in groups of 1, 2, 3, 4, $\cdots$: $1 - \frac{1}{2} - \frac{1}{3} + + + - - - - \cdots$;
   (iii) in groups of 1, 2, 4, 8, $\cdots$: $1 - \frac{1}{2} - \frac{1}{3} + + + + \cdots$.

Show that (i) and (ii) converge and (iii) diverges.   (Cf. Ex. 22.)   *Hint for* (ii):
In Abel's test, Ex. 22, let $a_n \equiv \pm \dfrac{1}{\sqrt{n}}$ and $b_n \equiv \dfrac{1}{\sqrt{n}}$.

★★25. If A is an arbitrary finite or denumerable set of real numbers, a_1, a_2, a_3, $\cdots$ (which may be discrete like the integers, or dense like the rational numbers, or anywhere in between), construct a bounded monotonic function whose set of points of discontinuity is precisely A, as follows: Let $\sum_{n=1}^{+\infty} p_n$ be a convergent series of positive numbers with sum p.   Define $f(x)$ to be 0 if x is any lower bound of A, and otherwise equal to the sum of all terms p_m of $\sum p_n$ such that $a_m < x$.   Prove the following five properties of $f(x)$: (i) $f(x)$ is monotonically increasing on $(-\infty, +\infty)$; (ii) $\lim_{x \to -\infty} f(x) = 0$; (iii) $\lim_{x \to +\infty} f(x) = p$; (iv) $f(a_n+) - f(a_n-) = p_n$ for every n; (v) $f(x)$ is continuous at every point not in A.

718. GROUPINGS AND REARRANGEMENTS

A series $\sum b_n$ is said to arise from a given series $\sum a_n$ by **grouping of terms** (or by the **introduction of parentheses**) if every b_n is the sum of a finite number of consecutive terms of $\sum a_n$, and every pair of terms a_m and a_n, where $m < n$, appear as terms in a unique pair of terms b_p and b_q, respectively, where $p \leq q$.   For example, the grouping

$$(a_1 + a_2) + (a_3) + (a_4 + a_5) + (a_6) + \cdots$$

gives rise to the series $\sum b_n$, where $b_1 = a_1 + a_2$, $b_2 = a_3$, $b_3 = a_4 + a_5$, $b_4 = a_6, \cdots$.

Theorem I.   *Any series arising from a convergent series by grouping of terms is convergent, and has the same sum as the original series.*

Proof.   The partial sums of the new series form a subsequence of the partial sums of the original.

Note.   The example

$$(2 - 1\tfrac{1}{2}) + (1\tfrac{1}{3} - 1\tfrac{1}{4}) + (1\tfrac{1}{5} - 1\tfrac{1}{6}) + \cdots$$

shows that grouping of terms may convert a divergent series into a convergent series.

A series $\sum b_n$ is said to arise from a given series $\sum a_n$ by **rearrangement** (of **terms**) if there exists a one-to-one correspondence between the terms of $\sum a_n$ and those of $\sum b_n$ such that whenever a_m and b_n correspond, $a_m = b_n$. For example, the series

$$\frac{1}{4} + 1 + \frac{1}{16} + \frac{1}{9} + \frac{1}{36} + \frac{1}{25} + \cdots$$

is a rearrangement of the p-series, with $p = 2$.

Theorem II. Dirichlet's Theorem. *Any series arising from an absolutely convergent series by rearrangement of terms is absolutely convergent, and has the same sum as the original series.*

Proof. We prove first that the theorem is true for nonnegative series. Let $\sum a_n$ be a given nonnegative series, convergent with sum A and let $\sum b_n$ be any rearrangement. If B_n is any partial sum of $\sum b_n$, the terms of B_n consist of a finite number of terms of $\sum a_n$, and therefore form a part of some partial sum A_m of $\sum a_n$. Since the terms are assumed to be nonnegative, $B_n \leqq A_m$, and hence, $B_n \leqq A$. Therefore the partial sums of the nonnegative series $\sum b_n$ are bounded, and $\sum b_n$ converges to a sum $B \leqq A$. Since $\sum a_n$ is a rearrangement of $\sum b_n$, the symmetric relation $A \leqq B$ also holds, and $A = B$.

If $\sum a_n$ is absolutely convergent, and if $\sum b_n$ is any rearrangement, the nonnegative and nonpositive parts of $\sum b_n$ are rearrangements of the nonnegative and nonpositive parts of $\sum a_n$, respectively. Since these latter both converge, say with sums P and Q, respectively, their rearrangements will also both converge, with sums P and Q, respectively, by the preceding paragraph. Finally, $\sum a_n = P - Q = \sum b_n$, and the proof is complete.

★**Theorem III.** *The terms of any conditionally convergent series can be rearranged to give either a divergent series or a conditionally convergent series whose sum is an arbitrary preassigned number.*

★*Proof.* We prove one case, and leave the rest as an exercise. (Ex. 2, § 721.) Let $\sum a_n$ be a conditionally convergent series, with divergent nonnegative and nonpositive parts $\sum p_n$ and $\sum q_n$, respectively, and let c be an arbitrary real number. Let the rearrangement be determined as follows: first put down terms $p_1 + p_2 + \cdots + p_{m_1}$ until the partial sum first exceeds c. Then attach terms $-q_1 - q_2 - q_3 - \cdots - q_{n_1}$ until the total partial sum first falls short of c. Then attach terms $p_{m_1+1} + \cdots + p_{m_2}$ until the total partial sum first exceeds c. Then terms $-q_{n_1+1} - \cdots - q_{n_2}$, etc. Each of these steps is possible because of the divergence of $\sum p_n$ and $\sum q_n$. The resulting rearrangement of $\sum a_n$ converges to c since $p_n \to 0$ and $q_n \to 0$.

Example. Rearrange the terms of the series obtained by doubling all terms of the alternating harmonic series so that the resulting series is the alternating harmonic series, thus convincing the unwary that $2 = 1$.

Solution. Write the terms

$$2[1 - \tfrac{1}{2} + \tfrac{1}{3} - \tfrac{1}{4} + \tfrac{1}{5} - \tfrac{1}{6} + \tfrac{1}{7} - \tfrac{1}{8} + \tfrac{1}{9} - \cdots]$$
$$= 2 - 1 + \tfrac{2}{3} - \tfrac{1}{2} + \tfrac{2}{5} - \tfrac{1}{3} + \tfrac{2}{7} - \tfrac{1}{4} + \tfrac{2}{9} - \cdots$$
$$= (2 - 1) - \tfrac{1}{2} + (\tfrac{2}{3} - \tfrac{1}{3}) - \tfrac{1}{4} + (\tfrac{2}{5} - \tfrac{1}{5}) - \tfrac{1}{6} + \cdots$$
$$= 1 - \tfrac{1}{2} + \tfrac{1}{3} - \tfrac{1}{4} + \tfrac{1}{5} - \tfrac{1}{6} + \tfrac{1}{7} - \tfrac{1}{8} + \tfrac{1}{9} - \cdots .$$

719. ADDITION, SUBTRACTION, AND MULTIPLICATION OF SERIES

Definition I.　*If $\sum a_n$ and $\sum b_n$ are two series, their* **sum** *$\sum c_n$ and* **difference** *$\sum d_n$ are series defined by the equations*

$$(1) \qquad\qquad c_n \equiv a_n + b_n, \quad d_n \equiv a_n - b_n.$$

Theorem I.　*The sum and difference of two convergent series, $\sum a_n = A$ and $\sum b_n = B$, converge to $A + B$ and $A - B$, respectively. The sum and difference of two absolutely convergent series are absolutely convergent.*

The proof is left as an exercise (Ex. 3, § 721).

The product of two series is a more difficult matter. The definition of a product series is motivated by the form of the product of polynomials or, more generally, power series (treated in Chapter 8):

$$(a_0 + a_1 x + a_2 x^2 + \cdots)(b_0 + b_1 x + b_2 x^2 + \cdots)$$
$$= a_0 b_0 + (a_0 b_1 + a_1 b_0)x + (a_0 b_2 + a_1 b_1 + a_2 b_0)x^2 + \cdots .$$

For convenience we revise slightly our notation for an infinite series, letting the terms have subscripts $0, 1, 2, \cdots$, and write

$$\sum a_n = \sum_{n=0}^{+\infty} a_n \quad \text{and} \quad \sum b_n = \sum_{n=0}^{+\infty} b_n.$$

Definition II.　*If $\sum\limits_{n=0}^{+\infty} a_n$ and $\sum\limits_{n=0}^{+\infty} b_n$ are two series, their* **product** *$\sum\limits_{n=0}^{+\infty} c_n$ is defined:*

$$(2) \qquad c_0 = a_0 b_0, \; c_1 = a_0 b_1 + a_1 b_0, \; \cdots ,$$

$$c_n = \sum_{k=0}^{n} a_k b_{n-k} = a_0 b_n + a_1 b_{n-1} + \cdots + a_n b_0, \; \cdots ,$$

$$\cdot \quad \cdot \quad \cdot \quad \cdot \quad \cdot \quad \cdot \quad \cdot \quad \cdot \quad \cdot \quad \cdot \quad \cdot \quad \cdot \quad \cdot \quad \cdot \quad \cdot$$

The basic questions are these: If $\sum a_n$ and $\sum b_n$ converge, with sums A and B, and if $\sum c_n$ is their product series, does $\sum c_n$ converge? If $\sum c_n$ converges to C is $C = AB$? If $\sum c_n$ does not necessarily converge, what conditions on $\sum a_n$ and $\sum b_n$ guarantee convergence of $\sum c_n$?

The answers, in brief, are: The convergence of $\sum a_n$ and $\sum b_n$ does not guarantee convergence of $\sum c_n$ (Ex. 5, § 721). If $\sum c_n$ does converge, then $C = AB$. (This result is due to Abel. Cf. Ex. 20, § 911.) If both $\sum a_n$ and $\sum b_n$ converge, and if *one* of them converges absolutely, then $\sum c_n$ converges (to AB). (This result is due to Mertens. Cf. Ex. 19, § 721.) If *both* $\sum a_n$ and $\sum b_n$ converge absolutely, then $\sum c_n$ converges absolutely (to AB). (This is our next theorem.)

Theorem II. *The product series of two absolutely convergent series is absolutely convergent. Its sum is the product of their sums.*

Proof. Let $\sum\limits_{n=0}^{+\infty} a_n$ and $\sum\limits_{n=0}^{+\infty} b_n$ be the given absolutely convergent series,

let $\sum\limits_{n=0}^{+\infty} c_n$ be their product series, and define the series $\sum\limits_{n=0}^{+\infty} d_n$ to be

$$a_0b_0 + a_0b_1 + a_1b_0 + a_0b_2 + a_1b_1 + a_2b_0$$
$$+ a_0b_3 + a_1b_2 + a_2b_1 + a_3b_0 + a_0b_4 + \cdots,$$

the terms following along the diagonal lines suggested in Figure 703.

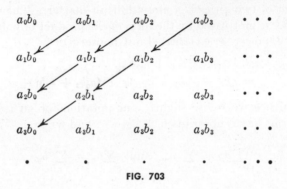

FIG. 703

Furthermore, let

$$A_n \equiv a_0 + a_1 + \cdots + a_n, \qquad B_n \equiv b_0 + b_1 + \cdots + b_n,$$
$$C_n \equiv c_0 + c_1 + \cdots + c_n, \qquad D_n \equiv d_0 + d_1 + \cdots + d_n.$$

Observe that every c_n is obtained by the grouping of $(n + 1)$ terms of the series $\sum d_n$, that every C_n is a partial sum of the series $\sum d_n$ with terms occupying a triangle in the upper left-hand corner of Figure 703, and that every A_nB_n is a sum (not a strict "partial sum") of certain terms of the series $\sum d_n$ occupying a square in the upper left-hand corner of Figure 703.

We prove the theorem first for the case of nonnegative series $\sum a_n$ and $\sum b_n$. In this case, since every finite set of terms from $\sum d_n$ is located in some square in the upper left-hand corner of Figure 703, *every* D_m is less than or equal to *some* A_nB_n. That is, if $A \equiv \lim\limits_{n\to+\infty} A_n$, and $B \equiv \lim\limits_{n\to+\infty} B_n$, the inequality $D_m \leq AB$ holds for every m. Therefore the series $\sum d_n$ converges, the limit $D \equiv \lim\limits_{n\to+\infty} D_n$ is finite, and $D \leq AB$. On the other hand, since A_nB_n is a sum of terms of the convergent series $\sum d_n$, the inequality $A_nB_n \leq D$ holds for every n, and hence $AB \leq D$. Thus $D = AB$. Finally, since $\{C_n\}$ is a subsequence of $\{D_n\}$ (resulting from introducing parentheses in the series $\sum d_n$), $C \equiv \lim\limits_{n\to+\infty} C_n = D = AB$.

If the given series, $\sum a_n$ and $\sum b_n$, have terms of arbitrary sign, the conclusion sought is a consequence of Dirichlet's Theorem (§ 718): Since, by the preceding paragraph, the series $\sum d_n$ converges absolutely, any rearrangement converges absolutely to the same sum. The sequence $\{C_n\}$ is a subsequence of the sequence of partial sums of $\sum d_n$, and the sequence $\{A_n B_n\}$ is a subsequence of the sequence of partial sums of an appropriate rearrangement of $\sum d_n$. Therefore $\lim_{n \to +\infty} C_n = \lim_{n \to +\infty} A_n B_n = \lim_{n \to +\infty} D_n$.

★720. SOME AIDS TO COMPUTATION

The only techniques available from the preceding sections of this chapter for evaluating series are (i) the sum $a/(1 - r)$ of a geometric series and (ii) the estimate $|S_n - S| < c_{n+1}$ for an alternating series. We give in this section some further means of estimating the sum of a convergent series, with illustrative examples. These will be available for computation work presented in the next chapter.

If a nonnegative series is dominated by a convergent geometric series, the formula $a/(1 - r)$ provides an estimate for the sum. A useful formulation of this method makes use of the test ratio (give the proof in Ex. 6, § 721):

Theorem I. *If* $a_n > 0$, $S_n \equiv a_1 + \cdots + a_n$, $S \equiv \sum_{n=1}^{+\infty} a_n$, $r_n \equiv \dfrac{a_{n+1}}{a_n}$, $r_n \downarrow$, *and* $r_n \to \rho < 1$, *then for any* n *for which* $r_n < 1$,

$$(1) \qquad S_n + \frac{a_{n+1}}{1 - \rho} < S < S_n + \frac{a_{n+1}}{1 - r_{n+1}}.$$

Example 1. Compute the sum of the series

$$1 + \frac{1}{3} + \frac{1}{2 \,! \cdot 5} + \frac{1}{3 \,! \cdot 7} + \cdots + \frac{1}{n \,! \, (2n + 1)} + \cdots,$$

to three decimal places. (The sum is $\int_0^1 e^{x^2} \, dx$. Cf. Example 4, § 810.)

Solution. The sum S_6 is between 1.4625 and 1.4626. Since $r_n \to \rho = 0$, we estimate:

$$\frac{a_7}{1 - 0} = 0.000107, \quad \text{and} \quad \frac{a_7}{1 - r_7} = \frac{0.000107}{1 - 0.121} < 0.00013.$$

Therefore, from (1), S must lie between 1.4626 and 1.4628. Its value to three decimal places is therefore 1.463.

If a nonnegative series is not dominated by a convergent geometric series $\left(\text{for example, if } \dfrac{a_{n+1}}{a_n} \to 1\right)$, Theorem I cannot be used. However, in this case the process of integration (cf. the integral test, § 706) can sometimes be used, as expressed in the following theorem (give the proof in Ex. 7, § 721):

Theorem II. *If $f(x)$ is a positive monotonically decreasing function,*

for $x \geq a$, if $\sum_{n=1}^{+\infty} a_n$ is a convergent positive series, with $f(n) = a_n$ for $n > a$,

if $S \equiv \sum a_n$, and if $S_n \equiv a_1 + \cdots + a_n$, then for $n > a$,

$$(6) \qquad S_n + \int_{n+1}^{+\infty} f(x)\,dx < S < S_n + \int_{n}^{+\infty} f(x)\,dx.$$

A much sharper estimate is provided by the following theorem (hints for a proof are given in Ex. 21, § 721):

★★**Theorem III.** *Under the hypotheses of Theorem II and the additional assumption that $f''(x)$ is a positive monotonically decreasing function for $x \geq a$, then for $n > a$,*

$$(7) \quad S_n + \frac{a_{n+1}}{2} + \int_{n+1}^{+\infty} f(x)\,dx - \frac{f'(n+2)}{12}$$

$$< S < S_n + \frac{a_{n+1}}{2} + \int_{n+1}^{+\infty} f(x)\,dx - \frac{f'(n)}{12}.$$

Example 2. Estimate the sum of the p-series with $p = 2$, using 10 terms.

Solution. With the aid of a table of reciprocals we find that $S_{10} = 1.549768$. With $f(x) \equiv x^{-2}$, $\int_{11}^{+\infty} f(x)\,dx = \frac{1}{11} = 0.090909$ and $\int_{10}^{+\infty} f(x)\,dx = \frac{1}{10} = 0.100000$. Thus the estimate of Theorem II places the sum S between 1.640 and 1.650, with an accuracy of one digit in the second decimal place.

★★Further computations give $\frac{1}{2} a_{11} = 0.004132$, $-\frac{1}{12} f'(12) = \frac{1}{6 \cdot 12^3} = 0.000096$, and $-\frac{1}{12} f'(10) = \frac{1}{6 \cdot 10^3} = 0.000167$. Thus the estimate of Theorem III places the sum S between 1.6449 and 1.6450, with an accuracy of one digit in the fourth decimal place.

Note. The sum in Example 2 can be specifically evaluated by means of the techniques of Fourier series (cf. H. S. Carslaw, *Fourier's Series and Integrals,* 3rd ed. (New York, Dover Publications, Inc., 1930), p. 234):

$$\frac{\pi^2}{6} = 1 + \frac{1}{2^2} + \frac{1}{3^2} + \frac{1}{4^2} + \cdots .$$

If an alternating series converges slowly, the estimate given in the alternating series test (§ 715) is very crude unless an excessively large number of terms is used. For example, to compute the value of the alternating harmonic series to four decimal places would require at least ten thousand terms! This particular series happens to converge to $\ln 2$ (cf. § 807), and this fortuitous circumstance permits a simpler and more speedy evaluation (cf. Example 4, § 813). However, this series will be used in the following example to illustrate a technique frequently useful in evaluating slowly converging alternating series:

Example 3. Evaluate the alternating harmonic series,

$$S = 1 - \tfrac{1}{2} + \tfrac{1}{3} - \tfrac{1}{4} + \cdots$$

to four decimal places.

Solution. We start by evaluating the sum of the first 10 terms: $S_{10} = 0.645635$. We wish to estimate the remainder:

$$x \equiv \tfrac{1}{11} - \tfrac{1}{12} + \tfrac{1}{13} - \tfrac{1}{14} + \cdots.$$

If we double, remove parentheses (the student should justify this step), and introduce parentheses, we find

$$2x = (\tfrac{1}{11} + \tfrac{1}{11}) - (\tfrac{1}{12} + \tfrac{1}{12}) + (\tfrac{1}{13} + \tfrac{1}{13}) - \cdots$$
$$= \tfrac{1}{11} + \tfrac{1}{11} - \tfrac{1}{12} - \tfrac{1}{12} + \tfrac{1}{13} + \tfrac{1}{13} - \cdots$$
$$= \tfrac{1}{11} + (\tfrac{1}{11} - \tfrac{1}{12}) - (\tfrac{1}{12} - \tfrac{1}{13}) + (\tfrac{1}{13} - \tfrac{1}{14}) - \cdots$$
$$= \frac{1}{11} + \frac{1}{11 \cdot 12} - \frac{1}{12 \cdot 13} + \frac{1}{13 \cdot 14} - \cdots.$$

Again doubling, and removing and introducing parentheses, we have

$$4x = \frac{2}{11} + \frac{1}{11 \cdot 12} + \frac{2}{11 \cdot 12 \cdot 13} - \frac{2}{12 \cdot 13 \cdot 14} + \cdots,$$

or

$$2x = \frac{25}{11 \cdot 24} + \frac{1}{11 \cdot 12 \cdot 13} - \frac{1}{12 \cdot 13 \cdot 14} + \cdots.$$

Once more:

$$4x = \frac{25}{11 \cdot 12} + \frac{1}{11 \cdot 12 \cdot 13} + \frac{3}{11 \cdot 12 \cdot 13 \cdot 14} - \frac{3}{12 \cdot 13 \cdot 14 \cdot 15} + \cdots.$$

The sum of the first two terms of this series is 0.189977, and the remainder is less than the term $3/11 \cdot 12 \cdot 13 \cdot 14 < 0.000126$. Therefore x is between 0.04749, and 0.04753, and S is between 0.69312 and 0.69317. An estimate to four places is 0.6931+. (The actual value to five places is 0.69315.)

721. EXERCISES

1. Prove that any series arising from a divergent nonnegative series by grouping of terms is divergent. Equivalently, if the introduction of parentheses into a nonnegative series produces a convergent series, the original series is convergent.

2. Prove that the terms of a conditionally convergent series can be rearranged to give a series whose partial sums (*i*) tend toward $+\infty$, (*ii*) tend toward $-\infty$, (*iii*) tend toward ∞ but neither $+\infty$ nor $-\infty$, (*iv*) are bounded and have no limit.

3. Prove Theorem I, § 719.

★4. Prove that if $\sum a_n$ and $\sum b_n$ are nonnegative series with sums A and B, respectively, and if $\sum c_n$ is their product series, with sum C, then $C = AB$ under all circumstances of convergence or divergence, with the usual conventions about infinity $((+\infty) \cdot (+\infty) = +\infty$, (positive number) $\cdot (+\infty) = +\infty)$ and the additional convention $0 \cdot (+\infty) = 0$.

★5. Prove that if $\sum\limits_{n=0}^{+\infty} a_n$ and $\sum\limits_{n=0}^{+\infty} b_n$ are both the series

$$1 - \frac{1}{\sqrt{2}} + \frac{1}{\sqrt{3}} - \frac{1}{\sqrt{4}} + \cdots$$

and if $\sum\limits_{n=0}^{+\infty} c_n$ is their product series, then $\sum a_n$ and $\sum b_n$ converge, while $\sum c_n$ diverges. *Hint:* Show that $|c_n| \geqq 1$.

★6. Prove Theorem I, § 720.

★7. Prove Theorem II, § 720.

★8. Prove the commutative law for product series: The product series of $\sum a_n$ and $\sum b_n$ is the same as the product series of $\sum b_n$ and $\sum a_n$.

★9. Prove the associative law for product series: Let $\sum d_n$ be the product series of $\sum a_n$ and $\sum b_n$, and let $\sum e_n$ be the product series of $\sum b_n$ and $\sum c_n$. Then the product series of $\sum a_n$ and $\sum e_n$ is the same as the product series of $\sum d_n$ and $\sum c_n$.

★10. Prove the distributive law for multiplying and adding series: The product series of $\sum a_n$ and $\sum (b_n + c_n)$ is the sum of the product series of $\sum a_n$ and $\sum b_n$ and the product series of $\sum a_n$ and $\sum c_n$.

★11. Using the evaluation of the series $\sum n^{-2}$ given in the Note, § 720, show that

$$\frac{\pi^2}{8} = 1 + \frac{1}{3^2} + \frac{1}{5^2} + \frac{1}{7^2} + \cdots .$$

★12. Using the evaluation of the series $\sum n^{-2}$ given in the Note, § 720, show that

$$\frac{\pi^2}{12} = 1 - \frac{1}{2^2} + \frac{1}{3^2} - \frac{1}{4^2} + \cdots .$$

In Exercises 13-18, compute to four significant digits.

★13. $(e =)$ $1 + \dfrac{1}{1!} + \dfrac{1}{2!} + \dfrac{1}{3!} + \cdots .$

★14. $(\ln 2 =)$ $\dfrac{1}{2} + \dfrac{1}{2 \cdot 2^2} + \dfrac{1}{3 \cdot 2^3} + \dfrac{1}{4 \cdot 2^4} + \cdots .$

★15. $(\zeta(3) =)$ $1 + \dfrac{1}{2^3} + \dfrac{1}{3^3} + \dfrac{1}{4^3} + \cdots .$

★16. $\dfrac{5}{2^2 \cdot 3^2} + \dfrac{9}{4^2 \cdot 5^2} + \dfrac{13}{6^2 \cdot 7^2} + \dfrac{17}{8^2 \cdot 9^2} + \cdots .$

★17. $\left(\dfrac{\pi}{4} = \right)$ $1 - \dfrac{1}{3} + \dfrac{1}{5} - \dfrac{1}{7} + \cdots .$

★18. $\left(\ln \dfrac{3}{2} = \right)$ $\dfrac{1}{2} - \dfrac{1}{2 \cdot 2^2} + \dfrac{1}{3 \cdot 2^3} - \dfrac{1}{4 \cdot 2^4} + \cdots .$

★★19. Prove that the sequence

$$\{C_n\} \equiv \left\{ 1 + \frac{1}{2} + \cdots + \frac{1}{n} - \ln n \right\}$$

is decreasing and bounded below. Hence $C \equiv \lim\limits_{n \to +\infty} C_n$ exists. (The number

C is known as **Euler's constant.** It is believed to be transcendental, but its transcendence has never been established.)   (Cf. Ex. 22.)

★★20. Prove the theorem of Mertens: *If* $\sum\limits_{n=0}^{+\infty} a_n$ *converges absolutely to* A *and if* $\sum\limits_{n=0}^{+\infty} b_n$ *converges to* B, *then the product series* $\sum\limits_{n=0}^{+\infty} c_n$ *converges to* AB.   *Hint:* By virtue of Exs. 8-10, it may be assumed without loss of generality that $\sum a_n$ is nonnegative, $A > 0$, and $B = 0$.   Under these assumptions prove that $\sum c_n$ converges to 0: Define $A_n \equiv \sum\limits_{k=0}^{n} a_k$, $B_n \equiv \sum\limits_{k=0}^{n} b_k$, $C_n \equiv \sum\limits_{k=0}^{n} c_k$.   Then

$$C_n = a_0b_0 + (a_0b_1 + a_1b_0) + \cdots + (a_0b_n + \cdots + a_nb_0)$$
$$= a_0B_n + a_1B_{n-1} + \cdots + a_nB_0.$$

For a given $\epsilon > 0$, first choose N such that $m > N$ implies $|B_m| < \epsilon/2A$, and therefore

$$|a_0B_n + \cdots + a_{n-N-1}B_{N+1}| < \tfrac{1}{2}\epsilon.$$

Then choose $N' > N$ such that $n > N'$ implies

$$|a_{n-N}| < \frac{\epsilon}{2(N+1)} \cdot \max\left(|B_0|, |B_1|, \cdots, |B_N|, 1\right).$$

★★21. Prove Theorem III, § 720.   *Hints:* Let $R_n \equiv a_{n+1} + a_{n+2} + \cdots = \tfrac{1}{2}a_{n+1} + \tfrac{1}{2}(a_{n+1} + a_{n+2}) + \tfrac{1}{2}(a_{n+2} + a_{n+3}) + \cdots \equiv \tfrac{1}{2}a_n + T_{n+1}$. Interpret T_{n+1} as a sum of areas of trapezoids, and use the trapezoidal formula error estimate (Ex. 22, § 503) to write $\tfrac{1}{2}(a_m + a_{m+1}) = \int_m^{m+1} f(x)\, dx + \tfrac{1}{12} f''(\xi_m)$, where $m < \xi_m < m + 1$.   Thus $T_{n+1} - \int_{n+1}^{+\infty} f(x)\, dx = \tfrac{1}{12} \sum\limits_{m=n+1}^{+\infty} f''(\xi_m)$.   But

$$\tfrac{1}{12} \int_{n+2}^{+\infty} f''(x)\, dx < \tfrac{1}{12} \sum_{m=n+1}^{+\infty} f''(m) < \sum_{m=n+1}^{+\infty} f''(\xi_m) < \tfrac{1}{12} \sum_{m=n}^{+\infty} f''(m)$$
$$< \tfrac{1}{12} \int_n^{+\infty} f''(x)\, dx.$$

★★22. Find an estimate of Euler's constant (Ex. 19), by using the technique of the proof of Theorem III, § 720 (Ex. 21), and $9\tfrac{1}{2}$ terms of the harmonic series:

$$C = 1 + \tfrac{1}{2} + \cdots + \tfrac{1}{9} + \tfrac{1}{2} \cdot \tfrac{1}{10} - \ln 10$$
$$+ \lim_{n \to +\infty} \left\{ \left[\tfrac{1}{2}\left(\tfrac{1}{10} + \tfrac{1}{11}\right) - \int_{10}^{11} \frac{dx}{x}\right] + \left[\tfrac{1}{2}\left(\tfrac{1}{11} + \tfrac{1}{12}\right) - \int_{11}^{12} \frac{dx}{x}\right] + \cdots \right\}.$$

8

Power Series

.

~~~~~~

801. INTERVAL OF CONVERGENCE

A series of the form

(1)
$$\sum a_n x^n = \sum_{n=0}^{+\infty} a_n x^n = a_0 + a_1 x + a_2 x^2 + \cdots$$

is called a **power series in x.** A series of the form

(2)
$$\sum a_n (x - a)^n = \sum_{n=0}^{+\infty} a_n (x - a)^n = a_0 + a_1(x - a) + \cdots$$

is called a **power series in (x − a).** More generally, a series of the form

(3)
$$\sum a_n [u(x)]^n = \sum_{n=0}^{+\infty} a_n [u(x)]^n = a_0 + a_1 u(x) + \cdots,$$

where $u(x)$ is a function of x, is called a **power series in u(x).** It is principally series (1) or (2) that will be of interest in this chapter, and the single expression *power series* will be used to mean either series (1) or series (2).

A power series is an example of a series of *functions.* For any fixed value of x the series becomes a series of *constants;* but convergence or divergence of this series of constants depends, ordinarily, on the value of x. One is frequently interested in the question, "For what values of x does a given power series converge?" The answer is fairly simple: The values of x for which a power series converges always form an interval, which may degenerate to a single point, or encompass all real numbers, or be a finite interval, open, closed, or half-open. To prove this result we formulate it for simplicity for the power series $\sum a_n x^n$, first establishing a lemma:

Lemma. *If a power series $\sum a_n x^n$ converges for $x = x_1$ and if $|x_2| < |x_1|$, then the series converges absolutely for $x = x_2$.*

Proof. Assume $\sum a_n x_1^n$ converges. Then $\lim\limits_{n \to +\infty} a_n x_1^n = 0$. Therefore the sequence $\{a_n x_1^n\}$, being convergent, is bounded. Let $|a_n x_1^n| < K$ for all n. If $|x_2| < |x_1|$, we may write

(4) $$|a_n x_2{}^n| = |a_n x_1{}^n| \cdot \left|\frac{x_2}{x_1}\right|^n < Kr^n, \text{ where } 0 \leq r < 1.$$

The series $\sum Kr^n$ is a convergent geometric series. Therefore, by comparison, $\sum |a_n x_2{}^n|$ converges, and $\sum a_n x_2{}^n$ converges absolutely.

What this lemma says, in part, is that *any* point of convergence of the power series $\sum a_n x^n$ is at least as close to 0 as *any* point of divergence.

Theorem I. *Let S be the set of points x for which a power series $\sum a_n x^n$ converges. Then either (i) S consists only of the point $x = 0$, or (ii) S consists of all real numbers, or (iii) S is an interval of one of the following forms: $(-R, R), [-R, R], (-R, R],$ or $[-R, R),$ where R is a positive real number.*

★*Proof.* The simplest proof rests on the concept of *least upper bound* (§ 114). (For a proof based on convergent sequences, cf. Ex. 17, § 802.) If neither (i) nor (ii) holds, then (by the preceding lemma) the series $\sum a_n x^n$ must converge for some positive number x_C and diverge for some larger positive number x_D. That is, S contains some positive numbers and is bounded above. Let R be defined to be the least upper bound of S. Then (iii) is a consequence of the Lemma. (Why?)

Note 1. The statements just established for the power series (1) apply to the power series (2), the only change being that the interval of convergence has the point $x = a$ instead of the point $x = 0$ as midpoint.

The set S of points x for which a power series $\sum a_n (x - a)^n$ converges is called the **interval of convergence,** and the number R of Theorem I (and Note 1) is called the **radius of convergence**† of $\sum a_n (x - a)^n$. In case (i) of Theorem I we define $R \equiv 0$, and in case (ii) we write $R \equiv +\infty$, so that in general $0 \leq R \leq +\infty$.

A further consequence of the Lemma is the Theorem:

Theorem II. *At any point interior to the interval of convergence of a power series the convergence is absolute.*

Note 2. All of the eventualities stated in Theorem I exist (Ex. 13, § 802).

Note 3. At an end-point of the interval of convergence a power series may diverge, converge conditionally, or converge absolutely. At the two end-points all combinations are possible, except that if a power series converges absolutely at one end-point it must also converge absolutely at the other end-point. (Cf. Ex. 14, § 802.)

The usual procedure in determining the interval of convergence of a power series is to start with the ratio test, although this may fail (cf. Ex-

---

† R is called the *radius of convergence* because of the analogous situation with complex numbers, where the *interval* of convergence is replaced by a *circle* of convergence whose radius is R.

ample 3). The success of the ratio test depends on the existence of the limit of the ratio of successive coefficients. We specify this relationship:

Theorem III.   *The radius of convergence of the power series $\sum a_n(x - a)^n$ is*

$$(5) \qquad\qquad R = \lim_{n \to +\infty} \left| \frac{a_n}{a_{n+1}} \right|,$$

where $0 \leq R \leq +\infty$, provided this limit exists.

Proof. We give the details for $0 < R < +\infty$. (Cf. Ex. 15, § 802.) The test ratio for the series $\sum a_n(x - a)^n$ is $\dfrac{a_{n+1}(x - a)}{a_n}$, whose absolute value has the limit $\lim\limits_{n \to +\infty} \left| \dfrac{a_{n+1}}{a_n} \right| \cdot |x - a| = \dfrac{|x - a|}{R}$. Therefore, by the ratio test, $\sum a_n(x - a)^n$ converges absolutely if $|x - a| < R$ and diverges if $|x - a| > R$.

After the radius of convergence has been found, the end-points of the interval of convergence should be tested. For such points the ratio test cannot give any information, for if $\dfrac{a_{n+1}}{a_n} R$ had a limit for $R > 0$, the limit (5) would exist, and the absolute value of the test ratio must have the limit 1. To test the end-points one is forced to use some type of comparison test, or a refined test of the type discussed in § 712. (The root test also fails at the end-points—cf. Ex. 16, § 802.)

★NOTE 4. A universally valid formula for the radius of convergence of a power series $\sum a_n(x - a)^n$ makes use of *limit superior* (Ex. 16, § 305):

$$R = \frac{1}{\varlimsup\limits_{n \to +\infty} \sqrt[n]{|a_n|}},$$

with the conventions $1/0 = +\infty$, $1/+\infty = 0$. (Give the proof in Ex. 18, § 802, and cf. Ex. 16, § 802.)

Example 1.   Determine the interval of convergence for the series

$$1 + x^2 + \frac{x^4}{2!} + \frac{x^6}{3!} + \cdots .$$

(Cf. § 807.)

Solution. This should be treated as a power series in powers of x^2. The radius of convergence is

$$R = \lim_{n \to +\infty} \frac{(n + 1)!}{n!} = \lim_{n \to +\infty} (n + 1) = +\infty.$$

Therefore the interval of convergence is $(-\infty, +\infty)$.

Example 2.   Determine the interval of convergence for the series

$$(x - 1) - \frac{(x - 1)^2}{2} + \frac{(x - 1)^3}{3} - \frac{(x - 1)^4}{4} + \cdots .$$

(Cf. § 807.)

Solution. The radius of convergence is $R = \lim\limits_{n \to +\infty} \dfrac{n+1}{n} = 1$, and the midpoint of the interval of convergence is $x = 1$. We test for convergence at the end-points of the interval, $x = 2$ and $x = 0$. The value $x = 2$ gives the convergent alternating harmonic series and $x = 0$ gives minus the divergent harmonic series. The interval of convergence is $(0, 2]$.

Example 3. Determine the interval of convergence for the series

$$\frac{1}{2} + \frac{x}{3} + \frac{x^2}{2^2} + \frac{x^3}{3^2} + \frac{x^4}{2^3} + \frac{x^5}{3^3} + \frac{x^6}{2^4} + \frac{x^7}{3^4} + \cdots .$$

(Cf. Example 2, § 708.)

Solution. The limit (5) does not exist. However, the intervals of convergence of the two series

$$\frac{1}{2} + \frac{x^2}{2^2} + \frac{x^4}{2^3} + \cdots \quad \text{and} \quad \frac{x}{3} + \frac{x^3}{3^2} + \frac{x^5}{3^3} + \cdots$$

are $(-\sqrt{2}, \sqrt{2})$ and $(-\sqrt{3}, \sqrt{3})$, respectively. Therefore the given series converges absolutely for $|x| < \sqrt{2}$ and diverges for $|x| \geq \sqrt{2}$. The interval of convergence is $(-\sqrt{2}, \sqrt{2})$.

Example 4. Determine the values of x for which the series

$$xe^{-x} + 2x^2e^{-2x} + 3x^3e^{-3x} + 4x^4e^{-4x} + \cdots$$

converges.

Solution. Either the ratio test or the root test shows that the series converges absolutely for $|x\,e^{-x}| < 1$ (otherwise it diverges). The inequality $|x\,e^{-x}| < 1$ is equivalent to $|x| < e^x$, and is satisfied for all nonnegative x. To determine the negative values of x which satisfy this inequality, we let $\alpha = -x$, and solve the equation $\alpha = e^{-\alpha}$ ($\alpha = 0.567$, approximately). Then the given series converges if and only if $x > -\alpha$, and the convergence is absolute.

802. EXERCISES

In Exercises 1-10, determine the interval of convergence, and specify the nature of any convergence at each end-point of the interval of convergence.

1. $1 - \dfrac{2x}{1!} + \dfrac{(2x)^2}{2!} - \dfrac{(3x)^3}{3!} + \cdots .$

2. $x - \dfrac{x^3}{3} + \dfrac{x^5}{5} - \dfrac{x^7}{7} + \cdots .$

3. $1 + \dfrac{x^2}{2!} + \dfrac{x^4}{4!} + \dfrac{x^6}{6!} + \cdots .$

4. $1 + x + 2!x^2 + 3!x^3 + 4!x^4 + \cdots .$

5. $(x+1) - \dfrac{(x+1)^2}{4} + \dfrac{(x+1)^3}{9} - \dfrac{(x+1)^4}{16} + \cdots .$

6. $(x-2) + \dfrac{(x-2)^3}{3!} + \dfrac{(x-2)^5}{5!} + \dfrac{(x-2)^7}{7!} + \cdots .$

7. $\dfrac{(\ln 2)(x-5)}{\sqrt{2}} + \dfrac{(\ln 3)(x-5)^2}{\sqrt{3}} + \dfrac{(\ln 4)(x-5)^3}{\sqrt{4}} + \cdots .$

8. $(x - 1) + \dfrac{(x - 1)^3}{3} + \dfrac{(x - 1)^5}{5} + \dfrac{(x - 1)^7}{7} + \cdots$.

★9. $1 - \dfrac{1}{2} x + \dfrac{1 \cdot 3}{2 \cdot 4} x^2 - \dfrac{1 \cdot 3 \cdot 5}{2 \cdot 4 \cdot 6} x^3 + \dfrac{1 \cdot 3 \cdot 5 \cdot 7}{2 \cdot 4 \cdot 6 \cdot 8} x^4 - \cdots$.

★10. $x + \dfrac{x^3}{6} + \dfrac{1 \cdot 3}{2 \cdot 4} \cdot \dfrac{x^5}{5} + \dfrac{1 \cdot 3 \cdot 5}{2 \cdot 4 \cdot 6} \dfrac{x^7}{7} + \cdots$.

11. Determine the values of x for which the series

$$\frac{1}{x - 3} + \frac{1}{2(x - 3)^2} + \frac{1}{3(x - 3)^3} + \frac{1}{4(x - 3)^4} + \cdots;$$

converges, and specify the type of convergence.

12. Determine the values of x for which the series

$$\sin x - \frac{\sin^3 x}{3} + \frac{\sin^5 x}{5} - \frac{\sin^7 x}{7} + \cdots.$$

converges, and specify the type of convergence.

13. Prove Note 2, § 801.

14. Prove Note 3, § 801.

15. Prove Theorem III, § 801, for the cases $R = 0$ and $R = +\infty$.

16. Prove Note 4, § 801, for the case where $\lim\limits_{n \to +\infty} \sqrt[n]{a_n}$ exists (replacing $\overline{\lim}$ by lim).

★17. Give a proof of Theorem I, § 801, based on convergent sequences, as follows: Assume that neither condition (*i*) nor (*ii*) of that theorem holds. Show first that there exist positive points of convergence and of divergence which are arbitrarily close. Then construct two sequences $\{c_n\}$ and $\{d_n\}$ of points of convergence and divergence, respectively, where $0 \leqq c_n \leqq c_{n+1} < d_{n+1} \leqq d_n$, for $n = 1, 2, \cdots$, and define R to be their common limit. Prove that R is the radius of convergence of the given series.

★18. Prove Note 4, § 801. (Cf. Ex. 32, § 711.)

★19. Apply Note 4, § 801 to Example 3, § 801. (Cf. Ex. 33, § 711.)

★20. Show by examples that Theorem III, § 801, cannot be generalized in the manner of Note 4, § 801, by the use of limits superior or inferior. (Cf. Exs. 31-33, § 711.)

803. TAYLOR SERIES

We propose to discuss in this section some formal procedures, nearly all of which need justification and will be discussed in future sections. The purpose of this discussion is to motivate an important formula, and raise some questions.

Let us suppose that a power series $\sum a_n(x - a)^n$ has a positive radius of convergence $(0 < R \leqq +\infty)$, and let $f(x)$ be the function defined by this series wherever it converges. That is,

$$(1) \qquad f(x) \equiv a_0 + a_1(x - a) + a_2(x - a)^2 + \cdots.$$

We now differentiate term-by-term, as if the infinite series were simply a finite sum:

$$f'(x) = a_1 + 2a_2(x - a) + 3a_3(x - a)^2 + \cdots .$$

Again:

$$f''(x) = 2a_2 + 2 \cdot 3a_3(x - a) + 3 \cdot 4a_4(x - a)^2 + \cdots .$$

And so forth:

$$f'''(x) = 3 ! a_3 + 2 \cdot 3 \cdot 4a_4(x - a) + 3 \cdot 4 \cdot 5a_5(x - a)^2 + \cdots ,$$

. . . .

Upon substitution of $x = a$, we have:

$$f(a) = a_0, f'(a) = a_1, f''(a) = 2 ! a_2, f'''(a) = 3 ! a_3, \cdots ,$$

or, if we solve for the coefficients a_n:

(2) $$a_0 = f(a), a_1 = f'(a), a_2 = \frac{f''(a)}{2 !}, \cdots , a_n = \frac{f^{(n)}(a)}{n !}, \cdots .$$

This suggests that if a power series $\sum a_n(x - a)^n$ converges to a function $f(x)$, then the coefficients of the power series should be determined by the values of that function and its successive derivatives according to equations (2). In other words, we should expect:

(3) $$f(x) = f(a) + f'(a)(x - a) + \frac{f''(a)}{2 !} (x - a)^2 + \cdots$$
$$+ \frac{f^{(n)}(a)}{n !} (x - a)^n + \cdots ,$$

and, in particular, for $a = 0$:

(4) $$f(x) = f(0) + f'(0)x + \cdots + \frac{f^{(n)}(0)}{n !} x^n + \cdots .$$

Now suppose $f(x)$ has derivatives of all orders, at least in a neighborhood of the point $x = a$. Then $f^{(n)}(a)$ is defined for every n, and the series (3) exists. Regardless of any question of convergence or (in case of convergence) equality in (3), we *define* the series $\sum_{n=0}^{+\infty} \frac{f^{(n)}(a)}{n !} (x - a)^n$† on the right-hand side of (3) as the **Taylor series for the function $f(x)$ at $x = a$.** The particular case $\sum_{n=0}^{+\infty} \frac{f^{(n)}(0)}{n !} x^n$ given in (4) is known as the **Maclaurin series for $f(x)$.**

We ask two questions:

(*i*) For a given function $f(x)$, is the Taylor series expansion (3) universally valid in some neighborhood of $x = a$, and if not, what criteria are there for the relation (3) to be true?

† For convenience in notation we define $f^{(0)}(x) \equiv f(x)$, and recall that $0 ! \equiv 1$. Although for $x = a$ and $n = 0$ an indeterminacy 0^0 develops, let us agree that *in this instance* 0^0 shall be defined to be 1.

The answer to this question is a major concern of the remaining sections of this chapter.

(*ii*) For a given power series $\sum a_n (x - a)^n$, converging to a function $f(x)$ in an interval with positive radius of convergence, is the Taylor series equation (3) true?

We answer this second question affirmatively, now, but defer the proof to the next chapter (Ex. 13, § 911):

Theorem I. *If* $\sum\limits_{n=0}^{+\infty} a_n (x - a)^n$ *has a positive radius of convergence, and if* $f(x) \equiv \sum a_n(x - a)^n$ *in the interval of convergence of the series, then throughout the interior of that interval* $f(x)$ *is continuous and has (continuous) derivatives of all orders, and relations (2) hold:* $a_n = f^{(n)}(a)/n$!, *for* $n = 0, 1, 2, \cdots$. *The given series is the Taylor series for the function* $f(x)$ *at* $x = a$.

One immediate consequence of this theorem is the uniqueness of a power series $\sum a_n(x - a)^n$ converging to a given function:

Theorem II. Uniqueness Theorem. *If a function* $f(x)$ *is equal to the sum of a power series* $\sum a_n(x - a)^n$ *in a neighborhood of* $x = a$, *and if* $f(x)$ *is also equal to the sum of a power series* $\sum b_n(x - a)^n$ *in a neighborhood of* $x = a$, *then these two power series are identical, coefficient by coefficient:* $a_n = b_n, n = 0, 1, 2, \cdots$.

Proof. Each power series is the Taylor series for $f(x)$ at $x = a$.

804. TAYLOR'S FORMULA WITH A REMAINDER

In § 407 we obtained from the Extended Law of the Mean a formulation for expanding a function $f(x)$ in terms closely related to the Taylor series discussed in the preceding section. Let us repeat the formula of Note 3, § 407, with a slight change in notation, in the following Definition and Theorem I:

Definition. *If* $f^{(n)}(x)$ *exists at every point of an interval* I *containing the point* $x = a$, *then the* **Taylor's Formula with a Remainder** *for the function* $f(x)$, *for any point* x *of* I, *is*

$$(1) \quad f(x) = f(a) + f'(a)(x - a) + \frac{f''(a)}{2\,!}\,(x - a)^2 + \cdots$$
$$+ \frac{f^{(n-1)}(a)}{(n - 1)\,!}\,(x - a)^{n-1} + R_n\,(x).$$

The quantity $R_n(x)$ *is called the* **remainder after n terms.**

The principal substance of Note 3, § 407, is an explicit evaluation of the remainder $R_n(x)$:

Theorem I.   Lagrange Form of the Remainder.   *Let n be a fixed positive integer.   If $f^{(n)}(x)$ exists at every point of an interval I (open, closed, or half-open) containing $x = a$, and if x is any point of I, then there exists a point ξ_n between a and x ($\xi_n = a$ if $x = a$) such that the remainder after n terms, in Taylor's Formula with a Remainder, is*

$$(2) \qquad R_n(x) = \frac{f^{(n)}(\xi_n)}{n!}(x - a)^n.$$

The principal purpose of this section is to obtain two other forms of the remainder $R_n(x)$. We first establish an integral form of the remainder (Theorem II), from which both the Lagrange form and the Cauchy form (Theorem III) can be derived immediately (cf. Ex. 1, § 806).

Assuming continuity of all of the derivatives involved, we start with the obvious identity $\int_0^{x-a} f'(x - t)\,dt = f(x) - f(a)$, and integrate by parts, repeatedly:

$$f(x) - f(a) = \int_0^{x-a} f'(x - t)\,dt = \Big[\, t f'(x - t)\,\Big]_0^{x-a} + \int_0^{x-a} t f''(x - t)\,dt$$

$$= f'(a)(x - a) + \int_0^{x-a} f''(x - t)\, d\!\left(\frac{t^2}{2!}\right)$$

$$= f'(a)(x - a) + \left[\frac{t^2}{2!} f''(x - t)\right]_0^{x-a} + \int_0^{x-a} \frac{t^2}{2!} f'''(x - t)\,dt$$

$$= f'(a)(x - a) + \frac{f''(0)}{2!}(x - a)^2 + \int_0^{x-a} f'''(x - t)\, d\!\left(\frac{t^3}{3!}\right)$$

$$= \cdots\cdots .$$

Iteration of this process an appropriate number of times leads to the formula written out in the following theorem:

Theorem II.   Integral Form of the Remainder.   *Let n be a fixed positive integer.   If $f^{(n)}(x)$ exists and is continuous throughout an interval I containing the point $x = a$, and if x is any point of I, then the remainder after n terms, in Taylor's Formula with a Remainder, can be written*

$$(3) \qquad R_n(x) = \frac{1}{(n-1)!} \int_0^{x-a} t^{n-1} f^{(n)}(x - t)\,dt.$$

Suppose for the moment that $x > a$. Then $x - a > 0$ and, by the First Mean Value Theorem for Integrals (Theorem XI, § 501) there exists a number η_n such that $0 < \eta_n < x - a$ and, from (3),

$$R_n(x) = \frac{1}{(n-1)!}\, \eta_n{}^{n-1} f^{(n)}(x - \eta_n)\cdot(x - a).$$

In other words, there exists a number $\xi_n \equiv x - \eta_n$ between a and x such that

$$R_n(x) = \frac{1}{(n-1)!} (x - \xi_n)^{n-1} f^{(n)}(\xi_n) \cdot (x - a).$$

On the other hand, if $x \leq a$, we obtain the same result by reversing the inequalities or replacing them by equalities. We have the conclusion:

Theorem III. **Cauchy Form of the Remainder.** *Let n be a fixed positive integer. If $f^{(n)}(x)$ exists and is continuous throughout an interval I containing the point $x = a$, and if x is any point of I, then there exists a point ξ_n between a and x ($\xi_n = a$ if $x = a$) such that the remainder after n terms, in Taylor's Formula with a Remainder is*

(4) $$R_n(x) = \frac{(x - a)(x - \xi_n)^{n-1}}{(n-1)!} f^{(n)}(\xi_n).$$

805. EXPANSIONS OF FUNCTIONS

Definition. *A series of functions $\sum u_n(x)$ **represents** a function $f(x)$ on a certain set A if and only if for every point x of the set A the series $\sum u_n(x)$ converges to the value of the function $f(x)$ at that point.*

Immediately after the question of *convergence* of the Taylor series of a function comes the question, "Does the Taylor series of a given function *represent* the function throughout the interval of convergence?" The clue to the answer lies in Taylor's Formula with a Remainder. To clarify the situation we introduce the notation of partial sums (which now depend on x):

(1) $$S_n(x) \equiv f(a) + f'(a)(x - a) + \cdots + \frac{f^{(n-1)}(a)}{(n-1)!} (x - a)^{n-1}.$$

Taylor's Formula with a Remainder now assumes the form

(2) $$f(x) = S_n(x) + R_n(x),$$

or

(3) $$R_n(x) = f(x) - S_n(x).$$

Immediately from (3) and the definition of the sum of a series, we have the theorem:

Theorem. *If I is an interval containing $x = a$ at each point of which $f(x)$ and all of its derivatives exist, and if $x = x_0$ is a point of I, then the Taylor series for $f(x)$ at $x = a$ represents $f(x)$ at the point x_0 if and only if*

$$\lim_{n \to +\infty} R_n(x_0) = 0.$$

Determining for a particular function whether its Taylor series at $x = a$ represents the function for some particular $x = x_0$, reduces, then, to determining whether $R_n(x_0) \to 0$. Techniques for doing this vary with the function concerned. In the following section we shall make use of different forms of the remainder, in order to show that certain specific expansions represent the given functions. To make any general statement specifying conditions under which a given function is represented by its Taylor series is extremely difficult. We can say that some functions, such as polynomials, e^x, and $\sin x$ (cf. Example 1, below, Examples 5 and 6, § 808, and § 815) are *always* represented by *all* of their Taylor series, and that other functions, such as $\ln x$ and $\tan x$, are represented by Taylor series for only *parts* of their domains. Example 2, below, gives an extreme case of a function possessing a Taylor series which converges everywhere but represents the function only at one point!

Example 1. Prove that every polynomial is everywhere represented by all of its Taylor series.

Solution. If $f(x)$ is a polynomial, $f^{(n)}(x)$ exists for all n and x, and $f^{(n)}(x) = 0$ if n is greater than the degree of the polynomial. Therefore, if the Lagrange form of the remainder is used, $R_n(x)$ is identically zero for sufficiently large n, and $\lim_{n \to +\infty} R_n(x) = 0$.

Example 2. Show that the function $f(x)$ defined to be 0 when $x = 0$, and otherwise $f(x) \equiv e^{-1/x^2}$, is not represented by its Maclaurin series, although the function has derivatives of all orders everywhere.

Solution. The function has (continuous) derivatives of all orders at every point except possibly $x = 0$. At $x = 0$, $f^{(n)}(x) = 0$ for every $n = 0, 1, 2, \cdots$ (cf. Ex. 52, § 419), so that $f^{(n)}(x)$ exists and is continuous for every $n = 0, 1, 2, \cdots$ and every x. The Maclaurin series for $f(x)$ is thus

$$0 + 0 \cdot x + 0 \cdot x^2 + 0 \cdot x^3 + \cdots$$

which represents the function identically 0 everywhere, but the function $f(x)$ only at $x = 0$.

806. EXERCISES

1. Derive the Lagrange form of the remainder in Taylor's formula (Theorem I, § 804) from the integral form (Theorem II, § 804), using the additional hypothesis of continuity of $f^{(n)}(x)$. *Hint:* Use the generalized form of the First Mean Value Theorem for Integrals (Ex. 6, § 503).

2. Show that $|x|$, $\ln x$, $\sqrt{x}$, and $\cot x$ have no Maclaurin series. Show that x^p has a Maclaurin series if and only if p is a nonnegative integer.

3. Show that the Taylor series for $f(x)$ at $x = a$ can be written in increment and differential notation:

$$\Delta y = dy + \frac{f''(a)}{2!} dx^2 + \frac{f'''(a)}{3!} dx^3 + \cdots .$$

Hence show that approximations by differentials (cf. § 411) are those provided by the partial sum S_1 (through terms of the first degree) of the Taylor series of the function.

807. SOME MACLAURIN SERIES

In this section we derive the Maclaurin series for the five functions e^x, $\sin x$, $\cos x$, $\ln (1 + x)$, and $(1 + x)^m$, and (sometimes with the aid of future exercises) show that in each case the function is represented by its Maclaurin series throughout the interval of convergence.

I. The exponential function, $f(x) = e^x$. Since, for $n = 0, 1, 2, \cdots$, $f^{(n)}(x) = e^x$, $f^{(n)}(0) = 1$, and the Maclaurin series is

$$(1) \qquad 1 + x + \frac{x^2}{2!} + \frac{x^3}{3!} + \cdots + \frac{x^n}{n!} + \cdots .$$

The test ratio is $\frac{x}{n}$, whose limit is 0. Therefore the series (1) converges absolutely for all x, and the radius of convergence is infinite: $R = +\infty$.

To show that *the series* (1) *represents the function* e^x *for all real* x, we choose an arbitrary $x \neq 0$, and use the Lagrange form of the remainder:

$$(2) \qquad R_n(x) = \frac{e^{\xi_n}}{n!} x^n,$$

where ξ_n is between 0 and x. We observe first that for a fixed x, ξ_n (although it depends on n and is not constant) satisfies the inequality $\xi_n < |x|$, and therefore e^{ξ_n} is bounded above by the constant $e^{|x|}$. Thus the problem has been reduced to showing that $\lim\limits_{n \to +\infty} \frac{x^n}{n!} = 0$. But $\frac{x^n}{n!}$ is the general term of (1), and since (1) has already been shown to converge for all x, the general term must tend toward 0.

II. The sine function, $f(x) = \sin x$. The sequence $\{f^{(n)}(x)\}$ is $\sin x$, $\cos x$, $-\sin x$, $-\cos x$, $\sin x$, $\cdots$, and the sequence $\{f^{(n)}(0)\}$ is $0, 1, 0, -1, 0, 1, \cdots$. Therefore the Maclaurin series is

$$(3) \qquad x - \frac{x^3}{3!} + \frac{x^5}{5!} - \frac{x^7}{7!} + \cdots + (-1)^{n-1} \frac{x^{2n-1}}{(2n-1)!} + \cdots .$$

(Here we have dropped all zero terms, and used n to indicate the sequence of remaining nonzero terms, instead of the original exponent for the series $\sum \frac{f^{(n)}(0)}{n!} x^n$.) The test ratio of (3) is

$$- \frac{x^2}{2n(2n + 1)},$$

whose limit is 0. Therefore (3) converges absolutely for all x, and the radius of convergence is infinite: $R = +\infty$.

To show that *the series* (3) *represents the function* $\sin x$ *for all real* x, we choose an arbitrary $x \neq 0$, and again use the Lagrange form of the remainder:

$$(4) \qquad\qquad R_n(x) = \frac{g_n(\xi_n)}{n\,!}\, x^n,$$

where ξ_n is between 0 and x, $g_n(x)$ is $\pm\sin x$ or $\pm\cos x$, and n is now used to indicate the number of terms in the original form $\sum \dfrac{f^{(n)}(0)}{n\,!}\, x^n$ of the Maclaurin series. The proof that $\lim\limits_{n\to+\infty} R_n(x) = 0$ follows the same lines as the proof for e^x, with the aid of the inequality $|g_n(\xi_n)| \leqq 1$.

III. The cosine function, $f(x) = \cos x$. The details of the analysis are similar to those for $\sin x$. The Maclaurin series is

$$(5) \qquad 1 - \frac{x^2}{2\,!} + \frac{x^4}{4\,!} - \frac{x^6}{6\,!} + \cdots + (-1)^{n-1}\frac{x^{2n}}{(2n)\,!},$$

which converges absolutely for all real x $(R = +\infty)$. *The series (5) represents the function $\cos x$ for all real x.*

IV. The natural logarithm, $f(x) = \ln(1 + x)$. The sequence $\{f^{(n)}(x)\}$ is

$$\ln(1+x),\ (1+x)^{-1},\ -(1+x)^{-2},\ 2\,!\,(1+x)^{-3},\ -3\,!\,(1+x)^{-4},$$
$$\cdots,\ (-1)^{n-1}(n-1)\,!\,(1+x)^{-n},\ \cdots,$$

and hence the sequence $\{f^{(n)}(0)\}$ is

$$0,\ 1,\ -1,\ 2\,!,\ -3\,!,\ \cdots,\ (-1)^{n-1}(n-1)\,!,\ \cdots.$$

Therefore the Maclaurin series is

$$(6) \qquad x - \frac{x^2}{2} + \frac{x^3}{3} - \frac{x^4}{4} + \cdots + (-1)^{n-1}\frac{x^n}{n} + \cdots.$$

Theorem III, § 801, gives the radius of convergence: $R = 1$. If $x = 1$, the series (6) is the conditionally convergent alternating harmonic series, and if $x = -1$, the series (6) is the divergent series $\sum -\dfrac{1}{n}$. The interval of convergence is therefore $-1 < x \leqq 1$.

To show that *the series (6) represents the function* $\ln(1 + x)$ *throughout the interval of convergence,* we shall derive a form of the remainder appropriate to $\ln(1 + x)$ alone. Using a formula from College Algebra for the sum of a geometric progression, we have, for any $t \neq -1$:

$$(7) \qquad 1 - t + t^2 - t^3 + \cdots + (-t)^{n-2} = \frac{1 - (-t)^{n-1}}{1 + t}.$$

Therefore, if we solve for $\dfrac{1}{1+t}$, and integrate from 0 to x, where $-1 < x \leqq 1$, we have:

$$\int_0^x \frac{dt}{1+t} = \int_0^x [1 - t + \cdots + (-1)^n\, t^{n-2}]\, dt + (-1)^{n-1}\int_0^x \frac{t^{n-1}\, dt}{1 + t},$$

or

$$(8) \qquad \ln(1+x) = x - \frac{x^2}{2} + \frac{x^3}{3} - \cdots + (-1)^n \frac{x^{n-1}}{n-1} + R_n(x),$$

where

(9)
$$R_n(x) = (-1)^{n-1} \int_0^x \frac{t^{n-1}\, dt}{1+t}.$$

If $0 \leqq x \leqq 1$, $|R_n(x)| \leqq \int_0^x t^{n-1}\, dt = \dfrac{x^n}{n} \leqq \dfrac{1}{n}$, and $\lim\limits_{n \to +\infty} R_n(x) = 0$. If $-1 < x < 0$,

$$|R_n(x)| \leqq \left| \int_0^x \left| \frac{t^{n-1}}{1+t} \right| dt \right| \leqq \frac{1}{1+x} \left| \int_0^x |t^{n-1}|\, dt \right|$$

$$= \frac{1}{1+x} \left| \int_0^x t^{n-1}\, dt \right| = \frac{|x|^n}{n(1+x)} < \frac{1}{n(1+x)},$$

and $\lim\limits_{n \to +\infty} R_n(x) = 0$. Therefore the series (6) converges to $\ln (1 + x)$ for $-1 < x \leqq 1$. In particular, if $x = 1$, an interesting special case results:

(10)
$$\ln 2 = 1 - \frac{1}{2} + \frac{1}{3} - \frac{1}{4} + \cdots .$$

V. The binomial function $f(x) = (1 + x)^m$, where m is any real number. The sequence $\{f^{(n)}(x)\}$ is

$$(1 + x)^m,\ m(1 + x)^{m-1},\ m(m - 1)(1 + x)^{m-2},\ \cdots ,$$

and the sequence $\{f^{(n)}(0)\}$ is 1, m, $m(m - 1)$, $\cdots$. Therefore the Maclaurin series is the **binomial series**

(11)
$$1 + mx + \frac{m(m - 1)}{2!}\, x^2 + \cdots + \binom{m}{n} x^n + \cdots ,$$

where

(12)
$$\binom{m}{n} \equiv \frac{m(m - 1) \cdots (m - n + 1)}{n!},$$

and is called the **binomial coefficient** of x^n. If m is a nonnegative integer the binomial series (11) has only a finite number of nonzero terms and hence converges to $f(x) = (1 + x)^m$ for all real x. Assume now that m is not a nonnegative integer. Since $\binom{m}{n} \Big/ \binom{m}{n+1} = \dfrac{n+1}{m-n} \to -1$, we know from Theorem III, § 801, that the radius of convergence is 1. The behavior of (11) at the endpoints of the interval of convergence depends on the value of m. We state the facts here, but defer the proofs to the Exercises (Ex. 36, § 811):

(i) $m \geqq 0$: (11) converges absolutely for $x = \pm 1$.

(ii) $m \leqq -1$: (11) diverges for $x = \pm 1$.

(iii) $-1 < m < 0$: (11) converges conditionally for $x = 1$, and diverges for $x = -1$.

The binomial series (11) *represents the binomial function* $(1 + x)^m$ *throughout the interval of convergence.* In proving this we shall call upon both the Lagrange and the Cauchy forms of the remainder, depending on whether $0 < x \leqq 1$ or $-1 \leqq x < 0$:

Assume $0 < x \leqq 1$. Then the Lagrange form of the remainder is

$$(13) \qquad R_n(x) = \binom{m}{n} (1 + \xi_n)^{m-n} x^n,$$

where $0 < \xi_n < x$. Since, for $n > m$, the inequality $1 + \xi_n > 1$ implies $(1 + \xi_n)^{m-n} < 1$, $|R_n(x)| \leqq \left| \binom{m}{n} x^n \right|$ for sufficiently large n. Since $\binom{m}{n} x^n$ is the general term of the binomial series (11), it must tend toward zero whenever that series converges. Therefore $\lim\limits_{n \to +\infty} R_n(x) = 0$ for $0 < x \leqq 1$ whenever (11) converges, and we conclude that the binomial series represents the binomial function throughout the interval $0 \leqq x < 1$, and also at the point $x = 1$ whenever the series converges there (that is, for $m > -1$).

Assume $-1 \leqq x < 0$. Then the Cauchy form of the remainder is

$$(14) \qquad R_n(x) = nx \, (x - \xi_n)^{n-1} \binom{m}{n} (1 + \xi_n)^{m-n},$$

where $x < \xi_n < 0$. We rewrite (14):

$$(15) \qquad R_n(x) = n \binom{m}{n} x^n (1 + \xi_n)^{m-1} \left(\frac{1 - \dfrac{\xi_n}{x}}{1 + \xi_n} \right)^{n-1}.$$

For $-1 \leqq x < \xi_n < 0$, $0 < 1 - \frac{\xi_n}{x} < 1 + \xi_n$ (check this), so that the last factor of (15) is less than 1 for $n > 1$. Also, if $m > 1$, the inequality $1 + \xi_n < 1$ implies $(1 + \xi_n)^{m-1} < 1$, while if $m < 1$ the inequality $1 + \xi_n > 1 + x$ implies $(1 + \xi_n)^{m-1} < (1 + x)^{m-1}$. In any case, then, the last two factors of (15) remain bounded as $n \to +\infty$. The problem before us has been simplified, then, to showing (under the appropriate conditions) that

$$(16) \qquad \lim_{n \to +\infty} n \binom{m}{n} x^n = 0.$$

In case $-1 < x < 0$, the relation (16) is easily established by the ratio test (check the details in Ex. 27, § 811). Finally, if $x = -1$, the last item remaining in the proof is to show that $n \binom{m}{n} \to 0$ for $m > 0$. A technique for doing this is suggested in Exercise 37, § 811. We conclude that the binomial series represents the binomial function throughout the interval of convergence.

808. ELEMENTARY OPERATIONS WITH POWER SERIES

From results obtained in Chapter 7 for series of constants (§§ 702, 719) we have the theorem for power series (expressed here for simplicity in terms of powers of x, although similar formulations are valid for power series in powers of $(x - a)$):

Theorem. Addition, Subtraction, and Multiplication. *Let* $\sum\limits_{n=0}^{+\infty} a_n x^n$ *and* $\sum\limits_{n=0}^{+\infty} b_n x^n$ *be two power series representing the functions* $f_1(x)$ *and* $f_2(x)$, *respectively, within their intervals of convergence, and let* γ *be an arbitrary constant. Then* (*i*) *the power series* $\sum \gamma a_n x^n$ *represents the function* $\gamma f_1(x)$ *throughout the interval of convergence of* $\sum a_n x^n$; (*ii*) *the power series* $\sum (a_n \pm b_n) x^n$ *represents the function* $f_1(x) \pm f_2(x)$ *for all points common to the intervals of convergence of the two given power series; and* (*iii*) *if* $c_n \equiv \sum\limits_{k=0}^{n} a_k b_{n-k}$, $n = 0$, 1, 2, $\cdots$, *then the power series* $\sum\limits_{n=0}^{+\infty} c_n x^n$ *represents the function* $f_1(x) f_2(x)$ *for all points interior to both intervals of convergence of the two given power series* (cf. § 909).

In finding the Maclaurin or Taylor series for a given function, it is well to bear in mind the import of the uniqueness theorem (Theorem II, § 803) for power series. This means that the Maclaurin or Taylor series need not be obtained by direct substitution in the formulas defining those series. Any means that produces an appropriate power series representing the function automatically produces the Maclaurin or Taylor series.

Example 1. Since the series for e^x is $1 + x + \dfrac{x^2}{2!} + \cdots$, the series for e^{-x} is found by substituting $-x$ for x:

$$e^{-x} = 1 - x + \frac{x^2}{2!} - \frac{x^3}{3!} + \cdots.$$

This series expansion is valid for all real x, and is therefore the Maclaurin series for e^{-x}.

Example 2. The Maclaurin series for $\cos 2x$ is

$$\cos 2x = 1 - \frac{(2x)^2}{2!} + \frac{(2x)^4}{4!} - \frac{(2x)^6}{6!} + \cdots,$$

and is valid for all real x.

Example 3. The Maclaurin series for $\sinh x = \frac{1}{2}(e^x - e^{-x})$ is

$$\frac{1}{2}\left(1 + x + \frac{x^2}{2!} + \cdots\right) - \frac{1}{2}\left(1 - x + \frac{x^2}{2!} - \cdots\right) = x + \frac{x^3}{3!} + \frac{x^5}{5!} + \cdots,$$

and is valid for all real x.

Example 4. Find the Maclaurin series for $\sin\left(\dfrac{\pi}{6} + x\right)$.

Solution. Instead of proceeding in a routine manner, we expand $\sin\left(\dfrac{\pi}{6} + x\right)$

$= \sin\dfrac{\pi}{6}\cos x + \cos\dfrac{\pi}{6}\sin x$, and obtain:

$$\frac{1}{2}\left[1 - \frac{x^2}{2!} + \frac{x^4}{4!} - \cdots\right] + \frac{\sqrt{3}}{2}\left[x - \frac{x^3}{3!} + \frac{x^5}{5!} - \cdots\right]$$

$$= \frac{1}{2} + \frac{\sqrt{3}}{2}x - \frac{1}{2}\frac{x^2}{2!} - \frac{\sqrt{3}}{2}\frac{x^3}{3!} + \frac{1}{2}\frac{x^4}{4!} + \frac{\sqrt{3}}{2}\frac{x^5}{5!} - \cdots.$$

Example 5. The Taylor series for e^x at $x = a$ is most easily obtained by writing $e^x = e^a e^{x-a}$ and expanding the second factor by means of the Maclaurin series already established:

$$e^x = e^a\left[1 + (x - a) + \frac{(x-a)^2}{2!} + \frac{(x-a)^3}{3!} + \cdots\right].$$

Example 6. The Taylor series for $\sin x$ at $x = a$ can be found by writing
$$\sin x = \sin[a + (x - a)] = \sin a \cos(x - a) + \cos a \sin(x - a)$$

$$= \sin a\left[1 - \frac{(x-a)^2}{2!} + \frac{(x-a)^4}{4!} - \cdots\right]$$

$$+ \cos a\left[(x - a) - \frac{(x-a)^3}{3!} + \frac{(x-a)^5}{5!} - \cdots\right].$$

If $a = \frac{\pi}{6}$, the coefficients are those of Example 4.

Example 7. The Taylor series for $\ln x$ at $x = a > 0$ can be found by writing

$$\ln x = \ln[a + (x - a)] = \ln a + \ln\left[1 + \frac{x - a}{a}\right]$$

$$= \ln a + \frac{x - a}{a} - \frac{(x - a)^2}{2a^2} + \frac{(x - a)^3}{3a^3} - \cdots.$$

This is valid for $0 < x \leqq 2a$.

Example 8. The Taylor series for x^m at $x = a > 0$ can be found by writing

$$x^m = [a + (x - a)]^m = a^m\left[1 + \left(\frac{x - a}{a}\right)\right]^m$$

$$= a^m\left[1 + m\left(\frac{x - a}{a}\right) + \frac{m(m - 1)}{2!}\left(\frac{x - a}{a}\right)^2 + \cdots\right].$$

This is valid for $0 < x < 2a$; also at 0 for $m > 0$ and at $2a$ for $m > -1$.

Example 9. The Maclaurin series for $e^x \sin ax$ is found by multiplying the series:

$$\left[1 + x + \frac{x^2}{2!} + \frac{x^3}{3!} + \cdots\right]\left[ax - \frac{a^3x^3}{3!} + \frac{a^5x^5}{5!} - \cdots\right].$$

If we wish the terms of degree $\leqq 5$, we have

$$\left(1 + x + \frac{x^2}{2} + \frac{x^3}{6} + \frac{x^4}{24} + \cdots\right)\left(ax - \frac{a^3x^3}{6} + \frac{a^5x^5}{120} + \cdots\right)$$

$$= ax + ax^2 + \frac{a}{6}(3 - a^2)x^3 + \frac{a}{6}(1 - a^2)x^4 + \frac{a}{120}(5 - 10a^2 + a^4)x^5 + \cdots.$$

809. SUBSTITUTION OF POWER SERIES

Sometimes it is important to obtain a power series for a composite function, where each of the constituent functions has a known power series.

The most useful special case of a general theorem for such substitutions is the principal theorem of this section. We begin with a lemma:

★**Lemma.** *If the terms of the doubly infinite array*

(1)
$$c_{11}, c_{12}, c_{13}, \cdots$$
$$c_{21}, c_{22}, c_{23}, \cdots$$
$$c_{31}, c_{32}, c_{33}, \cdots$$
$$\cdots \cdots \cdots \cdots,$$

when arranged in any manner to form an infinite series, give an absolutely convergent series whose sum is C, then every row series $c_{m1} + c_{m2} + \cdots$ converges absolutely, and if $c_m \equiv \sum\limits_{n=1}^{+\infty} c_{mn}$, then $\sum\limits_{m=1}^{+\infty} c_m$ converges absolutely, with sum C.

★*Proof.* We first assume that every $c_{mn} \geq 0$. Then any partial sum of terms in any row is bounded by C, so that each row series converges. Furthermore, the sum of the terms in the rectangle made up of the elements of the first M rows and the first n columns is bounded by C, so that when $n \to +\infty$ we have in the limit $\sum\limits_{m=1}^{M} c_m \leq C$, and hence $\sum\limits_{m=1}^{+\infty} c_m \leq C$. On the other hand, if $\epsilon > 0$, there exists a finite sequence of terms of (1) whose sum exceeds $C - \epsilon$. If M is the largest index of the rows from which these terms are selected, then $\sum\limits_{m=1}^{M} c_m$ must also exceed $C - \epsilon$. Therefore $\sum\limits_{m=1}^{+\infty} c_m \geq C - \epsilon$ and, since ϵ is arbitrarily small, $\sum\limits_{m=1}^{+\infty} c_m \geq C$. In combination with a preceding inequality this gives $\sum\limits_{m=1}^{+\infty} c_m = C$.

We now remove the assumption that $c_{mn} \geq 0$, and (by splitting the entire array into nonnegative and nonpositive parts in the manner of § 716) immediately draw every conclusion stated in the lemma, except the equality $\sum\limits_{m=1}^{+\infty} c_m = C$. But this equality follows from the fact that for any $\epsilon > 0$ there exists a number M such that the sum of the absolute values of all terms of (1) appearing below the Mth row is less than ϵ (check the details of this carefully in Ex. 28, § 811). This completes the proof.

Theorem I. Substitution. *Let*

(1)
$$y = f(u) \equiv a_0 + a_1 u + a_2 u^2 + \cdots, \text{ and}$$
(2)
$$u = g(x) \equiv b_1 x + b_2 x^2 + \cdots,$$

where both power series have positive radii of convergence. Then the composite function $h(x) \equiv f(g(x))$ is represented by a power series having a positive radius of convergence, obtained by substituting the entire series (2) for the quantity u in (1), expanding, and collecting terms:

(3) $y = h(x) = a_0 + a_1(b_1x + b_2x^2 + \cdots) + a_2(b_1x + \cdots)^2 + \cdots$

$\qquad = a_0 + a_1b_1x + (a_1b_2 + a_2b_1^2)\, x^2$

$\qquad + (a_1b_3 + 2a_2b_1b_2 + a_3b_1^3)\, x^3$

$\qquad + (a_1b_4 + 2a_2b_1b_3 + a_2b_2^2 + 3a_3b_1^2b_2)\, x^4 + \cdots\cdots$

★*Proof.* We first exploit the continuity of $g(x)$ at $x = 0$ (Theorem I, § 803) and observe that if x belongs to a sufficiently small neighborhood of $x = 0$ and if u is defined in terms of x by (2), then u belongs to the interior of the interval of convergence of (1), and the expansions indicated by (1) and the first line of (3) are valid. It now remains to justify the removal of parentheses and the subsequent rearrangement in (3). For this purpose we shall insist on restricting x to so small an interval about $x = 0$ that

$$v \equiv \sum_{n=1}^{+\infty} |b_n x^n| \text{ is inside the interval of convergence of (1). Then, as a con-}$$

sequence of the absolute convergence of all series concerned, we can apply the preceding lemma to the double array

(4)

$a_0,$	$0,$	$0,$	$0,$	$\cdots$
$0,$	$a_1b_1x,$	$a_1b_2x^2,$	$a_1b_3x^3,$	$\cdots$
$0,$	$0,$	$a_2b_1^2x^2,$	$2a_2b_1b_2x^3,$	$\cdots$

$$\cdot \quad \cdot \quad \cdot \quad \cdot \quad \cdot \quad \cdot \quad \cdot \quad \cdot \quad \cdot \quad \cdot$$

With a final appeal to § 718 the proof is complete. (Give precise details, particularly for the last step of the proof, in Ex. 29, § 811.)

Example 1. Find the terms of the Maclaurin series for $e^{\sin x}$, through terms of degree 5.

Solution. The series (1) and (2) are

$$y = f(u) = e^u = 1 + u + \frac{u^2}{2!} + \frac{u^3}{3!} + \frac{u^4}{4!} + \cdots,$$

$$u = g(x) = \sin x = x - \frac{x^3}{3!} + \frac{x^5}{5!} - \cdots.$$

The double array (4) becomes

$1,$	$0,$	$0,$	$0,$	$0,$	$0,$	$\cdots$
$0,$	$x,$	$0,$	$-\dfrac{x^3}{6},$	$0,$	$\dfrac{x^5}{120},$	$\cdots$
$0,$	$0,$	$\dfrac{x^2}{2},$	$0,$	$-\dfrac{x^4}{6},$	$0,$	$\cdots$
$0,$	$0,$	$0,$	$\dfrac{x^3}{6},$	$0,$	$-\dfrac{x^5}{12},$	$\cdots$
$0,$	$0,$	$0,$	$0,$	$\dfrac{x^4}{24},$	$0,$	$\cdots$
$0,$	$0,$	$0,$	$0,$	$0,$	$\dfrac{x^5}{120},$	$\cdots$

$$\cdot \quad \cdot \quad \cdot \quad \cdot \quad \cdot \quad \cdot \quad \cdot \quad \cdot \quad \cdot$$

Therefore the series sought is

$$1 + x + \frac{x^2}{2} - \frac{x^4}{8} - \frac{x^5}{15} + \cdots .$$

★The radius of convergence is infinite, since each basic series converges absolutely, everywhere.

Example 2. Find the terms of the Maclaurin series for $e^{\cos x}$ through terms of degree 6.

Solution. The Maclaurin series for $\cos x$ has a nonzero constant term. Therefore we write

$$e^{\cos x} = e^{1+g(x)} = e \cdot e^{g(x)},$$

where $g(x) = -\frac{x^2}{2} + \frac{x^4}{24} - \frac{x^6}{720} + \cdots$. We proceed as before, obtaining

$$e^{\cos x} = e \left\{ 1 + \left[-\frac{x^2}{2} + \frac{x^4}{24} - \cdots \right] + \frac{1}{2} \left[-\frac{x^2}{2} + \frac{x^4}{24} - \cdots \right]^2 + \cdots \right\}$$

$$= e \left\{ 1 + \left[-\frac{x^2}{2} + \frac{x^4}{24} - \frac{x^6}{720} \right] + \frac{1}{2} \left[\frac{x^4}{4} - \frac{x^6}{24} \right] + \frac{1}{6} \left[-\frac{x^6}{8} \right] + \cdots \right\}$$

$$= e \left(1 - \frac{x^2}{2} + \frac{x^4}{6} - \frac{31x^6}{720} + \cdots \right)$$

Before presenting more examples, let us record for future use a convenient device, which sometimes simplifies the work connected with the method of undetermined coefficients, illustrated in the second solution of Example 3, below:

Theorem II. *If $\sum\limits_{n=0}^{+\infty} a_n x^n$ represents a function $f(x)$ in a neighborhood I of $x = 0$, then (i) if $f(x)$ is an even function in I the power series $\sum a_n x^n$ consists of only even degree terms, and (ii) if $f(x)$ is an odd function in I the power series $\sum a_n x^n$ consists of only odd degree terms.*

Proof. We shall give the details only for part (*i*) (cf. Ex. 32, § 811, for (*ii*)). Since

$$f(x) = a_0 + a_1 x + a_2 x^2 + a_3 x^3 + \cdots ,$$

$$f(-x) = a_0 - a_1 x + a_2 x^2 - a_3 x^3 + \cdots ,$$

and therefore

$$f(x) - f(-x) = 2a_1 x + 2a_3 x^3 + 2a_5 x^5 + \cdots .$$

If $f(x)$ is even, the function $f(x) - f(-x)$ is identically 0 in I, and every coefficient in its power series expansion must vanish, by the uniqueness theorem (Theorem II, § 803).

Example 3. Find the terms of the Maclaurin series for $\sec x$ through terms of degree 8, and ★ determine an interval within which the series converges.

First Solution. Since $\sec x = \dfrac{1}{\cos x} = \dfrac{1}{1 - g(x)}$, where $g(x) = \dfrac{x^2}{2!} - \dfrac{x^4}{4!} +$

$\cdots$, the Maclaurin series for sec x is found by substituting the power series for $g(x)$ in the series

$$\frac{1}{1-u} = 1 + u + u^2 + u^3 + \cdots .$$

We therefore collect terms from

$$1 + \left[\frac{x^2}{2!} - \frac{x^4}{4!} + \frac{x^6}{6!} - \frac{x^8}{8!}\right] + \left[\frac{x^2}{2!} - \frac{x^4}{4!} + \frac{x^6}{6!}\right]^2 + \left[\frac{x^2}{2!} - \frac{x^4}{4!}\right]^3 + \left[\frac{x^2}{2!}\right]^4,$$

and get

$$\sec x = 1 + \frac{x^2}{2} + \frac{5x^4}{24} + \frac{61x^6}{720} + \frac{277x^8}{8064} + \cdots .$$

★The above procedures have been validated for any interval such that $\frac{x^2}{2!} + \frac{x^4}{4!} + \frac{x^6}{6!} + \cdots < 1$, or $\cosh x < 2$. Therefore the series found for sec x converges to sec x within (at least) the interval $(-1.3, 1.3)$. Actually, as is easily shown by the theory of analytic functions of a complex variable, the interval of convergence is $\left(-\frac{\pi}{2}, \frac{\pi}{2}\right)$.

Second Solution. Since sec x is an even function and is represented by its Maclaurin series (cf. the first solution), its Maclaurin series must have the form

$$\sec x = a_0 + a_2 x^2 + a_4 x^4 + a_6 x^6 + \cdots ,$$

all coefficients of odd degree terms being 0. We form the product of this series and that of cos x and have

$$1 = (a_0 + a_2 x^2 + a_4 x^4 + \cdots)\left(1 - \frac{x^2}{2!} + \frac{x^4}{4!} - \cdots\right)$$

$$= a_0 + \left(-\frac{a_0}{2!} + a_2\right)x^2 + \left(\frac{a_0}{4!} - \frac{a_2}{2!} + a_4\right)x^4$$

$$+ \left(-\frac{a_0}{6!} + \frac{a_2}{4!} - \frac{a_4}{2!} + a_6\right)x^6 + \left(\frac{a_0}{8!} - \frac{a_2}{6!} + \frac{a_4}{4!} + \frac{a_2}{2!} + a_0\right)x^8 + \cdots .$$

Equating corresponding coefficients, we have the recursion formulas $a_0 = 1$, $a_2 = \frac{a_0}{2!}$, $a_4 = \frac{a_2}{2!} - \frac{a_0}{4!}$, $\cdots$, from which we can evaluate the coefficients, one after the other. The result is the same as that of the first solution.

810. INTEGRATION AND DIFFERENTIATION OF POWER SERIES

As useful adjuncts to the methods of the two preceding sections, we state three theorems, the second and third of which are proved in the next chapter:

Theorem I. *A power series* $\sum\limits_{n=0}^{+\infty} a_n(x-a)^n$ *and its* **derived series** $\sum\limits_{n=1}^{+\infty} na_n(x-a)^{n-1}$ *have the same radius of convergence.*

Proof. For simplicity of notation, we assume that $a = 0$. In the first place, since $|a_n| \leqq n\,|a_n|$, for $n = 1, 2, \cdots$, if the derived series converges absolutely for some particular $x = x_0$, then $x_0(\sum na_n x_0^{n-1}) = \sum na_n x_0^n$ converges absolutely and $\sum a_n x_0^n$ also converges absolutely. That is, the radius of convergence of the derived series can be no larger than that of the original series. On the other hand, it can be no smaller, for let $0 < \alpha < \beta$, and assume that the original series converges absolutely for $x = \beta$. We shall show that the derived series converges absolutely for $x = \alpha$. This will conclude the proof (why?). Our contention follows from the fact that $n a_n \alpha^n = O(|a_n \beta^n|)$ for the nonzero terms of the series, and this fact in turn follows by means of the ratio test from the limit:

$$\lim_{n \to +\infty} \frac{n a_n \alpha^n}{a_n \beta^n} = \lim_{n \to +\infty} n \left(\frac{\alpha}{\beta}\right)^n = \lim_{n \to +\infty} \frac{n}{e^{n \ln \frac{\beta}{\alpha}}} = 0.$$

For an alternative proof, see Ex. 38, § 811.

Theorem II. *If $f(x)$ is represented by a power series $\sum a_n(x - a)^n$ in its interval of convergence I, and if α and β are any two points interior to I, then the series can be integrated term by term:*

$$\int_\alpha^\beta f(x)\, dx = \sum_{n=0}^{+\infty} a_n \int_\alpha^\beta (x - a)^n\, dx = \sum_{n=0}^{+\infty} \frac{a_n}{n + 1}\left[(\beta - a)^{n+1} - (\alpha - a)^{n+1}\right].$$

(Cf. Ex. 11, § 911.)

Theorem III. *A function $f(x)$ represented by a power series $\sum a_n(x - a)^n$ in the interior of its interval of convergence is differentiable there, and its derivative is represented there by the derived series:*

$$f'(x) = \sum_{n=1}^{+\infty} n a_n(x - a)^{n-1}.$$

(Cf. Ex. 12, § 911.)

Example 1. The series

$$\frac{1}{1 + t} = 1 - t + t^2 - t^3 + \cdots$$

has radius of convergence $R = 1$. Therefore, for $|x| < 1$, integration from 0 to x gives

$$\ln(1 + x) = x - \frac{x^2}{2} + \frac{x^3}{3} - \cdots.$$

Example 2. The series

$$(1 + t)^{-\frac{1}{2}} = 1 - \frac{1}{2} t + \frac{1 \cdot 3}{2 \cdot 4} t^2 - \frac{1 \cdot 3 \cdot 5}{2 \cdot 4 \cdot 6} t^3 + \cdots$$

has radius of convergence $R = 1$. Therefore the same is true for

$$(1 - t^2)^{-\frac{1}{2}} = 1 + \frac{1}{2} t^2 + \frac{1 \cdot 3}{2 \cdot 4} t^4 + \frac{1 \cdot 3 \cdot 5}{2 \cdot 4 \cdot 6} t^6 + \cdots.$$

From this, by integrating from 0 to x, where $|x| < 1$, we find

$$\text{Arcsin } x = x + \frac{1}{2} \frac{x^3}{3} + \frac{1 \cdot 3}{2 \cdot 4} \frac{x^5}{5} + \frac{1 \cdot 3 \cdot 5}{2 \cdot 4 \cdot 6} \frac{x^7}{7} + \cdots.$$

Example 3. Find the terms of the Maclaurin series for tan x through terms of degree 9.

First Solution. Multiply the power series for sin x and sec x (Example 3, § 809):

$$\tan x = \left(x - \frac{x^3}{3!} + \frac{x^5}{5!} - \cdots \right)\left(1 + \frac{x^2}{2} + \frac{5x^4}{24} + \cdots \right)$$

$$= x + \frac{x^3}{3} + \frac{2x^5}{15} + \frac{17x^7}{315} + \frac{62x^9}{2835} + \cdots .$$

Second Solution. Since tan x is an odd function its Maclaurin series (which exists and represents the function, by the first solution) has the form

$$\tan x = a_1 x + a_3 x^3 + a_5 x^5 + \cdots .$$

Furthermore, since $\cos x \tan x = \sin x$, the coefficients of the product series for $\cos x \tan x$ must be identically equal to those of the sine series:

$$a_1 = 1, \quad -\frac{a_1}{2} + a_3 = -\frac{1}{6}, \quad \frac{a_1}{24} - \frac{a_3}{2} + a_5 = \frac{1}{120}, \cdots .$$

The result of solving these recursion formulas is the same as that found in the first solution.

Third Solution. As in the second solution, let

$$\tan x = a_1 x + a_3 x^3 + a_5 x^5 + a_7 x^7 + \cdots .$$

Differentiation and use of the identity $\sec^2 x = 1 + \tan^2 x$ give

$$a_1 + 3a_3 x^2 + 5a_5 x^4 + 7a_7 x^6 + 9a_9 x^8 + \cdots$$

$$= 1 + [a_1 x + a_3 x^3 + a_5 x^5 + a_7 x^7 + \cdots]^2$$

$$= 1 + a_1^2 x^2 + 2a_1 a_3 x^4 + (2a_1 a_5 + a_3^2)x^6 + \cdots .$$

Equating corresponding coefficients produces the recursion formulas $a_1 = 1$, $3a_3 = a_1^2$, $5a_5 = 2a_1 a_3$, $\cdots$, and the result of the first solution. This is by far the shortest of the three methods.

Example 4. Find the exact sum of the series

$$\frac{1}{1! \cdot 3} + \frac{1}{2! \cdot 4} + \frac{1}{3! \cdot 5} + \cdots + \frac{1}{n! \, (n+2)} + \cdots .$$

Solution. Start with the series

$$e^x = 1 + x + \frac{x^2}{2!} + \frac{x^3}{3!} + \cdots .$$

Multiply by x and integrate from 0 to 1:

$$\int_0^1 x e^x \, dx = \frac{1}{2} + \frac{1}{3} + \frac{1}{2! \cdot 4} + \frac{1}{3! \cdot 5} + \cdots .$$

Since the value of the integral is 1, the original series converges to $\frac{1}{2}$.

811. EXERCISES

In Exercises 1-12, find the Maclaurin series for the given function.

1. $\cosh x = \dfrac{e^x - e^{-x}}{2}.$

2. $\dfrac{1}{1 + x^2}.$

3. $\text{Arctan } x = \displaystyle\int_0^x \frac{dt}{1 + t^2}.$

4. $\sqrt{e^x}.$

5. $\cos x^2$.

6. $\ln (2 + 3x)$.

7. $(1 - x^4)^{-\frac{1}{2}}$.

8. $\sqrt{4 + x}$.

9. $\ln \dfrac{1 + x}{1 - x}$.

10. $\displaystyle\int_0^x \dfrac{\sin t}{t}\, dt$.

11. $\displaystyle\int_0^x e^{-t^2}\, dt$.

12. $\displaystyle\int_0^x \sin t^2\, dt$.

In Exercises 13-18, find the terms of the Maclaurin series for the given function through terms of the specified degree.

13. $\dfrac{1}{1 + e^x}$; 5.

14. $e^x \cos x$; 5.

15. $\tanh x$; 7.

16. $e^{\tan x}$; 5.

17. $\ln \dfrac{\sin x}{x}$; 6.

18. $\ln \cos x$; 8.

In Exercises 19-22, find the Taylor series for the given function at the specified value of $x = a$.

19. $\cos x$; a.

20. $\cos x$; $\dfrac{\pi}{4}$.

21. $\ln x$; e.

22. x^m; 1.

In Exercises 23-26, find the exact sum of the infinite series.

23. $1 + 2x + 3x^2 + 4x^3 + \cdots + (n + 1)x^n + \cdots$.

24. $\dfrac{x^3}{1\cdot3} - \dfrac{x^5}{3\cdot5} + \dfrac{x^7}{5\cdot7} - \dfrac{x^9}{7\cdot9} + \cdots$.

25. $1 - 2x^2 + 3x^4 - 4x^6 + \cdots$.

26. $\dfrac{1}{1\cdot2\cdot2} - \dfrac{1}{2\cdot3\cdot2^2} + \dfrac{1}{3\cdot4\cdot2^3} - \dfrac{1}{4\cdot5\cdot2^4} + \cdots$.

27. Prove relation (16), § 807, for $-1 < x < 0$.

★28. Check the final details of the proof of the lemma, § 809.

★29. Give the details requested at the end of the proof of Theorem I, § 809.

30. Prove part (*ii*) of Theorem II, § 809.

★31. By reasoning analogous to that used in part IV, § 807, for the function $\ln (1 + x)$, show that

$$\text{Arctan } x = x - \frac{x^3}{3} + \frac{x^5}{5} - \frac{x^7}{7} + \cdots,$$

for $|x| \leqq 1$. In particular, derive the formula

$$\frac{\pi}{4} = 1 - \frac{1}{3} + \frac{1}{5} - \frac{1}{7} + \cdots.$$

★32. Prove that if

$$f(x) = a_k x^k + a_{k+1} x^{k+1} + \cdots,$$

where k is a nonnegative integer and $a_k \neq 0$, within some neighborhood of $x = 0$, then $f(x)$ and x^k are of the same order of magnitude as $x \to 0$. What is the order of magnitude of $1/f(x)$?

★**33.** Prove that if

$$f(x) = \frac{a_0 + a_1x + a_2x^2 + \cdots}{x^k},$$

where k is a nonnegative integer and $a_0 \neq 0$, within some deleted neighborhood of $x = 0$, then $f(x)$ and x^{-k} are of the same order of magnitude as $x \to 0$. What is the order of magnitude of $1/f(x)$?

★**34.** Prove that e is irrational. *Hint:* Assume $e = p/q$, where p and q are positive integers, and write $e = S + R$, where

$$S = 1 + \frac{1}{1!} + \frac{1}{2!} + \cdots + \frac{1}{q!},$$

$$R = \frac{1}{(q+1)!} + \frac{1}{(q+2)!} + \cdots,$$

and show that the integer $eq!$ has the form $Sq! + Rq!$, where $Sq!$ is an integer and $Rq!$ is not.

★**35.** The numbers B_n in the Maclaurin series

$$(1) \qquad\qquad \frac{x}{e^x - 1} = \sum_{n=0}^{+\infty} \frac{B_n x^n}{n!},$$

called **Bernoulli numbers,** play an important role in the theory of infinite series (for instance, the coefficients in the Maclaurin series for $\tan x$ are expressible in terms of the Bernoulli numbers). (Cf. Knopp, *Theory and Application of Infinite Series* (Blackie, London, 1928).) By equating the function x and the product of the series (1) and the Maclaurin series for $e^x - 1$, obtain the recursive formula

$$\frac{B_0}{n!\,0!} + \frac{B_1}{(n-1)!\,1!} + \frac{B_2}{(n-2)!\,2!} + \cdots + \frac{B_{n-1}}{1!\,(n-1)!} = 0.$$

Use this to evaluate $B_0, B_1, \cdots, B_{10}$. Prove that $B_{2n+1} = 0$ for $n = 1, 2, \cdots$.

Hint: What kind of a function is $\dfrac{x}{e^x - 1} + \dfrac{1}{2}x$?

★**36.** Prove the facts given in Part V, § 807, regarding convergence at the endpoints of the interval of convergence of the binomial series. *Hints:* Consider only values of $n > m$. Then $\left|\dfrac{a_n}{a_{n+1}}\right| = \dfrac{n+1}{n-m}$. If $m > 0$ use Raabe's test. If $m \leq -1$, $\left|\dfrac{a_n}{a_{n+1}}\right| \leq 1$ and $a_n \nrightarrow 0$. For $-1 < m < 0$ and $x = -1$, use Raabe's test, the terms being ultimately of one sign. For $-1 < m < 0$ and $x = 1$, the series is alternating, $|a_{n+1}| < |a_n|$, and the problem is to show that $a_n \to 0$. To do this, let k be a positive integer greater than $1/(m+1)$, and show that $a_n{}^k \to 0$, as $n \to +\infty$, by establishing the convergence of $\sum a_n{}^k$ with the aid of Raabe's test.

★**37.** Prove that $\lim\limits_{n \to +\infty} n \binom{m}{n} = 0$, for $m > 0$. *Hint:* Use the method suggested in the hints of Ex. 36, k being a positive integer $> 1/m$.

★★**38.** Prove Theorem I, § 810, by using limits superior and the formula of Note 4, § 801.

812. INDETERMINATE EXPRESSIONS

It is frequently possible to find a simple evaluation of an indeterminate expression by means of Maclaurin or Taylor series. This can often be expedited by the "big O" or "order of magnitude" concepts. (Cf. Ex. 10, § 713.)

Example 1. Find $\lim\limits_{x \to 0} \dfrac{1 - \cos x}{x^2}$.

Solution. Since

$$\cos x = 1 - \frac{x^2}{2!} + \frac{x^4}{4!} - \cdots = 1 - \frac{x^2}{2} + O(x^4), \quad \frac{1 - \cos x}{x^2} = \frac{1}{2} + O(x^2) \to \frac{1}{2}.$$

Example 2. Find $\lim\limits_{n \to +\infty} n\{\ln (n + 1) - \ln n\}$.

Solution. We write the expression

$$\ln (n + 1) - \ln n = \ln \left(1 + \frac{1}{n}\right) = \frac{1}{n} + O\left(\frac{1}{n^2}\right).$$

Therefore $n\{\ln (n + 1) - \ln n\} = 1 + O\left(\dfrac{1}{n}\right) \to 1$.

Example 3. Find $\lim\limits_{x \to 0} \dfrac{\ln (1 + x)}{e^{2x} - 1}$.

Solution. $\dfrac{\ln (1 + x)}{e^{2x} - 1} = \dfrac{x + O(x^2)}{2x + O(x^2)} = \dfrac{1 + O(x)}{2 + O(x)}$

$$= [1 + O(x)][\tfrac{1}{2} + O(x)] = \tfrac{1}{2} + O(x) \to \tfrac{1}{2}.$$

813. COMPUTATIONS

The principal techniques most commonly used for computations by means of power series have already been established. In any such computation one wishes to obtain some sort of definite range within which the sum of a series must lie. The usual tools for this are (*i*) an estimate provided by a dominating series (Theorem I, § 720), (*ii*) an estimate provided by the integral test (Theorems II and III, § 720), (*iii*) the alternating series estimate (Theorem, § 715), and (*iv*) some form of the remainder in Taylor's Formula (§ 804).

Another device is to seek a different series to represent a given quantity. For instance, some logarithms can be computed more efficiently with the series

$$(1) \qquad\qquad \ln \frac{1 + x}{1 - x} = 2\left[x + \frac{x^3}{3} + \frac{x^5}{5} + \frac{x^7}{7} + \cdots\right]$$

(cf. Ex. 9, § 811) than with the Maclaurin series for $\ln (1 + x)$.

Finally, one must not forget that infinite series are not the only means for computation. We include in Example 5 one illustration of the use of an approximation (Simpson's Rule) to a definite integral.

We illustrate some of these techniques in the following examples:

Example 1. Compute the sine of one radian to five decimal places.

Solution. $\sin 1 = 1 - \dfrac{1}{3!} + \dfrac{1}{5!} - \dfrac{1}{7!} = 0.84147$ with an error of less than $1/9! < 0.000003$.

Example 2. Compute $\sqrt{89}$ to six decimal places.

Solution. We approximate first by 9.4, whose square is 88.36, and write

$$\sqrt{89} = \sqrt{88.36 + .64} = 9.4\sqrt{1 + 0.64/88.36}.$$

Computing $(1 + x)^{\frac{1}{2}}$, where $x = 0.64/88.36$, we have, from the binomial series,

$$1 + \frac{1}{2}x - \frac{1 \cdot 1}{2 \cdot 4}x^2 = 1.00361991,$$

with an error of $R_3(x) = \dfrac{1 \cdot 1 \cdot 3}{2 \cdot 4 \cdot 6}\xi^3$, from (13), § 807. This error is between 0 and 0.000000003, so that $\sqrt{1 + x}$ is between 1.00361991 and 1.00361992, and $\sqrt{89}$ is between 9.4340271 and 9.4340273. To six decimal places, $\sqrt{89} = 9.434027$.

Example 3. Compute e to five decimal places.

Solution. Substitution of $x = 1$ in the Maclaurin series for e^x gives

$$e = 1 + \frac{1}{2!} + \frac{1}{3!} + \cdots + \frac{1}{9!} + R_{10}(1), \quad = 2.718281 + \frac{e^\xi}{10!}$$

where $R_{10}(1)$ is between 0 and $\dfrac{e}{10!} < 0.000001$. Therefore e lies between 2.718281 and 2.718282, and is equal to 2.71828, to five decimal places.

Example 4. Compute $\ln 2$ by use of series (1), to five decimal places.

Solution. Solving $\dfrac{1 + x}{1 - x} = 2$ for x, we have $x = \dfrac{1}{3}$, and

$$\ln 2 = 2[\tfrac{1}{3} + \tfrac{1}{3}(\tfrac{1}{3})^3 + \tfrac{1}{5}(\tfrac{1}{3})^5 + \cdots] = 0.6931468 + [\tfrac{2}{13}(\tfrac{1}{3})^{13} + \cdots].$$

The remainder, in brackets, by the fact that it is dominated by a convergent geometric series with ratio 1/9, is less than $[\tfrac{2}{13}(\tfrac{1}{3})^{13}] \div [1 - \tfrac{1}{9}]$ (cf. Theorem I, § 720). This quantity, in turn, is less than 0.0000001. Therefore $\ln 2$ is between 0.693146 and 0.693148. To five places, $\ln 2 = 0.69315$. (Cf. Example 3, § 720.)

Example 5. Compute π to five significant digits.

First Solution. One method is to evaluate $\dfrac{\pi}{4}$ by use of the series for Arctan x (cf. Exs. 3 and 31, § 811) with $x = 1$:

$$\frac{\pi}{4} = 1 - \frac{1}{3} + \frac{1}{5} - \frac{1}{7} + \cdots.$$

Although this series converges very slowly, its terms can be combined in the manner of Example 3, § 720, to produce a manageable series for computation.

However, if use is made of such a trigonometric identity as

$$\text{Arctan } 1 = \text{Arctan } \tfrac{1}{2} + \text{Arctan } \tfrac{1}{3},$$

two much more rapidly converging series are obtained:

$$\frac{\pi}{4} = \left[\frac{1}{2} - \frac{1}{3}\left(\frac{1}{2}\right)^3 + \frac{1}{5}\left(\frac{1}{2}\right)^5 - \cdots\right] + \left[\frac{1}{3} - \frac{1}{3}\left(\frac{1}{3}\right)^3 + \frac{1}{5}\left(\frac{1}{3}\right)^5 - \cdots\right].$$

(Complete the details in Ex. 21, § 814.)

The student may be interested in finding other trigonometric identities which give even more rapidly converging series. Two such identities are $\text{Arctan } 1 = 2 \text{ Arctan } \tfrac{1}{3} + \text{Arctan } \tfrac{1}{7}$ and $\text{Arctan } 1 = 4 \text{ Arctan } \tfrac{1}{5} - \text{Arctan } \tfrac{1}{239}$.

Second Solution. Since

$$\frac{\pi}{4} = \int_0^1 \frac{dx}{1 + x^2} = \text{Arctan } 1,$$

an estimate of π is given by use of Simpson's Rule (Ex. 23, § 503). For simplicity, we take $n = 10$ and complete the table:

x_k	$1 + x_k^2$	y_k	$y_k, 2y_k, 4y_k$
0	1	1.000000	1.000000
0.1	1.01	0.990099	3.960396
0.2	1.04	0.961538	1.923076
0.3	1.09	0.917431	3.669724
0.4	1.16	0.862069	1.724138
0.5	1.25	0.800000	3.200000
0.6	1.36	0.735294	1.470588
0.7	1.49	0.671141	2.684564
0.8	1.64	0.609756	1.219512
0.9	1.81	0.552486	2.209944
1.0	2.00	0.500000	0.500000
			23.561942

Therefore $\dfrac{\pi}{4} = \dfrac{23.561942}{30} = 0.785398$ (rounding off to six places to allow for previous round-off errors). Since the fourth derivative of $(1 + x^2)^{-1}$ is numerically less than 24 for $0 \leqq x \leqq 1$, the error estimate (Ex. 23, § 503) is less than $(24/180)(.1)^4 < 0.000013$. Thus, to four decimal places, $\pi = 3.1416$.

814. EXERCISES

In Exercises 1-10, evaluate the limit by use of Maclaurin or Taylor series.

1. $\displaystyle\lim_{x \to 0} \frac{1 - \cos x}{\tan^2 x}$.

2. $\displaystyle\lim_{x \to 0} \frac{\sin x - x}{\tan x - x}$.

3. $\displaystyle\lim_{x \to 0} \frac{\text{Arcsin } x - x - \dfrac{x^3}{6}}{\text{Arctan } x - x + \dfrac{x^3}{3}}$.

4. $\displaystyle\lim_{x \to 0} \frac{2 - x - 2\sqrt{1 - x}}{x^2}$.

5. $\lim\limits_{x\to 0}\left[\dfrac{\sin x}{x^7} - \dfrac{1}{x^6} + \dfrac{1}{6x^4} - \dfrac{1}{120x^2}\right].$ **6.** $\lim\limits_{x\to 1}\dfrac{(x-1)\ln x}{\sin^2(x-1)}.$

7. $\lim\limits_{x\to 0}\dfrac{(1+x)^{\frac{2}{3}} - (1-x)^{\frac{2}{3}}}{x}.$ **8.** $\lim\limits_{x\to 0}\dfrac{x\tan x}{\sqrt{1-x^2}-1}.$

9. $\lim\limits_{x\to 1}\dfrac{e^{2x} - e^2}{\ln x}.$

10. $\lim\limits_{n\to +\infty}\ln n\left[(n+1)\ln\dfrac{n+1}{n} - 1\right].$

In Exercises 11-20, compute the given quantity to the specified number of decimal places, by use of Maclaurin series.

11. e^2, 5.   **12.** $\sqrt{e}$, 5.

13. $\ln 3$, 4.   **14.** $\cos\frac{1}{2}$, 4.

15. $\sqrt[3]{10}$, 5.   **16.** $\tan 0.1$, 5.

17. $\displaystyle\int_0^{0.5}\dfrac{\sin t}{t}\,dt$, 4.   **18.** $\displaystyle\int_0^{0.1}\dfrac{\ln(1+x)}{x}\,dx$, 4.

19. $\displaystyle\int_0^{0.5}\sqrt{1-x^3}\,dx$, 4.   **20.** $\displaystyle\int_0^1 e^{-x^2}\,dx$, 4.

21. Complete the computation details in the first solution for Example 5, § 813.

★815. ANALYTIC FUNCTIONS

The property that a function may have of being represented by a Taylor series is of such basic importance in analysis that it is given a special name, *analyticity*, as specified in the definition:

Definition. *A function $f(x)$ is **analytic** at $x = a$ if and only if it has a Taylor series at $x = a$ which represents the function in some neighborhood of $x = a$.†*

We state here some of the more important theorems concerning analytic functions, leaving the proofs to the reader (Exs. 3-6, § 816):

Theorem I. *An analytic function of an analytic function is analytic.*

Theorem II. *The sum, difference, product, and quotient of analytic functions are analytic if division by 0 is not involved.*

Theorem III. *A function represented by a power series is analytic in the interior of the interval of convergence.*

Corollary. *If a function is analytic at a point, it is automatically analytic in a neighborhood of that point.*

---

† For functions of a complex variable this is only one of several definitions of analyticity, but for functions of a real variable this is the only practical definition in common use.

Theorem IV. *If two functions analytic on an interval I are identical on any subinterval, then they are identical throughout I. If a function analytic on an interval can be extended analytically to a larger interval (that is, if the domain of definition can be extended to a larger interval containing the original), then this extension is unique.*

NOTE 1. Theorem I, § 803 can be reworded: An analytic function has derivatives of all orders. Example 2, § 805, shows that the converse is not true. The function of that Example is not analytic at $x = 0$.

NOTE 2. Example 1, § 805, shows that polynomials are everywhere analytic.

NOTE 3. Theorems III and IV imply that if a function $f(x)$ is analytic throughout the interior I of the interval of convergence of a power series $\sum$, and if $\sum$ represents $f(x)$ in any subinterval (however small), it must represent $f(x)$ throughout I. They imply, then, that any identity involving analytic functions, such as $\sin x = \cos(\frac{1}{2}\pi - x)$ (cf. Example 2, below) is universally valid as soon as it has been established for any given interval. They also imply (for example) that a catenary (Ex. 35, § 419) and a parabola cannot coincide, even over an extremely short interval.

Example 1. Prove that the following functions are analytic for the indicated values of x:

$$e^x, \sin x, \cos x, \text{ for all real } x;$$

$$\ln x, x^m, \text{ for all positive } x.$$

Solution. For the functions e^x, $\sin x$, $\ln x$, and x^m, the result is implicit in Examples 5-8, § 808. Cf. Ex. 19, § 811, for $\cos x$.

Example 2. Establish the equation

$$(1) \qquad (1 + x)^m = 1 + mx + \frac{m(m-1)}{2!} x^2 + \cdots,$$

for $-1 < x < 1$ by use of the Lagrange form of the remainder only.

Solution. The Lagrange form of the remainder (§ 807) is

$$(2) \qquad R_n(x) = \binom{m}{n} (1 + \xi_n)^{m-n} x^n.$$

The ratio test shows that $R_n(x)$ tends toward 0 as a limit for any x such that $0 < x < 1$ (cf. § 807). By Example 1, the left-hand member of (1) is analytic for $x > -1$, and by Theorem III, the right-hand member of (1) is analytic for $-1 < x < 1$. Therefore, since the two members of (1) are identical for $0 < x < 1$, they must be identical for $-1 < x < 1$.

★816. EXERCISES

★1. Prove that $\tan x$, $\cot x$, $\sec x$, and $\csc x$ are analytic where defined.

★2. Prove that if I is a given interval, then there exists no polynomial identical with e^x throughout I.

★3. Prove Theorem I, § 815. *Hint:* Let $f(u)$ be analytic at $u = a$ and let $g(x)$ be analytic at $x = b$, where $a = g(b)$. Let $y = f(u) = a_0 + a_1(u - a) +$

$a_2(u - a)^2 + \cdots$ and $u = g(x) = a + b_1(x - b) + b_2(x - b)^2 + \cdots$. The proposition is a consequence of the substitution theorem (Theorem I) of § 809, with a translation of axes and a change in notation.

★**4.** Prove Theorem II, § 815.

★**5.** Prove Theorem III, § 815. *Hint:* Assume without loss of generality that the point under consideration is $x = 0$, lying within the interval of convergence of $f(x) \equiv \sum a_n(x - a)^n$. The series $\sum |a_n| \cdot |x - a|^n$ converges in a neighborhood I of $x = 0$. Let $\epsilon > 0$ belong to I. Then $\sum |a_n| \{|x| + \epsilon\}^n$ converges. Dirichlet's rearrangement theorem (Theorem II) of § 718 shows that

$$\{|a_0| + |a_1|\epsilon + |a_2|\epsilon^2 + \cdots\} + \{|a_1| + 2|a_2|\epsilon + 3|a_3|\epsilon^2 + \cdots\}x + \cdots$$

converges. Hence $\{a_0 + \cdots\} + \{a_1 + \cdots\}x + \cdots$ converges. Show that it converges to $f(x)$ by use of the Lemma, § 809.

★**6.** Prove Theorem IV, § 815.

★★**7.** A theorem regarding inverse functions, easily proved in the theory of analytic functions of a complex variable, but whose proof by use of techniques of real variable theory only is much more difficult (cf. K. Knopp, *Theory and Application of Infinite Series* (London, Blackie, 1928)) follows: *If $y = f(x)$ is analytic and has a nonzero derivative at $x = a$, then in some neighborhood of $b = f(a)$, a single-valued inverse function $x = \phi(y)$ is defined and is analytic.* This means that if $y = b + a_1(x - a) + a_2(x - a)^2 + \cdots$ in a neighborhood of a, and $a_1 \neq 0$, then it is possible to solve this equation for x in terms of a power series in powers of $(y - b)$. Prove that in a proof of this theorem it may be assumed without loss of generality that $a = b = 0$ and $a_1 = 1$. (Do not attempt to prove the theorem.)

★★**8.** Obtain a set of recursion formulas for the coefficients b_n, where

$$x = \phi(y) = b_1y + b_2y^2 + b_3y^3 + \cdots,$$

if $\phi(y)$ is the inverse function of

$$y = f(x) = x + a_2x^2 + a_3x^3 + \cdots.$$

(Cf. Ex. 7.) Use this method to obtain the first few terms of the Maclaurin series for $x = \tan y$, the inverse function of $y = \text{Arctan } x = x - \frac{1}{3}x^3 + \frac{1}{5}x^5 - \frac{1}{7}x^7 + \cdots$. (Cf. Example 3, § 810, Ex. 3, § 811.) *Hint:* Substitute the known series for y in the unknown series (or conversely) and equate coefficients in $x = \phi(f(x))$ (or $y = f(\phi(y))$).

9

★Uniform Convergence

~~~~~~

★901. UNIFORM CONVERGENCE OF SEQUENCES

Let

(1) $$S_1(x), S_2(x), \cdots, S_n(x), \cdots$$

be a sequence of functions defined on a set A. We say that this sequence of functions **converges on A** in case, for every fixed x of A, the sequence of constants $\{S_n(x)\}$ converges. Assume that (1) converges on A, and define

(2) $$S(x) \equiv \lim_{n \to +\infty} S_n(x).$$

Then the rapidity with which $S_n(x)$ approaches $S(x)$ can be expected to depend (rather heavily) on the value of x.

Let us write down explicitly the analytic formulation of (2):

Corresponding to any point x in A and any $\epsilon > 0$, there exists a number $N = N(x, \epsilon)$ (dependent on both x and ϵ) such that $n > N$ implies

$$|S_n(x) - S(x)| < \epsilon.$$

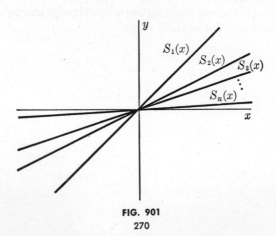

FIG. 901

Example 1. If $S_n(x) \equiv \dfrac{x}{n}$, and if $A = (-\infty, +\infty)$, then $\lim\limits_{n \to +\infty} S_n(x)$ exists and is equal to 0 for every x in A. (Cf. Fig. 901.) If $\epsilon > 0$, the inequality $|S_n(x) - S(x)| < \epsilon$ is equivalent to $n > |x|/\epsilon$. Therefore $N = N(x, \epsilon)$ can be defined to be $N(x, \epsilon) \equiv |x|/\epsilon$. We can see how N must depend on x. For instance, if we were asked, "How large must n be in order that $|S_n(x) - S(x)| = \dfrac{|x|}{n} < 0.001$?" we should be entitled to reply, "Tell us first how large x is." If $x = 0.001$, the second term of the sequence provides the desired degree of approximation, if $x = 1$, we must proceed at least past the 1000th term, and if $x = 1000$, we must choose $n > 1,000,000$.

If it is possible to find N, in the definition of (2), as a function of ϵ alone, independent of x, then a particularly powerful type of convergence occurs. This is prescribed in the definition:

Definition. *A sequence of functions* $\{S_n(x)\}$, *defined on a set* A, **converges uniformly on** A *to a function* $S(x)$ *defined on* A, *this being written*

$$S_n(x) \rightrightarrows S(x),$$

if and only if corresponding to $\epsilon > 0$ *there exists a number* $N = N(\epsilon)$, *dependent on ϵ alone and not on the point x, such that $n > N$ implies*

$$|S_n(x) - S(x)| < \epsilon$$

for every x in A. (Fig. 902.)

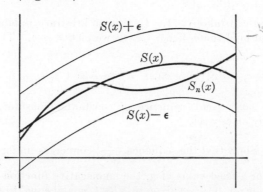

FIG. 902

Let us contrast the definitions of *convergence* and *uniform convergence*. (Cf. § 307.) The most obvious distinction is that convergence is defined *at a point*, whereas uniform convergence is defined *on a set*. These concepts are also distinguished by the order in which things happen. In the case of convergence we have (*i*) the point x, (*ii*) the number $\epsilon > 0$, and (*iii*) the number N, which depends on both x and ϵ. In the case of uniform convergence we have (*i*) the number $\epsilon > 0$, (*ii*) the number N, which depends only on ϵ, and (*iii*) the point x.

Example 2. If $S_n(x) \equiv \dfrac{x}{n}$, and if A is the interval $(-1000, 1000)$, then the sequence $\{S_n(x)\}$ *converges uniformly to* 0 *on the set* A. The function $N(\epsilon)$ can be chosen: $N(\epsilon) \equiv 1000/\epsilon$. Then

$$n > N(\epsilon) \text{ and } |x| \leq 1000$$

imply

$$|S_n(x) - S(x)| = \frac{|x|}{n} < \frac{1000}{1000/\epsilon} = \epsilon.$$

A quick and superficial reading of Example 1 might lead one to believe, since N seems to depend so thoroughly on x, that even when the set A is restricted as it is in Example 2 the convergence could not be uniform. We have seen, however, that it is. Are we really *sure*, now, that the convergence in Example 1 fails to be uniform? In order to show this, we formulate the negation of uniform convergence (give the proof in Ex. 25, § 904):

Negation of Uniform Convergence. *A sequence of functions* $\{S_n(x)\}$, *defined on a set* A, *fails to converge uniformly on* A *to a function* $S(x)$ *defined on* A *if and only if there exists a positive number* ϵ *having the property that for any number* N *there exist a positive integer* $n > N$ *and a point* x *of* A *such that* $|S_n(x) - S(x)| \geq \epsilon$.

Example 3. Show that the convergence of Example 1 is not uniform on the interval $(-\infty, +\infty)$.

Solution. We can take $\epsilon \equiv 1$. If N is an arbitrary number, let us choose any $n > N$, and hold this n fixed. Next we pick $x > n$. Then (for this pair n and x),

$$S_n(x) - S(x) = \frac{x}{n} > \frac{n}{n} = 1 = \epsilon.$$

NOTE. Any convergent sequence of constants (constant functions) converges uniformly on any set.

Example 4. Show that the sequence $\left\{\dfrac{x}{e^{nx}}\right\}$ converges uniformly on $[0, +\infty)$.

Solution. For a fixed value of n, the nonnegative function $f(x) \equiv xe^{-nx}$ has a maximum value on $[0, +\infty)$ given by $x = 1/n$, and equal to $1/ne$. Therefore the sequence approaches 0 uniformly on $[0, +\infty)$.

Example 5. Show that the sequence $\left\{\dfrac{nx}{e^{nx}}\right\}$ converges uniformly on $[\alpha, +\infty)$, for any $\alpha > 0$, but not uniformly on $(0, +\infty)$.

Solution. For $x \geq \alpha$, and a fixed $n > 1/\epsilon$, the function $f(x) \equiv nxe^{-nx}$ is monotonically decreasing, with a maximum value of $n\alpha e^{-n\alpha}$. This quantity is independent of x and approaches 0 as $n \to +\infty$. On the entire interval $(0, +\infty)$, the function $f(x) \equiv nxe^{-nx}$ has a maximum value given by $x = 1/n$ and equal to $1/e$. The convergence is therefore not uniform.

★902. UNIFORM CONVERGENCE OF SERIES

Let

$$(1) \qquad u_1(x) + u_2(x) + \cdots + u_n(x) + \cdots$$

be a series of functions defined on a set A, and let

$$S_n(x) \equiv u_1(x) + \cdots + u_n(x).$$

We say that this series of functions **converges on** A in case the sequence $\{S_n(x)\}$ converges on A. The series (1) **converges uniformly on** A if and only if the sequence $\{S_n(x)\}$ converges uniformly on A.

NOTE. Any convergent series of constants (constant functions) converges uniformly on any set.

Corresponding to the condition $a_n \to 0$ which is necessary for the convergence of the series of constants $\sum a_n$, we have:

Theorem. *If the series $\sum u_n(x)$ converges uniformly on a set A, then the general term $u_n(x)$ converges to 0 uniformly on A.*

Proof. By the triangle inequality, if $S_n(x) \equiv u_1(x) + \cdots + u_n(x)$ and $S(x) \equiv \sum_{n=1}^{+\infty} u_n(x),$

$$|u_n(x)| = |S_n(x) - S_{n-1}(x)| = |[S_n(x) - S(x)] + [S(x) - S_{n-1}(x)]|$$
$$\leq |S_n(x) - S(x)| + |S_{n-1}(x) - S(x)|.$$

Let $\epsilon > 0$ be given. If N is chosen such that $n > N - 1$ implies

$$|S_n(x) - S(x)| < \tfrac{1}{2}\epsilon$$

for all x in A, then $n > N$ implies $|u_n(x)| < \epsilon$ for all x in A.

Example. Show that the Maclaurin series for e^x converges uniformly on a set A if and only if A is bounded.

Solution. If the set A is bounded, it is contained in some interval of the form $[-\alpha, \alpha]$. Using the Lagrange form of the remainder in Taylor's formula for e^x at $x = a = 0$, we have (with the standard notation) for any x,

$$|S_n(x) - S(x)| = |R_n(x)| = \frac{e^{\xi_n}}{n!}|x|^n \leq \frac{e^{\alpha}}{n!}\alpha^n.$$

Since $\lim_{n \to +\infty} \frac{e^{\alpha}}{n!}\alpha^n = 0$ and $\frac{e^{\alpha}}{n!}\alpha^n$ is independent of x, the uniform convergence on A is established.

If the set A is unbounded, we can show that $\sum_{n=0}^{+\infty} \frac{x^n}{n!}$ fails to converge uniformly on A by showing that the general term does not approach 0 uniformly on A. This we do with the aid of the Negation of Uniform Convergence formulated in § 901: letting ϵ be 1 and n be any fixed positive integer, we can find an x in A such that $|x|^n > n$!

★903. DOMINANCE AND THE WEIERSTRASS M-TEST

The role of dominance in uniform convergence of series of functions is similar to that of dominance in convergence of series of constants (§ 708).

Definition. *The statement that a series of functions $\sum v_n(x)$ **dominates** a series of functions $\sum u_n(x)$ on a set A means that all terms are defined on A and that for any x in A $|u_n(x)| \leqq v_n(x)$ for every positive integer n.*

Theorem I. Comparison Test. *Any series of functions $\sum u_n(x)$ dominated on a set A by a series of functions $\sum v_n(x)$ which is uniformly convergent on A is uniformly convergent on A.*

Proof. From previous results for series of constants, we know that the series $\sum u_n(x)$ converges for every x in A. If $u(x) \equiv \sum u_n(x)$ and $v(x) \equiv \sum v_n(x)$, we have (cf. Theorem I, § 716):

$$|[u_1(x) + u_2(x) + \cdots + u_n(x)] - u(x)| = |u_{n+1}(x) + u_{n+2}(x) + \cdots|$$
$$\leqq v_{n+1}(x) + v_{n+2}(x) + \cdots = |[v_1(x) + v_2(x) + \cdots + v_n(x)] - v(x)|.$$

If $\epsilon > 0$ and if $N = N(\epsilon)$ is such that for $n > N$,

$$|[v_1(x) + \cdots + v_n(x)] - v(x)| < \epsilon$$

for all x in A, then $|[u_1(x) + \cdots + u_n(x)] - u(x)| < \epsilon$ for all x in A.

Corollary. *A series of functions converges uniformly on a set whenever its series of absolute values converges uniformly on that set.*

Example 1. Since the Maclaurin series for $\sin x$ and $\cos x$ are dominated on any set by the series obtained by substituting $|x|$ for x in the Maclaurin series for e^x, these series for $\sin x$ and $\cos x$ converge uniformly on any bounded set. Neither converges uniformly on an unbounded set. (Cf. the Example, § 902.)

Since any convergent series of constants converges uniformly on any set, we have as a special case of Theorem I the extremely useful test for uniform convergence due to Weierstrass:

Theorem II. Weierstrass M-Test. *If $\sum u_n(x)$ is a series of functions defined on a set A, if $\sum M_n$ is a convergent series of nonnegative constants, and if for every x of A,*

(1) $$|u_n(x)| \leqq M_n, n = 1, 2, \cdots,$$

then $\sum u_n(x)$ converges uniformly on A.

Example 2. Prove that the series $1 + e^{-x} \cos x + e^{-2x} \cos 2x +$ converges uniformly on any set that is bounded below by a positive constant.

Solution. If $\alpha > 0$ is a lower bound of the set A, then for any x in A, $|e^{-nx} \cos nx| \leqq e^{-nx} \leqq e^{-n\alpha}$. By the Weierstrass M-test, with $M_n \equiv e^{-n\alpha}$, the given series converges uniformly on A (the series $\sum e^{-n\alpha}$ is a geometric series with common ratio $e^{-\alpha} < 1$). (Cf. Ex. 26, § 904.)

★904. EXERCISES

In Exercises 1-10, use the Weierstrass M-test to show that the given series converges uniformly on the given set.

★1. $\sum n^2 x^n$; $[-\frac{1}{2}, \frac{1}{2}]$.

★2. $\sum \frac{x^n}{n^2}$; $[-1, 1]$.

★3. $\sum \frac{x^{2n-1}}{(2n-1)!}$; $(-1000, 2000)$.

★4. $\sum \frac{x^n}{n^n}$; $x = 1, 2, \cdots, K$.

★5. $\sum \frac{\sin nx}{n^2 + 1}$; $(-\infty, +\infty)$.

★6. $\sum \frac{\sin nx}{e^n}$; $(-\infty, +\infty)$.

★7. $\sum n e^{-nx}$; $[\alpha, +\infty)$, $\alpha > 0$.

★8. $\sum \frac{e^{nx}}{5^n}$; $(-\infty, \alpha]$, $\alpha < \ln 5$.

★9. $\sum \left(\frac{\ln x}{x}\right)^n$; $[1, +\infty)$.

★10. $\sum (x \ln x)^n$; $(0, 1]$.

In Exercises 11-20, show that the sequence whose general term is given converges uniformly on the first of the two given intervals, and that it converges but not uniformly on the second of the two given intervals. The letter η denotes an arbitrarily small positive number.

★11. $\sin^n x$; $[0, \frac{1}{2}\pi - \eta]$; $[0, \frac{1}{2}\pi)$.

★12. $\sqrt[n]{\sin x}$; $[\eta, \frac{1}{2}\pi]$; $(0, \frac{1}{2}\pi]$.

★13. $\frac{x}{x + n}$; $[0, b]$; $[0, +\infty)$.

★14. $\frac{x + n}{n}$; $[a, b]$; $(-\infty, +\infty)$.

★15. $\frac{nx}{1 + nx}$; $[\eta, +\infty)$; $(0, +\infty)$.

★16. $\frac{nx}{1 + n^2 x^2}$; $[\eta, +\infty)$; $(0, +\infty)$.

★17. $\frac{\ln (1 + nx)}{n}$; $[0, b]$; $[0, +\infty)$.

★18. $n^2 x^2 e^{-nx}$; $[\eta, +\infty)$; $(0, +\infty)$.

★ ____ $- \eta]$; $[0, 1)$.

★20. $\frac{\sin nx}{1 + nx}$; $[\eta, +\infty)$; $(0, +\infty)$.

In ____ 21-24, show that the given series converges uniformly on the first of the two given intervals, and that it converges but not uniformly on the second of the two given intervals. The letter η denotes an arbitrarily small positive number.

★21. $\sum x^n$; $[0, 1 - \eta]$; $[0, 1)$.

★22. $\sum \frac{x^n}{n}$; $[0, 1 - \eta]$; $[0, 1)$.

★23. $\sum \frac{1}{n^x}$; $[1 + \eta, +\infty)$; $(1, +\infty)$.

★24. $\sum \frac{nx}{e^{nx}}$; $[\eta, +\infty)$; $(0, +\infty)$.

★25. Prove the Negation of Uniform Convergence, § 901.

★26. Prove that the convergence of the series in Example 2, § 903, is not uniform on $(0, +\infty)$.

★27. Prove that if a sequence of functions converges uniformly on a set, then any subsequence converges uniformly on that set. Show by an example that the converse is false; that is, show that a sequence which converges nonuniformly on a set may have a uniformly convergent subsequence. (Cf. Ex. 28.)

★28. Prove that if a monotonic sequence of functions ($S_{n+1}(x) \leqq S_n(x)$ for each x) converges on a set and contains a uniformly convergent subsequence, then the convergence of the original sequence is uniform. (Cf. Ex. 27.)

★29. Prove that if a sequence converges uniformly on a set A, then it converges uniformly on any set contained in A.

★30. Prove that if a sequence converges uniformly on a set A and on a set B, then it converges uniformly on the combined set made up of points that belong either to A or to B (or to both). Show that any convergent sequence converges uniformly on every finite set. Show that if a sequence converges uniformly on an open interval (a, b) and converges at each endpoint, then the sequence converges uniformly on the closed interval $[a, b]$.

★31. Prove that if $S_n(x) \rightrightarrows S(x)$ on a set A, and if $S(x)$ is bounded on A, then the functions $S_n(x)$ are **uniformly bounded** on A: there exists a constant K such that $|S_n(x)| \leqq K$ for all n and all x in A.

★32. Prove that if $S_n(x) \rightrightarrows S(x)$ on a set A, and if each $S_n(x)$ is bounded on A (there exists a sequence of constants $\{K_n\}$ such that $|S_n(x)| \leqq K_n$ for each n and all x in A), then the functions $S_n(x)$ are uniformly bounded on A. (Cf. Ex. 31.)

★33. If $f(x)$ is defined on $[0, 1]$ and continuous at 1, prove that $\{x^n f(x)\}$ converges for every x of $[0, 1]$, and that this convergence is uniform if and only if $f(x)$ is bounded and $f(1) = 0$.

★34. If two sequences $\{f_n(x)\}$ and $\{g_n(x)\}$ converge uniformly on a set A, prove that their sum $\{f_n(x) + g_n(x)\}$ also converges uniformly on A. Show by an example that their product $\{f_n(x)g_n(x)\}$ need not converge uniformly on A. Prove, however, that if both original sequences are uniformly bounded (cf. Ex. 31), then the sequence $\{f_n(x)g_n(x)\}$ converges uniformly. What happens if only one of the sequences is uniformly bounded?

★35. Construct a series $\sum u_n(x)$ such that (*i*) $\sum u_n(x)$ converges on a [illegible] A, (*ii*) $u_n(x) \rightrightarrows 0$ on A, and (*iii*) $\sum u_n(x)$ does not converge unif[illegible]

★36. Prove the ratio test for uniform convergence: If $\sum$ [illegible] f nonvanishing functions on a set A, and if there exist constan[illegible] e $\rho < 1$, such that $\left|\dfrac{u_{n+1}(x)}{u_n(x)}\right| \leqq \rho$ for all $n > N$ and all x in A, then $\sum$ [illegible] verges uniformly on A. Use this test to prove that for any fixed x such that $|x| < 1$, the binomial series ((11), § 807), considered as a series of functions of m, converges uniformly for $|m| \leqq M$, where M is fixed.

In Exercises 37-42, find an appropriate function $N(\epsilon)$, as prescribed in the Definition of uniform convergence, § 901, for the sequence of the given Exercise (and the set specified in that exercise).

★37. Ex. 11. **★38.** Ex. 13. **★39.** Ex. 15.

★40. Ex. 17. *Hint:* The inequality $\ln (1 + nb) < \epsilon n$ is equivalent to $1 + nb < e^{\epsilon n}$; and $1 + \epsilon n + \dfrac{\epsilon^2 n^2}{2} < e^{\epsilon n}$. Thus require $1 + nb < 1 + \dfrac{\epsilon^2 n^2}{2}$.

★41. Ex. 18. *Hint:* $n^2x^2e^{-nx}$ is a decreasing function of x for $x > \dfrac{2}{n}$. First require $n > \dfrac{2}{\eta}$. Then guarantee $n^2\eta^2 < \epsilon e^{n\eta}$ (cf. Ex. 40).

★**42.** Ex. 19.

★**43.** Prove that the Cauchy condition for convergence of an infinite series $\sum a_n$ (Ex. 17, § 717) can be expressed in the form: $a_n + a_{n+1} + \cdots + a_{n+p} \rightrightarrows 0$, *uniformly in* $p > 0$. (Cf. Exs. 18, 20, § 717.)

★★**44.** Explain what you would mean by saying that a series of functions is **uniformly summable** $(C, 1)$ on a given set. Prove that a uniformly convergent series is uniformly summable, but not conversely. Generalize to uniform summability (C, r). Give examples. (Cf. Exs. 15-16, § 717.)

★**45.** Prove the **Cauchy criterion** for uniform convergence of a sequence of functions: *A sequence* $\{S_n(x)\}$ *converges uniformly on a set* A *if and only if corresponding to* $\epsilon > 0$ *there exists* $N = N(\epsilon)$ *such that* $m > N$ *and* $n > N$ *imply* $|S_m(x) - S_n(x)| < \epsilon$ *for every* x *in* A. *Hint:* By § 302, $S(x) \equiv \lim\limits_{n \to +\infty} S_n(x)$ exists. Assume that the convergence is not uniform, use the Negation of § 901, N as prescribed above for $\frac{1}{2}\epsilon$, and the triangle inequality, for fixed $n > N$ and arbitrary $m > N$:
$$|S_n(x) - S(x)| \leq |S_n(x) - S_m(x)| + |S_m(x) - S(x)|.$$

★**46.** State and prove the Cauchy criterion for uniform convergence of a series of functions. (Cf. Ex. 45, above, Exs. 17-19, § 717.)

★★**47.** Show that $\sum\limits_{n=1}^{+\infty} \dfrac{x}{1 + n^2 x^2}$ converges for all x, that it converges uniformly for $x \geqq \eta > 0$, and that it does not converge uniformly in any neighborhood of $x = 0$. *Hint:* Use the Cauchy criterion (Ex. 46), together with the ideas used in establishing the integral test (§ 706) to show that uniform convergence of the given series is equivalent to showing that
$$\int_m^n \frac{x\,dt}{1 + x^2 t^2} = \text{Arctan } mx - \text{Arctan } nx$$
is uniformly small for x in a given set, and large m and n.

★★**48.** Show that $\sum\limits_{n=1}^{+\infty} \dfrac{x}{n + n^2 x^2}$ converges uniformly for all x. *Hint:* See Ex. 47, and write $x \ln [(mnx^2 + m)/(mnx^2 + n)] = x \ln [1 + 1/nx^2] - x \ln [1 + 1/mx^2]$. Show that $x \ln [1 + 1/nx^2] < \frac{1}{2} \ln 5 n^{-\frac{1}{2}}$.

★★**49.** Prove the **Abel test** for uniform convergence: *If the partial sums of a series* $\sum\limits_{n=1}^{+\infty} u_n(x)$ *of functions are uniformly bounded on a set* A (Ex. 31), *and if* $\{v_n(x)\}$ *is a monotonically decreasing sequence of nonnegative functions converging uniformly to* 0 *on* A, *then the series* $\sum\limits_{n=1}^{+\infty} u_n(x)\, v_n(x)$ *converges uniformly on* A. (Cf. Ex. 22, § 717.)

★★**50.** Adapt and prove the Abel test of Exercise 23, § 717, for uniform convergence.

★★**51.** Prove the alternating series test for uniform convergence: *If* $\{v_n(x)\}$ *is a monotonically decreasing sequence of nonnegative functions converging uniformly to* 0 *on a set* A, *then* $\sum\limits_{n=1}^{+\infty} (-1)^{n-1} v_n(x)$ *converges uniformly on* A. (Cf. Ex. 49.)

★★52. Show that $\sum_{n=1}^{+\infty} \frac{(-1)^{n-1}}{n+x}$ converges uniformly for $x \geqq 0$, but does not converge absolutely for any x. (Cf. Ex. 51.)

★★53. Show that $\sum_{n=1}^{+\infty} \frac{(-1)^n x^{2n}}{1+x^{2n}}$ converges uniformly on $[-1+\eta, 1-\eta], \eta > 0$. (Cf. Ex. 51.)

★★54. Show that $\sum_{n=1}^{+\infty} \frac{(-1)^n}{n^x}$ converges uniformly for $x \geqq \eta > 0$, but not uniformly for $x > 0$. (Cf. Ex. 51.)

★★55. Show that $\sum_{n=1}^{+\infty} (-1)^n \frac{x^2+nx}{n^2}$ converges uniformly on every bounded set. Where does it converge absolutely? (Cf. Ex. 51.)

★★56. Show that $\sum_{n=1}^{+\infty} (-1)^n \frac{x}{n} e^{-\frac{x^2}{n^2}}$ converges uniformly on every bounded set, but absolutely only for $x = 0$. (Cf. Ex. 51.)

★905. UNIFORM CONVERGENCE AND CONTINUITY

The example $S_n(x) \equiv x^{\frac{1}{2n-1}}$, $-1 \leqq x \leqq 1$ (Fig. 903), shows that the limit of a sequence of continuous functions need not be continuous. The limit in this case is the signum function (Example 1, § 206), which is discontinuous at $x = 0$. As we shall see, this is possible because the convergence is not uniform. For example, let us set $\epsilon = \frac{1}{2}$. Then however large n may be there will exist a positive number x so small that the inequality

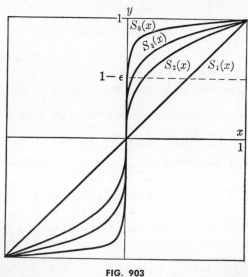

FIG. 903

$|S_n(x) - S(x)| < \epsilon$, which is equivalent to $1 - x^{\frac{1}{2n-1}} < \frac{1}{2}$, or $x^{\frac{1}{2n-1}} > \frac{1}{2}$, fails.

In case of uniform convergence we have the basic theorem:

Theorem. *If $S_n(x)$ is continuous at every point of a set A, $n = 1, 2, \cdots$, and if $S_n(x) \rightrightarrows S(x)$ on A, then $S(x)$ is continuous at every point of A.*

Proof. Let a be any point of A, and let $\epsilon > 0$. We first choose a positive integer N such that $|S_N(x) - S(x)| < \frac{1}{3}\epsilon$ for every x of A. Holding N fixed, and using the continuity of $S_N(x)$ at $x = a$, we can find a $\delta > 0$ such that $|x - a| < \delta$ implies $|S_N(x) - S_N(a)| < \frac{1}{3}\epsilon$. (The number δ apparently depends on *both* N and ϵ, but since N is determined by ϵ, δ is a function of ϵ alone—for the fixed value $x = a$.) Now we use the triangle inequality:

$$|S(x) - S(a)| \leq |S(x) - S_N(x)| + |S_N(x) - S_N(a)| + |S_N(a) - S(a)|.$$

Then $|x - a| < \delta$ implies

$$|S(x) - S(a)| < \tfrac{1}{3}\epsilon + \tfrac{1}{3}\epsilon + \tfrac{1}{3}\epsilon = \epsilon,$$

and the proof is complete.

Corollary. *If $f(x) \equiv \sum u_n(x)$, where the series converges uniformly on a set A, and if every term of the series is continuous on A, then $f(x)$ is continuous on A.* (Ex. 19, § 908.)

Example. Show that the function $f(x)$ defined by the series $\sum\limits_{n=0}^{+\infty} e^{-nx} \cos nx$ of Example 2, § 903, is continuous on the set $(0, +\infty)$—that is, for positive x.

Solution. Let $x = a > 0$ be given, and let $\alpha \equiv \frac{1}{2}a$. Then the given series converges uniformly on $[\frac{1}{2}a, +\infty)$, by Example 2, § 903. Therefore $f(x)$ is continuous on $[\frac{1}{2}a, +\infty)$ and, in particular, at $x = a$.

★906. UNIFORM CONVERGENCE AND INTEGRATION

The example illustrated in Figure 904 shows that the limit of the integral (of the general term of a convergent sequence of functions) need not equal the integral of the limit (function). The function $S_n(x)$ is defined to be $2n^2x$ for $0 \leq x \leq 1/2n$, $2n(1 - nx)$ for $1/2n \leq x \leq 1/n$, and 0 for $1/n \leq x \leq 1$. The limit function $S(x)$ is identically 0 for $0 \leq x \leq 1$. For every n, $\int_0^1 S_n(x)\, dx = \frac{1}{2}$ (the integral is the area of a triangle of altitude n and base $1/n$), but $\int_0^1 S(x)\, dx = 0$. Again, the reason that this kind of misbehavior is possible, is that the convergence is not uniform (cf. Ex. 22, § 908). (For another example of the same character, where the functions $S_n(x)$ are defined by single analytic formulas, see Ex. 25, § 908.)

In case of uniform convergence we have the theorem:

Theorem. *If $S_n(x)$ is integrable on $[a, b]$ for $n = 1, 2, \cdots$, and if $S_n(x) \rightrightarrows S(x)$ on $[a, b]$, then $S(x)$ is integrable on $[a, b]$ and*

$$(1) \qquad \lim_{n \to +\infty} \int_a^b S_n(x)\, dx = \int_a^b \lim_{n \to +\infty} S_n(x)\, dx = \int_a^b S(x)\, dx.$$

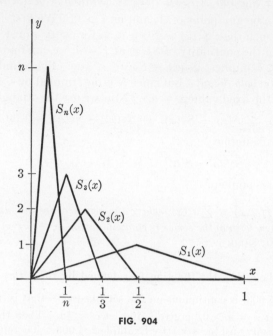

FIG. 904

Proof. We shall first prove that $S(x)$ is integrable on $[a, b]$. The idea is to approximate $S(x)$ by a particular $S_N(x)$, then to squeeze $S_N(x)$ between two step-functions (§ 502), and finally to construct two new step-functions that squeeze $S(x)$. Accordingly, for a given $\epsilon > 0$, we find an index N such that $|S_N(x) - S(x)| < \dfrac{\epsilon}{4(b - a)}$ for $a \leqq x \leqq b$. Since $S_N(x)$ is integrable on $[a, b]$, there must exist step-functions $\sigma_1(x)$ and $\tau_1(x)$ such that $\sigma_1(x) \leqq S_N(x) \leqq \tau_1(x)$ on $[a, b]$, and $\displaystyle\int_a^b [\tau_1(x) - \sigma_1(x)]\, dx < \tfrac{1}{2}\epsilon$. Define the new step-functions:

$$\sigma(x) \equiv \sigma_1(x) - \frac{\epsilon}{4(b - a)}, \; \tau(x) \equiv \tau_1(x) + \frac{\epsilon}{4(b - a)}.$$

Then, for $a \leqq x \leqq b$,

$$\sigma(x) < \sigma_1(x) + [S(x) - S_N(x)] \leqq S(x),$$

$$\tau(x) > \tau_1(x) + [S(x) - S_N(x)] \geqq S(x),$$

and

$$\int_a^b [\tau(x) - \sigma(x)]\, dx = \int_a^b \left\{ [\tau_1(x) - \sigma_1(x)] + \frac{\epsilon}{2(b-a)} \right\} dx < \tfrac{1}{2}\epsilon + \tfrac{1}{2}\epsilon = \epsilon.$$

By Theorem II, § 502, $S(x)$ is integrable on $[a, b]$.

We now wish to establish the limit (1). Since the difference between the integrals of two integrable functions is the integral of their difference, (1) is equivalent to

$$(2) \qquad\qquad \int_a^b [S_n(x) - S(x)]\, dx \to 0.$$

Finally, by Exercises 2 and 38, § 503,

$$\left| \int_a^b [S_n(x) - S(x)]\, dx \right| \le \int_a^b |S_n(x) - S(x)|\, dx,$$

so that if n is chosen so large that $|S_n(x) - S(x)| < \epsilon/(b-a)$ on $[a, b]$, then $\left| \int_a^b [S_n(x) - S(x)]\, dx \right| < [\epsilon/(b-a)](b-a) = \epsilon$, and the proof is complete.

Corollary. *If $f(x) \equiv \sum u_n(x)$, where the series converges uniformly on $[a, b]$, and if every term of the series is integrable on $[a, b]$, then $f(x)$ is integrable on $[a, b]$, and the series can be integrated term by term:*

$$\int_a^b f(x)\, dx = \int_a^b \sum u_n(x)\, dx = \sum \int_a^b u_n(x)\, dx.$$

(Ex. 20, § 908.)

Example. If $f(x)$ is the function defined by the series $\displaystyle\sum_{n=0}^{+\infty} e^{-nx} \cos nx$ of Example 2, § 903, and if $0 < a < b$, then

$$\int_a^b f(x)\, dx = \sum_{n=0}^{+\infty} \int_a^b e^{-nx} \cos nx\, dx.$$

★907. UNIFORM CONVERGENCE AND DIFFERENTIATION

The example $S_n(x) \equiv \dfrac{x}{1 + nx^2}$, $-1 \le x \le 1$ (Fig. 905), shows that even with uniform convergence of differentiable functions to a differentiable function, the limit of the derivatives may not equal the derivative of the limit. Since the maximum and minimum points of $S_n(x)$ are $(n^{-\frac{1}{2}}, \tfrac{1}{2}n^{-\frac{1}{2}})$ and $(-n^{-\frac{1}{2}}, -\tfrac{1}{2}n^{-\frac{1}{2}})$, respectively, $\{S_n(x)\}$ converges uniformly to the function $S(x)$ that is identically 0 on $[-1, 1]$. However,

$$\lim_{n \to +\infty} S_n'(x) = \lim_{n \to +\infty} \frac{1 - nx^2}{(1 + nx^2)^2} = \begin{cases} 1 \text{ if } x = 0, \\ 0 \text{ if } x \ne 0, \end{cases}$$

whereas $S'(x)$ is identically 0.

The clue to the problem lies in the uniform convergence of the sequence of *derivatives*, $\{S_n'(x)\}$. We state the basic theorem, and give a proof under an additional assumption (that of continuity of the derivatives), leaving to Exercise 38, § 908, a proof of the general theorem, with hints.

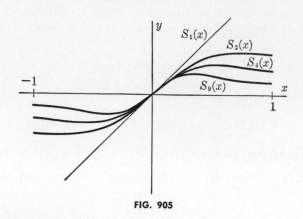

FIG. 905

Theorem. *Assume:*

    (*i*) $S_n(x)$ *is differentiable on* $[a, b]$, *for* $n = 1, 2, \cdots$;
    (*ii*) $\{S_n(x)\}$ *converges for some point* x_0 *of* $[a, b]$;
    (*iii*) $\{S_n'(x)\}$ *converges uniformly on* $[a, b]$.

Then

    (*iv*) $\{S_n(x)\}$ *converges uniformly on* $[a, b]$;
    (*v*) *if* $S(x) \equiv \lim\limits_{n \to +\infty} S_n(x)$, $S'(x)$ *exists on* $[a, b]$;
    (*vi*) $S'(x) = \lim\limits_{n \to +\infty} S_n'(x)$.

Proof if every $S_n'(x)$ *is continuous.* Under the assumption of continuity of $S_n'(x)$ we have, from the Fundamental Theorem of Integral Calculus (§ 504), $S_n(x) - S_n(x_0) = \int_{x_0}^{x} S_n'(t) \, dt$. Therefore, by the Theorem of § 906, the sequence $\{S_n(x) - S_n(x_0)\}$ converges for every x of $[a, b]$. Therefore the limit $\lim\limits_{n \to +\infty} S_n(x)$ exists for every x of $[a, b]$ (why?), and if we define $S(x) \equiv \lim\limits_{n \to +\infty} S_n(x)$ and $T(x) \equiv \lim\limits_{n \to +\infty} S_n'(x)$, we have (§ 906):

(1) $$S(x) = \int_{x_0}^{x} T(t) \, dt - S(x_0).$$

Since $T(x)$ is continuous on $[a, b]$ (§ 905), the function $S(x)$ is differentiable with derivative $S'(x) = T(x)$ (Theorem I, § 504). Finally, since

$$|S_n(x) - S(x)| = \left| \int_{x_0}^x [S_n'(t) - S'(t)] \, dt + [S_n(x_0) - S(x_0)] \right|$$

$$\leq \left| \int_{x_0}^x |S_n'(t) - S'(t)| \, dt \right| + |S_n(x_0) - S(x_0)|,$$

the convergence of $\{S_n(x)\}$ is uniform (cf. Ex. 23, § 908).

Corollary. *If $\sum u_n(x)$ is a series of differentiable functions on $[a, b]$, convergent at one point of $[a, b]$, and if the derived series $\sum u_n'(x)$ converges uniformly on $[a, b]$, then the original series converges uniformly on $[a, b]$ to a differentiable function whose derivative is represented on $[a, b]$ by the derived series.* (Ex. 21, § 908.)

Example. Show that if $f(x)$ is the function defined by the series $\sum_{n=0}^{+\infty} e^{-nx} \cos nx$ of Example 2, § 903, then

$$f'(x) = -\sum_{n=0}^{+\infty} ne^{-nx} (\cos nx + \sin nx),$$

for every $x > 0$.

Solution. Let x be a given positive number, and choose a and b such that $0 < a < x < b$. Since the original series has already been shown to converge (uniformly) on $[a, b]$, it remains only to show that the derived series converges uniformly there. This is easily done by the Weierstrass M-test, with $M_n \equiv 2ne^{-na}$ (check the details).

★908. EXERCISES

In Exercises 1–6, show that the convergence fails to be uniform by showing that the limit function is not continuous.

★1. $\lim\limits_{n \to +\infty} \sin^n x$, for $0 \leq x \leq \pi$. ★2. $\lim\limits_{n \to +\infty} e^{-nx^2}$, for $|x| \leq 1$.

★3. $\lim\limits_{n \to +\infty} \dfrac{x^n}{1 + x^n}$, for $0 \leq x \leq 2$.

★4. $\lim\limits_{n \to +\infty} S_n(x)$, where $S_n(x) \equiv \dfrac{\sin nx}{nx}$ for $0 < x \leq \pi$, and $S_n(0) \equiv 1$.

★5. $(1 - x) + x(1 - x) + x^2(1 - x) + \cdots$, for $0 \leq x \leq 1$.

★6. $x^2 + \dfrac{x^2}{1 + x^2} + \dfrac{x^2}{(1 + x^2)^2} + \cdots$, for $|x| \leq 1$.

In Exercises 7–12, show that the equation is true.

★7. $\lim\limits_{n \to +\infty} \displaystyle\int_{\frac{1}{2}\pi}^{\pi} \dfrac{\sin nx}{nx} \, dx = 0$. ★8. $\lim\limits_{n \to +\infty} \displaystyle\int_1^2 e^{-nx^2} \, dx = 0$.

★9. $\displaystyle\int_0^\pi \sum_{n=1}^{+\infty} \dfrac{\sin nx}{n^2} \, dx = \sum_{n=1}^{+\infty} \dfrac{2}{(2n - 1)^3}$.

★**10.** $\int_1^2 \sum_{n=1}^{+\infty} \frac{\ln nx}{n^2}\, dx = \sum_{n=1}^{+\infty} \frac{\ln 4n - 1}{n^2}.$

★**11.** $\int_0^\pi \sum_{n=1}^{+\infty} \frac{n \sin nx}{e^n}\, dx = \frac{2e}{e^2 - 1}.$

★**12.** $\int_1^2 \sum_{n=1}^{+\infty} ne^{-nx}\, dx = \frac{e}{e^2 - 1}.$

In Exercises 13-18, show that the equation is true.

★**13.** $\frac{d}{dx}\left[\sum_{n=1}^{+\infty} \frac{x^n}{n(n+1)}\right] = \sum_{n=0}^{+\infty} \frac{x^n}{n+2},$ for $|x| < 1.$

★**14.** $\frac{d}{dx}\left[\sum_{n=1}^{+\infty} \frac{n}{x^n}\right] = -\sum_{n=1}^{+\infty} \frac{n^2}{x^{n+1}},$ for $|x| > 1.$

★**15.** $\frac{d}{dx}\left[\sum_{n=1}^{+\infty} \frac{\sin nx}{n^3}\right] = \sum_{n=1}^{+\infty} \frac{\cos nx}{n^2},$ for any $x.$

★**16.** $\frac{d}{dx}\left[\sum_{n=1}^{+\infty} \frac{\sin nx}{n^3 x}\right] = \sum_{n=1}^{+\infty} \frac{\cos nx}{n^2 x} - \frac{\sin nx}{n^3 x^2},$ for $x \neq 0.$

★**17.** $\frac{d}{dx}\left[\sum_{n=1}^{+\infty} \frac{1}{n^3(1 + nx^2)}\right] = -2x \sum_{n=1}^{+\infty} \frac{1}{n^2(1 + nx^2)^2},$ for any $x.$

★**18.** $\frac{d}{dx}\left[\sum_{n=1}^{+\infty} e^{-nx} \sin knx\right] = \sum_{n=1}^{+\infty} ne^{-nx}[k \cos knx - \sin knx],$ for $x > 0.$

★**19.** Prove the Corollary to the Theorem of § 905.

★**20.** Prove the Corollary to the Theorem of § 906.

★**21.** Prove the Corollary to the Theorem of § 907.

★**22.** Prove that the convergence of the sequence illustrated in Figure 904, § 906, is not uniform.

★**23.** Complete the final details of the proof of § 907.

★**24.** Let $S_n(x) \equiv \frac{1}{n} e^{-nx},$ $S(x) \equiv \lim_{n \to +\infty} S_n(x).$ Show that $\lim_{n \to +\infty} S_n'(0) \neq S'(0).$

★**25.** Let $S_n(x) \equiv nxe^{-nx^2},$ $S(x) \equiv \lim_{n \to +\infty} S_n(x).$ Show that

$$\lim_{n \to +\infty} \int_0^1 S_n(x)\, dx \neq \int_0^1 S(x)\, dx.$$

★**26.** Construct an example to show that it is possible to have a sequence of continuous functions converge nonuniformly to a continuous function, on a closed interval $[a, b].$

★**27.** Construct an example to show that it is possible to have a sequence $\{S_n(x)\}$ of continuous functions converging to a continuous function $S(x)$ non-uniformly on a closed interval $[a, b],$ but still have $\int_a^b S_n(x)\, dx \to \int_a^b S(x)\, dx.$

Hint: Construct functions like those illustrated in Figure 904, § 906, but having uniform maximum values.

★**28.** Construct an example to show that it is possible to have $S_n(x) \rightrightarrows S(x)$ and $S_n'(x) \to S'(x)$ nonuniformly on an interval. *Hint:* Work backwards from

the result of Ex. 27, letting $\{S_n'(x)\}$ be the sequence of that exercise, and
$$S_n(x) \equiv \int_0^x S_n'(t)\, dt.$$

★**29.** Show that $S_n(x) \equiv \dfrac{n^2 x^2}{1 + n^2 x^2}$ furnishes an example of the type requested in Exercise **27,** for the interval $[-1, 1]$.

★**30.** Show that $S_n(x) \equiv \dfrac{\sin nx}{n} \rightrightarrows 0$ for all x, but that $\{S_n'(x)\}$ converges only for integral multiples of 2π.

★★**31.** Prove that
$$1 - m + \frac{m(m-1)}{2\,!} - \frac{m(m-1)(m-2)}{3\,!} + \cdots$$
converges, but not uniformly, for $0 \leqq m \leqq 1$. *Hint:* The limit function is discontinuous.

★★**32.** Show that although $nx(1-x)^n \rightarrow 0$ nonuniformly for $0 \leqq x \leqq 1$, $\displaystyle\int_0^1 nx(1-x)^n \rightarrow 0$. *Hint:* The functions are uniformly bounded (Ex. 31, § 904). Cf. Ex. 49, § 503, or proceed from first principles.

★★**33.** Show that the series $\displaystyle\sum_{n=1}^{+\infty} \frac{1}{n}\left(\frac{x}{x-1}\right)^n$ converges uniformly for $a \leqq x \leqq \frac{1}{2}$ and that the derived series converges uniformly for $a \leqq x \leqq b < \frac{1}{2}$.

★★**34.** Prove that if $u_n(x)$ is improperly integrable on $[a, +\infty)$, for $n = 1,$ $2, \cdots$, and if $\sum x^k u_n(x)$, where $k > 1$, is dominated by a convergent series of constants, then the series $\sum u_n(x)$ can be integrated term by term, from a to $+\infty$:
$$\int_a^{+\infty} \sum_{n=1}^{+\infty} u_n(x)\, dx = \sum_{n=1}^{+\infty} \int_a^{+\infty} u_n(x)\, dx.$$
Hint: Use Ex. 46, § 515. The hint given in that Exercise, together with the Weierstrass M-test provides a proof of the present proposition without the necessity of using Ex. 49, § 503.

★★**35.** Show by an example that uniform convergence of a sequence of functions on an infinite interval is not sufficient to guarantee that the integral of the limit is the limit of the integral. (Cf. Ex. 46, §515.) *Hint:* Consider $S_n(x) \equiv 1/n$ for $0 \leqq x \leqq n$, and $S_n(x) \equiv 0$ for $x > n$.

★★**36.** Prove that any monotonic convergence of continuous functions on a closed interval (more generally, on any compact set) to a continuous function there is uniform. *Hint:* Assume without loss of generality that for each x belonging to the closed interval A, $S_n(x) \downarrow$ and $S_n(x) \rightarrow 0$. If the convergence were *not* uniform there would exist a sequence $\{x_k\}$ of points of A such that $S_{n_k}(x_k) \geqq \epsilon > 0$. Assume without loss of generality that $\{x_k\}$ converges: $x_k \rightarrow \bar{x}$. Show that for every n, $S_n(\bar{x}) \geqq \epsilon$.

★★**37.** Prove the **Moore-Osgood Theorem:** *If $S_n(x)$ is a sequence of functions defined for x in a deleted neighborhood J of $x = c$, and if*

(i) $S_n \equiv \lim\limits_{x \to c} S_n(x)$ *exists and is finite for every* $n = 1, 2, \cdots$;

(ii) $f(x) \equiv \lim\limits_{n \to +\infty} S_n(x)$ *exists and is finite for every x in $J(x \neq c)$;*

(*iii*) *the convergence in* (*ii*) *is uniform in J;*

then

(*iv*) $\lim\limits_{n \to +\infty} S_n$ *exists and is finite;*

(*v*) $\lim\limits_{x \to c} f(x)$ *exists and is finite;*

(*vi*) *the limits in* (*iv*) *and* (*v*) *are equal.*

Similar results hold for $x \to c+$, $c-$, $+\infty$, $-\infty$, and ∞. *Hints:* For (*iv*), write

$$|S_m - S_n| \leqq |S_m - S_m(x)| + |S_m(x) - S_n(x)| + |S_n(x) - S_n|,$$

let N be such that $m > N$ and $n > N$ imply $|S_m(x) - S_n(x)| < \epsilon/3$, for all x in J, and let $x \to c$. For (*v*), write

$$|f(x') - f(x'')| \leqq |f(x') - S_n(x')| + |S_n(x') - S_n(x'')| + |S_n(x'') - f(x'')|,$$

let N be such that $n > N$ implies $|S_n(x) - f(x)| < \epsilon/3$ for all x in J, and use (*i*).

★★**38.** Prove the Theorem of § 907, without the assumption of continuity for the derivatives. *Hints:* First write

$$S_m(x) - S_n(x) = \{[S_m(x) - S_n(x)] - [S_m(x_0) - S_n(x_0)]\} + \{S_m(x_0) - S_n(x_0)\}$$
$$= [S_m'(\xi) - S_n'(\xi)] (x - x_0) + \{S_m(x_0) - S_n(x_0)\},$$

to establish $S_n(x) \rightrightarrows S(x)$. Then use the Moore-Osgood Theorem (Ex. 37) to obtain

$$\lim_{x \to c} \lim_{n \to +\infty} \frac{S_n(x) - S_n(c)}{x - c} = \lim_{n \to +\infty} \lim_{x \to c} \frac{S_n(x) - S_n(c)}{x - c},$$

by writing

$$\frac{S_m(x) - S_m(c)}{x - c} - \frac{S_n(x) - S_n(c)}{x - c} = \frac{S_m(x) - S_n(x)}{x - c} - \frac{S_m(c) - S_n(c)}{x - c}$$
$$= S_m'(\xi) - S_n'(\xi).$$

(Cf. Ex. 45, § 904.)

★★**39.** Prove that if a sequence of differentiable functions with uniformly bounded derivatives (Ex. 31, § 904) converges on a closed interval, then the convergence is uniform. *Hints:* Assume $S_n(x) \to S(x)$ and $|S_n'(x)| \leqq K$ on $[a, b]$. First use $|S_n(x') - S_n(x'')| \leqq K \cdot |x' - x''|$ and

$$|S(x') - S(x'')| \leqq |S(x') - S_n(x')| + |S_n(x') - S_n(x'')| + |S_n(x'') - S(x'')|$$

to show that $S(x)$ is continuous. Assume the convergence is not uniform, and let $x_k \to \bar{x}$ such that $|S_{n_k}(x_k) - S(x_k)| \geqq \epsilon > 0$. But

$$|S_{n_k}(x_k) - S(x_k)| \leqq |S_{n_k}(x_k) - S_{n_k}(\bar{x})| + |S_{n_k}(\bar{x}) - S(\bar{x})| + |S(\bar{x}) - S(x_k)|.$$

★★**40.** Let $f_n(x)$ and $f(x)$ be Riemann-Stieltjes integrable with respect to $g(x)$ on $[a, b]$, and assume $f_n(x) \rightrightarrows f(x)$ on $[a, b]$. Prove that

$$\int_a^b f_n(x) \, dg(x) \to \int_a^b f(x) \, dg(x).$$

★★**41.** Let $f_1(x)$, $f_2(x)$, $\cdots$ be a sequence of "sawtooth" functions (Fig. 906), defined for all real x, where the graph of $f_n(x)$ is made up of line segments of slope ± 1, such that $f_n(x) = 0$ for $x = \pm m \cdot 4^{-n}$, $m = 0, 1, 2, \cdots$, and $f_n(x) = \frac{1}{2} \cdot 4^{-n}$ for $x = \frac{1}{2} \cdot 4^{-n} + m \cdot 4^{-n}$, $m = 0, 1, 2, \cdots$. Let $f(x) \equiv \sum\limits_{n=0}^{+\infty} f_n(x)$. Prove that $f(x)$ is everywhere continuous and nowhere differentiable.[†] *Hint for non-*

[†] This example is modeled after one due to Van der Waerden. Cf. E. C. Titchmarsh, *Theory of Functions* (Oxford, Oxford University Press, 1932).

differentiability: If a is any fixed point, show that for any $n = 1, 2, \cdots$ a number h_n can be chosen as one of the numbers 4^{-n-1} or -4^{-n-1} such that $f_n(a + h_n) - f_n(a) = \pm h_n$. Then $f_m(a + h_n) - f_m(a)$ has the value $\pm h_n$ for $m \leqq n$, and otherwise vanishes. Hence the difference quotient $[f(a + h_n) - f(a)]/h_n$ is an integer of the same parity as n (even if n is even and odd if n is odd). Therefore its limit as $n \to +\infty$ cannot exist as a finite quantity.

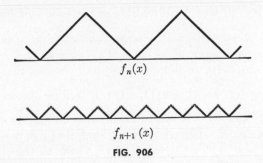

$$f_n(x)$$

$$f_{n+1}(x)$$

FIG. 906

★★42. Modify the construction of Exercise 41 to prove the following generalization (cf. the Note below): *Let $\rho(t)$ be a positive-valued function defined for $t > 0$ such that $\lim_{t \to 0+} \rho(t) = 0$. Then there exists a function $f(x)$, defined and continuous for all real x, having the property that corresponding to any real number a there is a sequence of numbers $\{h_n\}$ such that $h_n \to 0$ and $|f(a + h_n) - f(a)|/\rho(|h_n|) \to +\infty$.* Hint: Let $f_n(x)$ be a sawtooth function, somewhat like that of Ex. 41, having maximum value $\frac{1}{2} \cdot 4^{-n}$, and minimum value 0 occurring for $x =$ all integral multiples of a number α_n defined inductively to be a sufficiently high integral power of $\frac{1}{4}$ to ensure the following inequality, where $A_k \equiv 4^{-k}\alpha_k^{-1}$ is the absolute value of the slopes of the segments in the graph of $f_k(x)$, $k = 1$, $2, \cdots, n - 1$, (α_1 being defined to be $\frac{1}{4}$):

$$A_n > A_1 + A_2 + \cdots + A_{n-1} + n[\rho(\alpha_n/4)]/\alpha_n, \quad n > 1.$$

Then choose $h_n \equiv \pm\alpha_n/4$ such that $|f_n(a + h_n) - f_n(a)|/|h_n| = A_n$. Define $f(x) \equiv \sum_{n=1}^{+\infty} f_n(x)$.

★★Note. The statement of Exercise 42 is of interest in connection with the concept of **modulus of continuity** of a function $f(x)$ on an interval I, which is a function of a positive independent variable δ, denoted $\omega(\delta)$ and defined:

$$\omega(\delta) \equiv \sup |f(x_1) - f(x_2)|,$$

formed for all x_1 and x_2 of I such that $|x_1 - x_2| < \delta$. The function $\omega(\delta)$ is monotonic, and hence approaches a limit ω, as $\delta \to 0+$. The statement $\omega = 0$ is clearly equivalent to the statement that $f(x)$ is uniformly continuous on I. The example of Exercise 42 shows that for functions continuous (and hence uniformly continuous) over a closed interval, there is no bound to the slowness with which the modulus of continuity can approach 0 as $\delta \to 0+$. (With the notation of Ex. 42, $\omega(\delta_n) > \rho(\delta_n)$ for a sequence $\{\delta_n\}$ approaching 0.) The method of proof suggested in Exercise 42 is due to F. Koehler. Also cf. W. S. Loud, "Functions with Prescribed Lipschitz condition," *Proc. A. M. S.*, Vol. 2, No. 3 (June 1951), pp. 358-360.

★909. POWER SERIES. ABEL'S THEOREM

Chapter 8 contains three important theorems on power series (Theorem I, § 803, Theorems II and III, § 810), whose proofs have been deferred. These theorems (having to do with continuity, integration, and differentiation of power series within the interval of convergence) are simple corollaries (cf. Exs. 10-13, § 911) of the following basic theorem:

Theorem I. *A power series converges uniformly on any interval whose end-points lie in the interior of its interval of convergence.*

Proof. For simplicity of notation we shall assume that the series has the form $\sum_{n=0}^{+\infty} a_n x^n$ (cf. Ex. 9, § 911). Let $R > 0$ be the radius of convergence of $\sum a_n x^n$, and let I be an interval with endpoints α and β, where $\max(|\alpha|, |\beta|) = r < R$. Choose a fixed γ such that $r < \gamma < R$, and define $M_n \equiv |a_n \gamma^n|$, $n = 0, 1, \cdots$. Since γ is interior to the interval of convergence of $\sum a_n x^n$, $\sum a_n \gamma^n$ converges absolutely. Therefore the convergent series of constants $\sum M_n$ dominates the series $\sum a_n x^n$ throughout I, and by the Weierstrass M-test, the uniform convergence desired is established.

Theorem I and its corollaries in Chapter 8 have to do only with points in the *interior* of the interval of convergence of a power series. Behavior at the end-points of the interval usually involves more subtle and delicate questions. One of the most useful and elegant tools for treating convergence at and near the end-points is due to Abel. In this section we present the statement of Abel's Theorem, together with two corollaries (whose proofs are requested in Exercises 14 and 15, § 911). The proof of Abel's Theorem is given in the following section.

Theorem II. Abel's Theorem. *If $\sum_{n=0}^{+\infty} a_n$ is a convergent series of constants, then the power series $\sum_{n=0}^{+\infty} a_n x^n$ converges uniformly for $0 \leq x \leq 1$.*

Corollary I. *If a power series converges at an end-point P of its interval of convergence I, it converges uniformly on any closed interval that has P as one of its end-points and any interior point of I as its other end-point. If a power series converges at both end-points of its interval of convergence it converges uniformly throughout that interval.*

Corollary II. *If a function continuous throughout the interval of convergence of a power series is represented by that power series in the interior of that interval, then it is represented by that power series at any end-point of that interval at which the series converges.*

Example. Show that

$$(1) \qquad \ln(1 + x) = x - \frac{x^2}{2} + \frac{x^3}{3} - \cdots,$$

for $-1 < x \le 1$, by integrating $\sum\limits_{n=0}^{+\infty} (-1)^n x^n$.

Solution. The geometric series $\sum\limits_{n=0}^{+\infty} (-1)^n x^n$ converges for $|x| < 1$. Therefore the relation (1) is valid for $|x| < 1$ (Theorem II, § 810). Since $\ln(1 + x)$ is continuous at $x = 1$, the relation (1) is also true for $x = 1$, by Corollary II.

★★910. PROOF OF ABEL'S THEOREM

Notation. If $u_0, u_1, u_2, \cdots, u_n, \cdots$ is a sequence of real numbers, we denote by

$$(1) \qquad \max{}_m^n \big| u_m + u_{m+1} + \cdots + u_k \big|$$

the maximum of the $n - m + 1$ numbers

$$|u_m|, \ |u_m + u_{m+1}|, \ \cdots, \ |u_m + u_{m+1} + \cdots + u_n|.$$

Lemma. *If $\{a_n\}$ is any sequence of real numbers, and if $\{b_n\}$ is a monotonically decreasing sequence of nonnegative numbers ($b_n \downarrow$ and $b_n \ge 0$), then*

$$(2) \qquad \Big| \sum_{k=0}^{n} a_k b_k \Big| \le b_0 \cdot \max{}_0^n \big| a_0 + a_1 + \cdots + a_k \big|$$

and

$$(3) \qquad \Big| \sum_{k=m}^{n} a_k b_k \Big| \le b_m \cdot \max{}_m^n \big| a_m + a_{m+1} + \cdots + a_k \big|.$$

Proof. The two statements (2) and (3) are identical, except for notation. For convenience we shall prove (2), and then apply (3) in the proof of Abel's Theorem. Letting $A_n \equiv a_0 + a_1 + \cdots + a_n$, $n = 0, 1, 2, \cdots$, we can write the left-hand member of (2) in the form

$$|A_0 b_0 + (A_1 - A_0)b_1 + (A_2 - A_1)b_2 + \cdots + (A_n - A_{n-1})b_n|$$

$$= |A_0(b_0 - b_1) + A_1(b_1 - b_2) + \cdots + A_{n-1}(b_{n-1} - b_n) + A_n b_n|.$$

By the triangle inequality and the assumptions on $\{b_n\}$, this quantity is less than or equal to

$$|A_0|(b_0 - b_1) + |A_1|(b_1 - b_2) + \cdots + |A_{n-1}|(b_{n-1} - b_n) + |A_n|b_n$$

$$\le \{\text{maximum of } |A_0|, |A_1|, \cdots, |A_n|\} \cdot \{(b_0 - b_1) + \cdots + b_n\}$$

$$= b_0 \cdot \max{}_0^n \big| a_0 + \cdots + a_k \big|.$$

Proof of Abel's Theorem. By the Lemma, if $b_n \equiv x^n$,

$$\Big| \sum_{k=m}^{n} a_k x^k \Big| \le 1 \cdot \max{}_m^n \big| a_m + \cdots + a_n \big|.$$

The convergence of $\sum a_n$ implies that for any $\epsilon > 0$ there exists a number N such that $n \geq m > N$ implies $|a_m + \cdots + a_n| < \epsilon$. Therefore, by the Cauchy criterion for uniform convergence (Ex. 45, § 904), the proof is complete.

★911. EXERCISES

In Exercises 1-6, obtain the given expansions by integration, and justify the inclusion of the end-points specified.

★1. $\ln(1 - x) = -x - \dfrac{x^2}{2} - \dfrac{x^3}{3} - \cdots$; $-1 \leq x < 1$.

★2. $\text{Arctan } x = x - \dfrac{x^3}{3} + \dfrac{x^5}{5} - \cdots$; $|x| \leq 1$.

★3. $\text{Arcsin } x = x + \dfrac{1}{2}\dfrac{x^3}{3} + \dfrac{1\cdot 3}{2\cdot 4}\dfrac{x^5}{5} + \dfrac{1\cdot 3\cdot 5}{2\cdot 4\cdot 6}\dfrac{x^7}{7} + \cdots$; $|x| \leq 1$.

★4. $\ln(x + \sqrt{1 + x^2}) = x - \dfrac{1}{2}\dfrac{x^3}{3} + \dfrac{1\cdot 3}{2\cdot 4}\dfrac{x^5}{5} - \dfrac{1\cdot 3\cdot 5}{2\cdot 4\cdot 6}\dfrac{x^7}{7} + \cdots$, $|x| \leq 1$.

★★5. $\frac{1}{2}[x\sqrt{1 - x^2} + \text{Arcsin } x]$

$$= x - \dfrac{1}{2}\dfrac{x^3}{3} - \dfrac{1\cdot 1}{2\cdot 4}\dfrac{x^5}{5} - \dfrac{1\cdot 1\cdot 3}{2\cdot 4\cdot 6}\dfrac{x^7}{7} - \cdots \text{ ; } |x| \leq 1.$$

★★6. $\frac{1}{2}[x\sqrt{1 + x^2} + \ln(x + \sqrt{1 + x^2})]$

$$= x + \dfrac{1}{2}\dfrac{x^3}{3} - \dfrac{1\cdot 1}{2\cdot 4}\dfrac{x^5}{5} + \dfrac{1\cdot 1\cdot 3}{2\cdot 4\cdot 6}\dfrac{x^7}{7} - \cdots \text{ ; } |x| \leq 1.$$

★7. Show that

$$\int_0^x \ln(1 + t)\, dt = \dfrac{x^2}{1\cdot 2} - \dfrac{x^3}{2\cdot 3} + \dfrac{x^4}{3\cdot 4} - \cdots.$$

Hence evaluate $\dfrac{1}{1\cdot 2} - \dfrac{1}{2\cdot 3} + \dfrac{1}{3\cdot 4} - \cdots$.

★8. Show that

$$\int_0^x \text{Arctan } t\, dt = \dfrac{x^2}{1\cdot 2} - \dfrac{x^4}{3\cdot 4} + \dfrac{x^6}{5\cdot 6} - \cdots.$$

Hence evaluate $1 - \frac{1}{2} - \frac{1}{3} + \frac{1}{4} + \frac{1}{5} - \frac{1}{6} - \frac{1}{7} + + - - \cdots$.

★9. Prove Theorem I, § 909, for $\sum a_n(x - a)^n$.

★10. Prove that a function defined by a power series is continuous throughout the interval of convergence.

★11. Prove Theorem II, § 810.

★12. Prove Theorem III, § 810.

★13. Prove Theorem I, § 803.

★14. Prove Corollary I of Theorem II, § 909.

★15. Prove Corollary II of Theorem II, § 909.

★16. Show that

$$\int_0^1 \dfrac{\text{Arctan } x}{x}\, dx = \int_0^1 \dfrac{|\ln x|}{1 + x^2}\, dx = \sum_{n=0}^{+\infty} \dfrac{(-1)^n}{(2n + 1)^2}.$$

★**17.** Show that

$$\int_0^1 \frac{\text{Arcsin } x}{x}\, dx = \int_0^1 \frac{|\ln x|}{\sqrt{1 - x^2}}\, dx = \sum_{n=0}^{+\infty} \frac{1 \cdot 3 \cdot\, \cdots\, \cdot (2n - 1)}{2 \cdot 4 \cdot\, \cdots\, \cdot 2n} \cdot \frac{1}{(2n + 1)^2}.$$

★**18.** From the validity of the Maclaurin series for the binomial function $(1 + x)^m$ for $|x| < 1$, infer the validity of the expansion for any end-point of the interval of convergence at which the series converges.

★**19.** Show that

$$\int_0^1 \frac{x^m}{1 + x}\, dx = \frac{1}{m + 1} - \frac{1}{m + 2} + \frac{1}{m + 3} - \cdots,$$

for $m > -1$.

★**20.** Prove that if $\sum a_n$ and $\sum b_n$ are convergent series, with sums A and B, respectively, if $\sum c_n$ is their product series, and if $\sum c_n$ converges, with sum C, then $C = AB$. *Hint:* Define the three functions $f(x) \equiv \sum a_n x^n$, $g(x) \equiv \sum b_n x^n$, and $h(x) \equiv \sum c_n x^n$, for $0 \leq x \leq 1$. Examine the continuity of these functions for $0 \leq x \leq 1$, and the equation $h(x) = f(x)\, g(x)$ for $0 \leq x < 1$.

★★**21.** Verify the expansion of the following elliptic integral (cf. § 611):

$$\int_0^{\frac{\pi}{2}} \frac{dt}{\sqrt{1 - k^2 \sin^2 t}} = \frac{\pi}{2}\left[1 + \left(\frac{1}{2}\right)^2 k^2 + \left(\frac{1 \cdot 3}{2 \cdot 4}\right)^2 k^4 + \left(\frac{1 \cdot 3 \cdot 5}{2 \cdot 4 \cdot 6}\right)^2 k^6 + \cdots\right],$$

for $|k| \leq 1$. *Hint:* Expand by the binomial series:

$$(1 - k^2 \sin^2 t)^{-\frac{1}{2}} = 1 + \frac{1}{2}\, k^2 \sin^2 t + \frac{1 \cdot 3}{2 \cdot 4}\, k^4 \sin^4 t + \frac{1 \cdot 3 \cdot 5}{2 \cdot 4 \cdot 6}\, k^6 \sin^6 t + \cdots,$$

and use Wallis's formulas (Ex. 36, § 515).

★★**22.** Prove the **Weierstrass Uniform Approximation Theorem:** *If $f(x)$ is continuous on $[a, b]$, and if $\epsilon > 0$, then there exists a polynomial $P(x)$ such that $|f(x) - P(x)| < \epsilon$ for all x in $[a, b]$.*† *Suggested outline:* (*i*) The binomial series for $\sqrt{1 + x}$ converges uniformly to $\sqrt{1 + x}$ for $-1 \leq x \leq 0$. (*ii*) The corresponding series for $\sqrt{1 + (x^2 - 1)}$ converges uniformly to $|x|$ for $|x| \leq 1$. (*iii*) $|x|$ can be uniformly approximated by polynomials for $|x| \leq 1$. (*iv*) The theorem is true for any function of the form $m|x - c|$. (*v*) The theorem is true for any continuous function identically 0 for $a \leq x \leq c$ ($c \leq x \leq b$) and linear for $c \leq x \leq b$ ($a \leq x \leq b$). (*vi*) The theorem is true for any continuous function with a polygonal (broken-line) graph. (*vii*) Any continuous function on $[a, b]$ can be uniformly approximated on $[a, b]$ by a continuous function with a polygonal graph.

★★**23.** Prove that if $\int_a^b x^n f(x)\, dx = 0$ for $n = 0, 1, 2, \cdots$, and if $f(x)$ is continuous on $[a, b]$, then $f(x)$ is identically 0 on $[a, b]$. *Hint:* Use the Weierstrass Uniform Approximation Theorem (Ex. 22) to show that since $\int_a^b P(x)\, f(x)\, dx$ = 0 for any polynomial $P(x)$, $\int_a^b [f(x)]^2\, dx = 0$.

---

† Several proofs of this theorem have been given, the original by Weierstrass in 1885. The proof outlined here was given by Lebesgue in 1898. For references and additional discussion see Hobson, *Theory of Functions* (Washington, D. C., Harren Press, 1950).

Answers

12. $x > a + |b|$.

13. $-1 < x < 5$.

14. $x \leqq -5$ or $x \geqq -1$.

15. $x > 2$.

16. $x < 3$.

17. No values.

18. All values.

19. $-\sqrt{3} \leqq x \leqq -1$ or $1 \leqq x \leqq \sqrt{3}$.

20. $-3 < x < 5$.

21. No values.

22. $x < -\frac{5}{3}$ or $x > 5$.

23. $4 < x < 6$.

24. $2 < x < 4$ or $6 < x < 12$.

25. $|x| > |a|$.

26. $|x| < |a|$ or $x = a(a \neq 0)$.

27. $|x - 1| > 2$.

28. If $a = b$, no values; if $a < b$: $-|b| < x < 0$ or $x > |b|$; if $a > b$: $0 < x < |b|$ or $x < -|b|$.

17. $ad = bc$.

11. $\dfrac{2n}{2n - 1}$.

12. $\dfrac{(-1)^{n+1}}{n^2 + 2}$.

13. $\dfrac{(-1)^{n-1}}{(n - 1)!}$.

14. $(2n - 2)!$.

15. $1 \cdot 3 \cdot 5 \cdots (2n + 1) = \dfrac{(2n + 1)!}{2^n n!}$.

16. $a_{2n} = 2$, $a_{4n-1} = 3$, $a_{4n-3} = 1$.

17. $a_{3n} = a_{3n-1} = n$, $a_{3n-2} = -n$.

18. n even, $2^n n!$; n odd, $\dfrac{(2n)!}{2^n n!}$.

19. 2.

20. 1.

21. $\frac{1}{2}$.

22. $+\infty$.

23. ∞.

24. $-\infty$.

25. $N(\epsilon) \equiv 1$.

26. $N(\epsilon) \equiv 1/\epsilon$.

27. $N(\epsilon) \equiv 1/\epsilon$.

28. $N(B) \equiv B$.

29. $N(B) \equiv \frac{1}{5}(7B + 2)$.

30. $N(B) \equiv |B| + 10$.

21. 4.

22. $\frac{7}{13}$.

23. $\frac{11}{9}$.

24. $-\frac{1}{4}$.

25. $3a^2$.

26. ma^{m-1}.

33. (a) $-\infty$; (b) $+\infty$; (c) ∞; (d) $+\infty$; (e) $-\infty$; (f) ∞.
34. (c) 0; (e) 1; (f) 0; (a), (b), (d): there is no limit.
37. $\frac{5}{6}$.   **38.** $+\infty$.   **39.** $-\infty$.
40. $+\infty$.   **41.** 0.   **42.** $-\infty$.

59. 6; $\delta(\epsilon) \equiv \frac{\epsilon}{3}$.   **60.** 9; $\delta(\epsilon) \equiv \min\left(1, \frac{\epsilon}{7}\right)$.

61. 28; $\delta(\epsilon) \equiv \min\left(1, \frac{\epsilon}{22}\right)$.   **62.** $-\frac{1}{5}$; $\delta(\epsilon) \equiv \min(1, 20\epsilon)$.

63. $\frac{3}{7}$; $\delta(\epsilon) \equiv \min\left(1, \frac{\epsilon}{5}\right)$.   **64.** 6; $\delta(\epsilon) \equiv \min\left(\frac{1}{8}, \frac{\epsilon}{42}\right)$.

65. 0; $N(\epsilon) \equiv \frac{5}{\epsilon}$.   **66.** 0; $N(\epsilon) \equiv -\max\left(1, \frac{1}{\epsilon}\right)$.

67. 3; $N(\epsilon) \equiv \frac{17}{\epsilon}$.   **68.** $\frac{5}{3}$; $N(\epsilon) \equiv \max\left(1, \frac{1}{3\epsilon}\right)$.

69. $+\infty$; if $B > 0$, $\delta(B) \equiv \min\left(1, \frac{1}{B}\right)$; otherwise $\delta(B) \equiv 392$.

70. $-\infty$; if $B < 0$, $\delta(B) \equiv \min\left(1, \frac{1}{-2B}\right)$; otherwise $\delta(B) \equiv 1$.

§ 216, page 57

32. $\delta(\epsilon) \equiv \min(3, \epsilon)$.   **33.** $\delta(\epsilon) \equiv \min\left(1, \frac{\epsilon^2}{5}\right)$.

34. $\delta(\epsilon) \equiv \min\left(1, \frac{\epsilon}{5}\right)$.   **35.** $\delta(\epsilon) \equiv \min(5, \epsilon)$.

36. $\delta(\epsilon) \equiv \min(5, 6\epsilon)$.   **37.** $\delta(\epsilon) \equiv \min\left(\frac{7}{8}, \frac{\epsilon}{2}\right)$.

§ 305, page 66

19. 1; 0.   **20.** $+\infty$; $-\infty$.
21. 1; 0.   **22.** 1; 0.
29. $+\infty$; $-\infty$.   **30.** 1; -1.
31. 1; -1.   **32.** 1; -1.
33. 1; -1.   **34.** 1; -1.

§ 308, page 73

3. $\delta(\epsilon) \equiv \frac{\epsilon}{2}$.   **4.** $\delta(\epsilon) \equiv \frac{\epsilon}{4}$.

5. $\delta(\epsilon) \equiv 2\epsilon$.   **6.** $\delta(\epsilon) \equiv \epsilon^2$.

7. $\delta(\epsilon) \equiv \epsilon$.   **8.** $\delta(\epsilon) \equiv \frac{\epsilon^2}{4}$.

13. $\delta(\epsilon) \equiv \min\left(\frac{x_0}{2}, \frac{x_0^2\epsilon}{2}\right)$.   **14.** $\delta(\epsilon) \equiv \min\left(1, \frac{\epsilon}{1 + 2x_0}\right)$.

§ 404, page 91

1. $2x - 4$.   **2.** $3x^2$.

3. $-\frac{2}{x^3}$.   **4.** $-\frac{22}{(5x - 4)^2}$.

5. $\frac{1}{2\sqrt{x}}$.   **6.** $\frac{1}{3\sqrt[3]{x^2}}$.

15. Yes.   **16.** Yes.   **17.** No.

18. No.   **19.** No.   **20.** Yes.

21. $n > 1; n > 1.$ **22.** $n > k; n > k.$

23. $f'(x) = nx^{n-1} \sin \dfrac{1}{x} - x^{n-2} \cos \dfrac{1}{x}, x > 0; f'(0) = 0, n > 1.$ $n > 1.$ $n > 2.$

24. $f''(x) = [n(n - 1)x^{n-2} - x^{n-4}] \sin \dfrac{1}{x} - 2(n - 1)x^{n-3} \cos \dfrac{1}{x}, x > 0;$

$f''(0) = 0, n > 3.$ $n > 3.$ $n > 4.$

§ 408, page 100

1. $\pi, 2\pi,$ or $3\pi.$ **2.** $2 - \sqrt{2}.$

3. $e - 1.$ **4.** $\frac{1}{2}(a + b).$

5. $\dfrac{1}{e - 1}.$ **6.** $\frac{1}{2}.$

7. $\dfrac{a + b}{2}.$ **8.** $\frac{13}{6}.$

9. $1 - \sqrt[n+1]{1 - b}.$ **10.** $2/\sqrt[3]{\ln 27}.$

§ 412, page 111

1. Relative maximum $= 9$; relative minimum $= 5$; increasing on $(-\infty, 1]$ and $[3, +\infty)$; decreasing on $[1, 3].$

2. Absolute maximum $= 1$; absolute minimum $= -1$; increasing on $[-1, 1]$; decreasing on $(-\infty, -1]$ and $[1, +\infty).$

3. Relative maximum $= 3\sqrt[3]{20}/25$; relative minimum $= 0$; increasing on $[0, \frac{2}{5}]$; decreasing on $(-\infty, 0]$ and $[\frac{2}{5}, +\infty).$

4. Relative maximum $= 2\sqrt{3}/9$; absolute minimum $= 0$; increasing on $[0, \frac{1}{3}]$ and $[1, +\infty)$; decreasing on $[\frac{1}{3}, 1].$

5. Maximum $= \frac{1}{2}$; minimum $= -1.$

6. Maximum $= -4$; minimum $= -109/16.$

7. Maximum $= 2$; minimum $= -9/8.$

8. No maximum; minimum $= -1/e.$

15. (a) $x = 20$; (b) $x = 25$; (c) $x = 21$; (d) no profit possible.

16. (a) $x = 20$; (b) $x = 37.4$; (c) full speed, $x = 60.$

19. If $t \leqq s, x = b$; if $t > s, x = \min (b, as/\sqrt{t^2 - s^2}).$

20. $r \leqq -1$: no minimum; $-1 < r \leqq -\frac{1}{2}$: minimum $= -a^2/4(r + 1)$; $-\frac{1}{2} \leqq r \leqq 0$: minimum $= ra^2$; $r \geqq 0$: minimum $= 0.$

33. $\epsilon(\Delta x) = (6x^2 - 5)\Delta x + 4x\Delta x^2 + \Delta x^3.$

34. $\epsilon(\Delta x) = \Delta x/x^2(x + \Delta x).$

35. $\epsilon(\Delta x) = -\sqrt{x}\, \Delta x/2(x + \sqrt{x^2 + x\Delta x})^2.$

37. $10.48810.$ **38.** $h.$ **39.** $-0.06.$

40. $x.$ **41.** $x.$ **42.** $\dfrac{1}{2} - \dfrac{\sqrt{3}}{2}\left(x - \dfrac{\pi}{3}\right).$

43. $x.$ **44.** $1 + \dfrac{h}{n}.$ **45.** $0.$

46. $h.$ **47.** $1 + x.$ **48.** $0.$

§ 417, page 121

1. $\frac{13}{3}.$ **2.** $\frac{2}{3}.$ **3.** $\frac{1}{3}.$

4. $-\dfrac{\pi}{2}.$ **5.** $\frac{1}{24}.$ **6.** 1.

7. $\frac{1}{16}.$ **8.** 1.   **9.** $\dfrac{\ln a}{\ln b}.$

10. 2.   **11.** $\frac{8}{3}.$ **12.** 1.

13. 1.   **14.** Meaningless.   **15.** $\frac{1}{2}.$

16. 0.   **17.** 0.   **18.** $+\infty.$

19. 0.   **20.** $-\dfrac{2a}{\pi}.$ **21.** $-1.$

22. $\frac{1}{2}.$ **23.** 1.   **24.** $e^2.$

25. $e.$ **26.** $e^3.$ **27.** 0.

28. 1.   **29.** $e^{-2}.$ **30.** 0.

§ 503, page 143

14. $0;\ 3;\ \frac{1}{2}(n^2 - n).$

25. $\dfrac{\pi}{4}.$ **26.** $\dfrac{\pi}{6}.$ **27.** $\dfrac{\ln 2}{6}.$

§ 506, page 156

3. 0.   **4.** $\sin x^2.$

5. $-\sin x^2.$ **6.** $3x^2 \sin x^6.$

7. $4x^3 \sin x^8 - 3x^2 \sin x^6.$

8. $2x \cos x^2 \sin (\sin^2 x^2) - \sin 2x \sin (\sin^4 x).$

§ 508, page 160

3. No.   No.

§ 510, page 162

13. $-\frac{1}{6} \sin^5 x \cos x - \frac{5}{24} \sin^3 x \cos x - \frac{5}{16} \sin x \cos x + \frac{5}{16} x + C.$

14. $\frac{1}{5} \sin x \cos^4 x + \frac{4}{15} \sin x \cos^2 x + \frac{8}{15} \sin x + C.$

15. $-\dfrac{5}{4} \cot^4 \dfrac{x}{5} + \dfrac{5}{2} \cot^2 \dfrac{x}{5} + 5 \ln \sin \dfrac{x}{5} + C.$

16. $\frac{1}{6} \sec^5 x \tan x + \frac{5}{24} \sec^3 x \tan x + \frac{5}{16} \sec x \tan x + \frac{5}{16} \ln |\sec x + \tan x| + C.$

17. $\frac{1}{4} [(4x^3 - 6x) \sin 2x + (-2x^4 + 6x^2 - 3) \cos 2x] + C.$

18. $\frac{1}{3}(x^2 + 4x)^{\frac{3}{2}} - (x + 2)\sqrt{x^2 + 4x} + 4 \ln |x + 2 + \sqrt{x^2 + 4x}| + C.$

19. $\frac{1}{2}x^2 - \frac{1}{2}(x + \frac{1}{2})\sqrt{x^2 + x + 1} + \frac{5}{8} \ln |x + \frac{1}{2} + \sqrt{x^2 + x + 1}| + C.$

20. $-\frac{1}{20}(4x^2 + 21x + 105)(6x - x^2)^{\frac{3}{2}} + \frac{189}{8}(x - 3)\sqrt{6x - x^2}$
$$+ \frac{1701}{8} \operatorname{Arc} \sin \frac{x - 3}{3} + C.$$

§ 515, page 171

1. $\dfrac{\pi}{2}.$ **2.** 0.   **3.** Divergent.

4. 2.   **5.** 2.   **6.** Divergent.

7. $\dfrac{\pi}{2}.$ **8.** $\dfrac{1}{(k - 1)(\ln 2)^{k-1}},\ k > 1;$ divergent, $k \leqq 1.$ **9.** 2.   **10.** $\dfrac{\pi}{2}.$

15. Convergent.   **16.** Divergent

17. Convergent.

19. Divergent.

21. Convergent.

23. Divergent.

18. Convergent.

20. Convergent.

22. Convergent.

24. Convergent.

§ 518, page 184

1. $\frac{2}{3}$.

2. 3.

3. $\frac{\pi}{4}$.

4. $-(1 + e + e^2)$.

5. $e + e^{-1} - 2$.

6. $\pi - 2$.

35. $v(x) = x + [x]$; $p(x) = x$; $n(x) = [x]$.

36. $v(x) = 3 + 2x - x^2, -1 \leqq x \leqq 1$; $5 - 2x + x^2, 1 \leqq x \leqq 2$;

$p(x) = 3 + 2x - x^2, -1 \leqq x \leqq 1$; $4, 1 \leqq x \leqq 2$;

$n(x) = 0, -1 \leqq x \leqq 1$; $1 - 2x + x^2, 1 \leqq x \leqq 2$.

§ 606, page 196

1. $\frac{1}{5} \ln |\sec 5x| + C$.

2. $\frac{1}{4} \ln |\sec 4x + \tan 4x| + C$.

3. Arc sin $(x/\sqrt{2}) + C$, $x^2 < 2$.

4. $\frac{1}{2}(x + 2)\sqrt{x^2 + 4x} - 2 \ln |x + 2 + \sqrt{x^2 + 4x}| + C$, $x \geqq 0$ or $x \leqq -4$.

5. $\frac{1}{2} \ln |2x - 1 + \sqrt{4x^2 - 4x + 5}| + C$.

6. $\dfrac{6x - 1}{12} \sqrt{x - 3x^2} + \dfrac{\sqrt{3}}{72}$ Arc sin $(6x - 1) + C$, $0 < x < \frac{1}{3}$.

7. $\dfrac{1}{\sqrt{5}} \ln |(\sqrt{5 - 2x^2} - \sqrt{5})/x| + C$, $|x| < \sqrt{5/2}$.

8. sec $\sqrt{x}$ tan $\sqrt{x} + \ln |\sec \sqrt{x} + \tan \sqrt{x}| + C$, $x > 0$.

9. $\dfrac{1}{\sqrt{109}} \ln \left| \dfrac{6x + 5 - \sqrt{109}}{6x + 5 + \sqrt{109}} \right| + C$.

10. $\dfrac{2}{\sqrt{59}}$ Arc tan $\dfrac{6x + 5}{\sqrt{59}} + C$.

§ 609, page 200

1. $3 \sinh 3x$.

3. $-\text{sech}^2(2 - x)$.

5. $2 \coth 2x$.

2. $\sinh 2x$.

4. $\coth x^2 - 2x^2 \text{csch}^2 x^2$.

6. $e^{ax}(a \cosh bx + b \sinh bx)$.

7. $\dfrac{4}{\sqrt{1 + 16x^2}}$.

8. $\dfrac{e^x}{\sqrt{e^{2x} - 1}}$, $x > 0$.

9. $\dfrac{2x}{1 - x^4}$, $|x| < 1$.

10. $-\csc x$, $x \neq n\pi$.

11. $\frac{1}{6} \ln \cosh 6x + C$.

13. $\sinh x + \frac{1}{3} \sinh^3 x + C$.

15. $\frac{1}{4} \sinh 2x - \frac{1}{2}x + C$.

12. $\ln (\sinh e^x) + C$.

14. $x - \frac{1}{10} \tanh 10x + C$.

16. $\frac{1}{4}[(x^4 - 1) \tanh^{-1}x + \frac{1}{3}x^3 + x] + C$.

17. $\text{Cosh}^{-1} \dfrac{x}{\sqrt{2}} + C$.

18. $\dfrac{1}{2} \sinh^{-1} \dfrac{2x - 1}{2} + C$.

19. $-\dfrac{2}{\sqrt{109}} \coth^{-1} \dfrac{6x + 5}{\sqrt{109}} + C$.

20. $\dfrac{2}{\sqrt{109}} \tanh^{-1} \dfrac{6x + 5}{\sqrt{109}} + C$.

§ 707, page 211

1. $\dfrac{n}{n+1}$; 1.

2. $\dfrac{n}{2n+1}$; $\frac{1}{2}$.

3. $1 - (\frac{2}{3})^n$; 1.

4. $\dfrac{n(n+1)}{2}$; $+\infty$.

5. $2 + \frac{1}{2} + \frac{1}{6} + \frac{1}{12}$; $a_1 = 2$, $a_n = \dfrac{1}{n(n-1)}$, $n > 1$.

6. $1 + 2 - 2 + 2$; $a_1 = 1$, $a_n = 2(-1)^n$, $n > 1$.

7. $1.3 - 0.39 + 0.117 - 0.0351$; $1.3\,(-0.3)^{n-1}$.

8. $2 - 0.7 - 0.21 - 0.063$; $a_1 = 2$, $a_n = -0.7(0.3)^{n-2}$, $n > 1$.

9. $\frac{36}{5}$.

10. Divergent.

11. 0.3.

12. $\dfrac{10{,}201}{201}$.

13. $\frac{5}{9}$.

14. $\frac{2957}{900}$.

15. $\frac{679}{110}$.

16. $\frac{3}{7}$.

17. Divergent.

18. Divergent.

19. Convergent.

20. Convergent.

21. Convergent.

22. Divergent.

23. Divergent.

24. Convergent.

25. Convergent.

26. Convergent.

§ 711, page 219

1. Divergent.

2. Divergent.

3. Convergent.

4. Convergent.

5. Convergent.

6. Divergent.

7. Divergent.

8. Convergent.

9. Convergent.

10. Convergent.

11. Convergent.

12. Divergent.

13. Convergent.

14. Convergent.

15. Convergent for $\alpha > \frac{1}{2}$; divergent for $\alpha \leqq \frac{1}{2}$.

16. Convergent.

17. Divergent.

18. Convergent for $\alpha > 1$; divergent for $\alpha \leqq 1$.

19. Convergent.

20. Convergent for $0 < r < 1$; divergent for $r \geqq 1$ unless $\alpha = k\pi$.

§ 713, page 223

1. Divergent.

2. Convergent.

3. Divergent.

4. Convergent for $p > 2$; divergent for $p \leqq 2$.

§ 717, page 229

1. Conditionally convergent.

2. Divergent.

3. Conditionally convergent.

4. Absolutely convergent.

5. Absolutely convergent.

6. Absolutely convergent.

7. Absolutely convergent for $x > 0$; divergent for $x \leqq 0$.

8. Absolutely convergent for $|r| < 1$; divergent for $|r| \geqq 1$.

9. Absolutely convergent for $p > 1$; conditionally convergent for $p \leqq 1$.

10. Absolutely convergent for $p > 2$; conditionally convergent for $0 < p \leqq 2$; divergent for $p \leqq 0$.

§ 721, page 237

13. 2.718.

14. 0.6931.

15. 1.202.

16. 0.1775.

17. 0.7854.

18. 0.4055.

22. $0.5770 < C < 0.5774$.

§ 802, page 243

1. Absolutely convergent for $-\infty < x < +\infty$.
2. Absolutely convergent for $|x| < 1$; conditionally convergent for $x = \pm 1$.
3. Absolutely convergent for $-\infty < x < +\infty$.
4. Absolutely convergent for $x = 0$.
5. Absolutely convergent for $-2 \leqq x \leqq 0$.
6. Absolutely convergent for $-\infty < x < +\infty$.
7. Absolutely convergent for $4 < x < 6$; conditionally convergent for $x = 4$.
8. Absolutely convergent for $0 < x < 2$.
9. Absolutely convergent for $|x| < 1$; conditionally convergent for $x = 1$.
10. Absolutely convergent for $|x| \leqq 1$.
11. Absolutely convergent for $x < 2$ or $x > 4$; conditionally convergent for $x = 2$.
12. Absolutely convergent if $|x| \neq \dfrac{2n+1}{2}\pi$; conditionally convergent if $|x| = \dfrac{2n+1}{2}\pi$.

§ 811, page 261

1. $1 + \dfrac{x^2}{2!} + \dfrac{x^4}{4!} + \dfrac{x^6}{6!} + \cdots$.

2. $1 - x^2 + x^4 - x^6 + \cdots$.

3. $x - \dfrac{x^3}{3} + \dfrac{x^5}{5} - \dfrac{x^7}{7} + \cdots$.

4. $1 + \dfrac{x}{1!\cdot 2} + \dfrac{x^2}{2!\cdot 4} + \dfrac{x^3}{3!\cdot 8} + \cdots$.

5. $1 - \dfrac{x^4}{2!} + \dfrac{x^8}{4!} - \dfrac{x^{12}}{6!} + \cdots$.

6. $\ln 2 + \dfrac{3x}{1\cdot 2} - \dfrac{9x^2}{2\cdot 4} + \dfrac{27x^3}{3\cdot 8} - \cdots$.

7. $1 + \dfrac{1}{2}x^4 + \dfrac{1\cdot 3}{2\cdot 4}x^8 + \dfrac{1\cdot 3\cdot 5}{2\cdot 4\cdot 6}x^{12} + \cdots$.

8. $2 + \dfrac{2}{8}x - \dfrac{2\cdot 1}{8\cdot 16}x^2 + \dfrac{2\cdot 1\cdot 3}{8\cdot 16\cdot 24}x^3 - \dfrac{2\cdot 1\cdot 3\cdot 5}{8\cdot 16\cdot 24\cdot 32}x^4 + \cdots$.

9. $2\left[x + \dfrac{x^3}{3} + \dfrac{x^5}{5} + \dfrac{x^7}{7} + \cdots\right]$.

10. $x - \dfrac{x^3}{3\cdot 3!} + \dfrac{x^5}{5\cdot 5!} - \dfrac{x^7}{7\cdot 7!} + \cdots$.

11. $x - \dfrac{x^3}{3} + \dfrac{x^5}{2!\cdot 5} - \dfrac{x^7}{3!\cdot 7} + \cdots$.

12. $\dfrac{x^3}{3} - \dfrac{x^7}{3!\cdot 7} + \dfrac{x^{11}}{5!\cdot 11} - \dfrac{x^{15}}{7!\cdot 15} + \cdots$.

13. $\dfrac{1}{2} - \dfrac{x}{4} + \dfrac{x^3}{48} - \dfrac{x^5}{480}$.

14. $1 + x - \dfrac{x^3}{3} - \dfrac{x^4}{6} - \dfrac{x^5}{30}$.

15. $x - \dfrac{1}{3}x^3 + \dfrac{2}{15}x^5 - \dfrac{17}{315}x^7$.

16. $1 + x + \dfrac{x^2}{2} + \dfrac{x^3}{2} + \dfrac{3x^4}{8} + \dfrac{37x^5}{120}$.

17. $-\dfrac{x^2}{6} - \dfrac{x^4}{180} - \dfrac{x^6}{2835}$.

18. $-\dfrac{x^2}{2} - \dfrac{x^4}{12} - \dfrac{x^6}{45} - \dfrac{17x^8}{2520}$.

19. $\cos a \left[1 - \dfrac{(x-a)^2}{2!} + \dfrac{(x-a)^4}{4!} - \cdots\right]$

$\qquad - \sin a \left[(x-a) - \dfrac{(x-a)^3}{3!} + \dfrac{(x-a)^5}{5!} - \cdots\right]$.

20. $\dfrac{\sqrt{2}}{2}\left[1 - \left(x - \dfrac{\pi}{4}\right) - \dfrac{\left(x - \dfrac{\pi}{4}\right)^2}{2!} + \dfrac{\left(x - \dfrac{\pi}{4}\right)^3}{3!} + - - \cdots\right]$.

21. $1 + \dfrac{x-e}{e} - \dfrac{(x-e)^2}{2e^2} + \dfrac{(x-e)^3}{3e^3} - \cdots$.

22. $1 + m(x-1) + \dfrac{m(m-1)}{2!}(x-1)^2 + \cdots$.

23. $(1-x)^{-2}$.

24. $\frac{1}{2}[(x^2+1)\operatorname{Arc\,tan} x - x]$.

25. $(1 + x^2)^{-2}$.

26. $3 \ln \frac{3}{2} - 1$.

35. $B_0 = 1$, $B_1 = -\frac{1}{2}$, $B_2 = \frac{1}{6}$, $B_4 = -\frac{1}{30}$, $B_6 = \frac{1}{42}$, $B_8 = -\frac{1}{30}$, $B_{10} = \frac{5}{66}$.

§ 814, page 266

1. $\frac{1}{2}$. **2.** $-\frac{1}{2}$. **3.** $\frac{3}{8}$. **4.** $\frac{1}{4}$.

5. $-\dfrac{1}{7!}$. **6.** 1. **7.** $\frac{4}{3}$. **8.** -2.

9. $2e^2$. **10.** 0.

11. 7.38906. **12.** 1.64872.

13. 1.0986. **14.** 0.8776.

15. 2.15443. **16.** 0.10033.

17. 0.4931. **18.** 0.0976.

19. 0.4920. **20.** 0.7468.

§ 816, page 268

8. $b_1 = 1$, $b_2 + a_2 = 0$, $b_3 + 2a_2b_2 + a_3 = 0$, $b_4 + 3a_2b_3 + (a_2{}^2 + 2a_3)b_2 + a_4 = 0$.

§ 904, page 275

37. $\dfrac{\ln \epsilon}{\ln \sin \left(\frac{1}{2}\pi - \eta\right)}$. **38.** $\dfrac{b}{\epsilon}$.

39. $\dfrac{1}{\epsilon\eta}$. **40.** $\dfrac{2b}{\epsilon^2}$.

41. $\max \left(\dfrac{2}{\eta}, \dfrac{6}{\epsilon\eta}\right)$. **42.** $\dfrac{\ln \epsilon}{\ln (1 - \eta)}$.

§ 911, page 290

7. $\ln 4 - 1$. **8.** $\frac{1}{4}\pi - \frac{1}{2}\ln 2$.

INDEX

(The numbers refer to pages)